DON'T BE DISCOURAGED by that friend who is "lightning fast" with figures. It doesn't necessarily mean he's exceptionally gifted. More likely it simply means that he's learned the short-cuts.

Problem #2 on the back cover, for instance, is simple to solve in your head almost instantly if you know the "Double-and-Double" Method.

In dividing, it's often quicker to double the numbers. Here's how it works. The problem is to divide 315 by 4½. Double both numbers: 630 by 9. Easy. *Now* divide. The answer, 70, is instantaneous.

HIGH-SPEED MATH SELF-TAUGHT is a wonderful explanation of many tricks which make using figures easier and quicker and which eliminate paper work, because you can do the whole process faster in your head. There are over 1,000 examples and problems to make the explanations crystal clear. Originally published by the D. Van Nostrand Company, Inc., at $6.95, this new low-priced edition has been carefully abridged and revised.

HIGH-SPEED
MATH
Self-Taught

LESTER   MEYERS

Abridged and Revised by

MAXWELL   MARXE

POCKET BOOKS, INC. • NEW YORK

This CARDINAL GIANT edition has been especially abridged and revised for Pocket Books, Inc., from the original, higher-priced volume *High-Speed Math*. It is printed from brand-new plates made from completely reset, large, easy-to-read type.

HIGH-SPEED MATH SELF-TAUGHT

Van Nostrand edition published 1947

CARDINAL GIANT edition published September, 1959
1st printing.........................July, 1959

L

Publisher's Note

The value of the ability to make computations quickly and accurately has been increasing steadily with the growing importance of mathematical calculations. More and more, the operations of modern industry require closer control and faster analysis. More and more, management is turning to the men who have the necessary skill in mathematics. This work was written to impart this skill, and has proved helpful to many thousands of readers.

Dedicated to the

ROYAL SOCIETY OF ARTS, LONDON

whose certificate in Accounting, awarded the
author at the age of seventeen, inspired the
long-anticipated preparation of this book

PREFACE

The purpose of this book is threefold—namely, to show: (1) how a wide variety of problems in mathematics can be computed *quickly;* (2) how these problems can be computed *mentally* with a minimum of pencil-and-paper work; and (3) how, by means of one checking method or another, the possibility of *errors in computation can be virtually eliminated.* The third purpose is no less important than the others for, as most people know, some errors can be very costly. An unhurried study of this book should make it possible for the average reader to acquire the ability to compute the answers to thousands of different problems without making a single mistake. As a first step, note particularly "How to Read This Book" on page xix.

A knowledge of short-cuts in mathematics is of great practical importance. Everyone in industry is constantly confronted by mathematical problems of one kind or another, and one's industrial life can be made not only more profitable but more interesting and more pleasurable, when a wide variety of problems which may seem to be unsolvable without pencil and paper can be worked quickly, mentally and accurately in less time than it takes the uninitiated to pick up a pencil or depress the keys of a calculating machine.

Speed and accuracy are acquired through the mastery of technique—and techniques are the rock on which this book is built. These are not trick methods, but methods adapted to the rule rather than the exception. And once the technique of a short-cut is understood, the reader will find that its application with speed and accuracy is simple and easy, regardless of the seeming complexity of the problem.

Nothing more than a knowledge of simple arithmetic is necessary to understand the techniques discussed in these pages. There is no bothersome terminology to be memorized. There is not a word about algebra in the entire volume. Anyone who knows the simple rules of addition, subtraction, multiplication and division can sail through this book quickly and easily.

There is a range and richness to this fascinating subject, and for any reader who takes his industrial life seriously this book holds forth an additional promise of a satisfying adventure—an adventure of mental excursions to a world where one not only *sees* relationships between numbers, but *feels* them and *plays* with them . . . a world where computations become fun instead of work.

It is my hope that this book will constitute a welcome contribution, because it will save the reader precious minutes and be of added service when the use of pencil and paper is not expedient; because it will help speed production; and, last but not least, because the ability to compute speedily and accurately is a valuable attribute which will not fail to impress an employer.

I wish to express a deep obligation to my many business friends for their generous and valuable suggestions. And it is a special pleasure to thank Miss Harriet Bukarest for the diligence with which she applied herself to the tedious task of typing the manuscript.

LESTER MEYERS

January, 1957
New York, N.Y.

CONTENTS

CHAPTER I: THERE IS A SHORT-CUT FOR VIRTUALLY EVERY MULTIPLICATION PROBLEM

ARTICLE

CHAPTER V: MORE SHORT-CUTS IN MULTIPLICATION

CHAPTER VI: ALIQUOT PARTS

CHAPTER VII: PERCENTAGES AND DISCOUNTS

CHAPTER VIII: CHECKING RESULTS IN MULTIPLICATION

CHAPTER IX: SIMPLE INTEREST

CHAPTER X: AVOIDING ERRORS IN ADDITION

CHAPTER XI: AVOIDING ERRORS IN SUBTRACTION

CHAPTER XII: DIVISION CAN BE AS SIMPLE AS MULTIPLICATION

CHAPTER XIII: THE "DOUBLE-AND-DOUBLE" METHOD OF DIVISION

HOW TO READ THIS BOOK

As has been pointed out, anyone who knows the simple rules of addition, subtraction, multiplication and division can easily understand the techniques discussed in this book. However, any reader who is not sure of himself when confronted by problems which involve decimals and fractions is urged to make a careful study of Chapter XVI, preferably before he has progressed very far in his study of the other chapters. A quick review of this chapter is all that will be needed to understand any of the techniques discussed in the rest of the book.

Attention is called to the interrelation between Chapter I and Chapter II. For the sake of clarity and simplicity it was considered advisable to separate the subject matter of these two chapters. Should the reader have cause to hesitate even for a moment in following any of the discussions in Chapter I, he will find it helpful to read some of the material in Chapter II.

When he comes across what may appear to be a surprisingly simple problem, he should remember that the answer is to be computed by the method discussed in the text. In this way he will learn to compute mentally and with almost unbelievable ease a great many problems the solutions to which he would never heretofore have attempted without the use of pencil and paper.

The inclusion of stars and article references in the problem sections is an important feature of the book and should help speed up the reader's progress in his studies. The most practical way to use the article references is to work the problem first, and then—unless the reader is perfectly sure that he used the right technique—to check with the text in the indicated article.

INTRODUCTION

A brief glance through the table of contents will suffice to reveal the scope of this book. The author does not know of any other work that professes the object here sought— namely, to provide the reader with a wealth of ideas so he may know how to compute many different problems mentally and in the twinkling of an eye, and to conserve his time and energy in solving those problems which may require the use of pencil and paper.

To illustrate what is meant by being able to solve a problem in the twinkling of an eye, the reader is asked to multiply 35 by 28 the way he would ordinarily, then to turn to Example 1 in Art. 11 and learn how problems of this nature can be worked mentally in a few seconds. Let him also multiply 76 by 44 in his own way, then turn to Example 5 in the same article. Does the reader know how to compute a product with a multiplier like 436 without multiplying by more than a single digit? He will learn a simple and effortless way of doing so if he will refer to Example 7 in Art. 11.

The solution to the problem $5\frac{1}{2}$ times 126 may require pencil-and-paper work on the part of many; but the answers to this problem and to any number of others like it can be computed in just a few seconds with practically no effort and with full confidence in their accuracy by an incredibly simple method explained in Art. 13. And the same holds true for the problems $17\frac{1}{2}$ times 28 and $403\frac{1}{2}$ times 16, as explained in Art. 15.

A section of the book which will doubtless intrigue many

is Chapter V, "More Short-Cuts in Multiplication." It shows among other things how one mixed number can be multiplied by another—for example, $8\frac{3}{7}$ times $8\frac{4}{7}$—mentally, in a few seconds, and with confidence and assurance.

Perhaps no other part of the book gave the author more pleasure in the preparation than the two chapters on the subject of division. Examples of two typical problems in these chapters, each of which the reader will quickly learn to solve in a matter of seconds and without pencil and paper, are the division of 572 by 44 and the division of 560 by $2\frac{1}{3}$.

Some of the aforementioned examples are stressed because the respective techniques are discussed in three of the most important chapters in this book. They are Chapter II, "The Breakdown Method of Multiplication," Chapter III, "The 'Double-and-Halve' Method of Multiplication," and Chapter XIII, "The 'Double-and-Double' Method of Division." It is believed that many readers—those with an aptitude for figures and others who have always disliked mathematics—will discover here the key to something which may always have been a locked door to them. These chapters might be described as the core of the entire book. They contain information of much significance to anyone who wishes to learn some of the most important "secrets" of speed and accuracy in business mathematics. Although the terms "break-down method," "double-and-halve method" and "double-and-double method" may not be quite in accord with pedagogic procedure, the license of using them seems warranted because they describe the techniques of the methods most satisfactorily.

The reader, on whose part no previous knowledge of the subject is presupposed, will find in Chapter VII, "Percentages and Discounts," many interesting facts about per-cent rates, which hitherto may have escaped his notice. He will learn, for instance, how to compute the answer to virtually any interest problem in a few simple steps; how to compute percentages like 32 per cent of $27.50 and 16 per cent of $37.50 mentally, and in just a few seconds.

It would be impossible in the confines of this Introduction to emphasize in detail all of the other important parts of this book, for what may be important to one reader may not be quite so important to another. Stress, however, might be laid upon the following discussions: Art. 41, which shows how even a simple problem like 37 times 24 can be computed in at least six different ways—a discussion which should enable the reader to develop amazing accuracy in his calculations; Art. 5, wherein is discussed short and simple ways of multiplying and dividing by numbers which are divisible by 9; Arts. 76 and 77, on how to divide mentally and quickly by numbers which contain the fraction $\frac{1}{2}$.

For the benefit of those who have always believed that they were not mathematically inclined, an easy-to-follow chapter on the subject of decimals and fractions has been included at the end of this book. Decimals and fractions are really very simple, and a quick grasp of the subject, made possible by the bird's-eye view presentation in Chapter XVI, will provide a firm foundation and be of considerable help in attaining skill in the various techniques discussed in the main text.

One peculiarity—the arrangement and substance of the chapters—perhaps needs explanation. Since the aim has been to aid businessmen and businesswomen who are eager to get right down to essentials, much of the material which is found in the conventional texts intended for schoolroom use has been omitted, and no space has been used to discuss the elementary processes of arithmetic. The subject of speed in computing the answers to problems of the kind most frequently encountered in business—those concerned with multiplication—starts with the first chapter. And, whereas in conventional texts addition and subtraction are usually treated in the opening pages, their discussion, confined practically entirely to avoiding errors in these operations, has been reserved for Chapters X and XI.

The starring of problems at the end of the articles is another interesting feature. Realizing that many would like to read this book with arm-chair comfort, stars have been placed before those problems which can be worked mentally. In this way the reader who chooses to do so can quickly pass over those problems which require paper work. Of the approximately 1,000 problems (exclusive of illustrations) in this book, at least 400 are calculable mentally. So the reader can look forward to a thoroughly interesting and profitable time without going to the trouble of writing a single figure.

It is suggested that good use be made of the article references which follow the answers to many of the problems. These references are to previously discussed techniques which might be used advantageously in computing the answers. It should be remembered that this book is primarily one of techniques. So that, although it is important to obtain the correct answer, it is equally important to obtain the answer quickly and easily and, wherever possible, mentally.

Many readers will find it interesting to note the rich variety of the subject matter of the illustrations and problems at the end of the articles. These illustrations and problems are made up from facts about hundreds of different products, materials, operations, services and business practices.

Abundantly illustrated and completely void of intricate and useless exercises, this book will provide a valuable foundation to any reader who gives to it the surprisingly little effort needed—a foundation that will save for him *time* . . . the *physical effort* spent in making computations by conventional methods . . . and the expenditure of *mental energy* which often accompanies the hope that an important computation made by the conventional method is correct.

HIGH-SPEED
MATH
Self-Taught

CHAPTER I

THERE IS A SHORT-CUT FOR VIRTUALLY EVERY
MULTIPLICATION PROBLEM

It is hoped that few readers of this book will need to be informed that to multiply a number by 10, all that is necessary is to place a zero after the last figure; or, if there is a decimal point in the number, to move the decimal point one place to the right. Thus 47 multiplied by 10 becomes 470, and 38.9 multiplied by 10 equals 389. Similarly, the product of 47 multiplied by 100 is 4700, and 38.9 multiplied by 100 equals 3890.

All this may seem elementary—and it is. Yet many individuals with an aptitude for figures fail to apply this rule when multiplying by such numbers as $7\frac{1}{2}$, 9, 35, 45, 97, 185; or fail to take advantage of it for purposes of quick mental computation.

As a preliminary to the many other interesting and important short-cuts discussed in this book, the first four articles in this chapter show how it is possible to make many computations rapidly and easily—and oftentimes mentally—by the simple expedient of multiplying by 10 or by a multiple of 10, adding or subtracting a small mentally computed partial product.

1. How to Multiply Quickly by 5, 15, $7\frac{1}{2}$, 9, 18, 11, $12\frac{1}{2}$, $112\frac{1}{2}$, .125.

1-a. Multiplying by 5. Let us begin with a simple example: 5 times 48. To solve this problem the average individual would use the conventional method, going to the trouble of multiplying 8 by 5, setting down a zero and carrying 4, multiplying the 4 in the multiplicand by 5 and adding 4 to the product. Actually, this problem could readily be calculated mentally. Five is half of 10; why not, then, multiply 48 by 10 mentally and divide the result by 2 mentally? Or, if you like, divide 48 by 2 mentally and multiply the result by 10 mentally?

No matter how many figures it contains, the multiplicand can be multiplied by 5 mentally without any trouble at all and without the need to write down the multiplicand or the multiplier. Thus 5 times 184726 can be multiplied mentally as easily as 5 times 48; dividing 184726 by 2 mentally we write down the result, 92363, and annexing a zero supplies the answer, 923630.

1-b. Multiplying by 15. Here, too, there is no need to write down the multiplicand or the multiplier, or to multiply by 10 and by 5 on paper. We know that if 10 times the multiplicand is added to 5 times the multiplicand the total equals 15 times the multiplicand. To multiply 782 by 15, then all we need to do is add to the result of 782 multiplied by 10 (which is 7820) the result of 782 multiplied by 5 (which is half of 7820).

Notice in the following illustration the fewer figures and the simplicity of the procedure in computing the preceding problem under the suggested short method, as compared with the longer conventional method.

Conventional		
Method	*Short Method*	
782	782 multiplied by 10 *	= 7820
× 15	782 times 5 ($\frac{1}{2}$ of 7820) * =	3910
3910	782 multiplied by 15 *	= 11730
782		
11730		

1-c. Multiplying by $7\frac{1}{2}$. Can you multiply 44 by $7\frac{1}{2}$
mentally in a few seconds? If not, you will very likely be
able to do so presently. Seven and a half is equivalent to
three fourths of 10. Stated another way, $7\frac{1}{2}$ is equivalent
to 10 minus one fourth of 10. To multiply 44 by $7\frac{1}{2}$, then,
we simply multiply 44 by 10 and subtract from the result
one fourth of the result. Thus 44 multiplied by 10 equals
440; one fourth of 440 is 110; 440 minus 110 equals 330.
Three seconds is all it should take to do this simple problem mentally.

A more difficult example is $392.36 multiplied by $7\frac{1}{2}$.
Yet this should take but a few seconds longer. No need to
write down $392.36 or $7\frac{1}{2}$, and no need to multiply by 7
and by $\frac{1}{2}$. Merely write down the result of $392.36 multi-
plied by 10, and subtract one fourth, thus:

$392.36 multiplied by 10	= $3923.60
− 392.36 times $2\frac{1}{2}$ ($\frac{1}{4}$ of $3923.60) =	980.90
$392.36 multiplied by $7\frac{1}{2}$	= $2942.70

*This data is given here only for the purpose of explanation. In
actual practice only the products and their sum or difference, as the
case may be, need be written down.

1-d. Multiplying by 9. Nine is the equivalent of 10 minus 1. Bearing this in mind how would you go about multiplying 8754 by 9? Would you multiply each digit by 9? . . . first 4, then 5, then 7, and lastly 8? I hope not. You would find it more practical to set down the result of 8754 multiplied by 10, and then subtract 8754, thus:

$$8754 \text{ multiplied by } 10 = 87540$$
$$- 8754 \qquad\qquad\qquad = \quad 8754$$

$$8754 \text{ multiplied by } 9 \ = 78786$$

This simple method makes possible the computation of many different types of problems mentally. In computing 89 times 9, for instance, we need but to subtract 89 from 890, and in a few brief seconds we know that the answer is 801.

1-e. Multiplying by 18. As a multiplier 18 is an interesting number. It is the equivalent of 20 minus one tenth of 20. Let us multiply 8439 by 18, first by the conventional method, then by the short method which makes use of the aforementioned observation, and notice the ease and simplicity of the latter method.

*Conventional
  Method*   *Short Method*

      8439   8439 multiplied by 20 mentally = 168780
$\times$ 18 $- 8439$ times 2 ($\frac{1}{10}$ of 168780) $= \quad 16878$

      67512   8439 multiplied by 18 $= 151902$
      8439

     151902

The short method is obviously simpler and speedier than the conventional method.

1-f. Multiplying by 11. There is no need, in multiplying by 11, to multiply each figure in the multiplicand by 11. Write down the multiplicand; then, directly below, 10 times the multiplicand, and add. Thus 93 multiplied by 11 equals the sum of 93 and 930, or 1023.

When the multiplicand contains but two figures and their sum does not exceed 9, there is a still shorter way of multiplying by 11. Simply set down the multiplicand, leaving a little space between the figures, then insert in this space the sum of the two figures. Thus 43 multiplied by 11 equals 473; 70 multiplied by 11 equals 770, and so on.

To multiply a three-figure number in which the sum of the last two figures does not exceed 9, the method is equally simple. The last two figures are multiplied by 11 by the method described in the previous paragraph, and the result is added to the product of the hundreds digit multiplied by 11. Thus 834 multiplied by 11 equals 374 plus 8800, or 9174.

1-g. Multiplying by $12\frac{1}{2}$. Just as $7\frac{1}{2}$ is the equivalent of 10 *minus* one fourth of 10, $12\frac{1}{2}$ is the equivalent of 10 *plus* one fourth of 10. Or, we may say, $12\frac{1}{2}$ is one eighth of 100— so that the product of $12\frac{1}{2}$ times a number is equivalent to the product of 100 times that number, divided by 8. We, therefore, have a choice of two methods in multiplying by $12\frac{1}{2}$.

A little practice will enable one to determine which is the better method for the solution of any given problem. In computing $12\frac{1}{2}$ times 800, for instance, the second method is better, for 800 is easily divided by 8 mentally. The same would apply to numbers like 400, 1200, 48, 96.

On the other hand, a problem like 137 multiplied by $12\frac{1}{2}$ might be computed more easily by the first method—that is, by multiplying by 10 and adding to the product one fourth of the product.

1-h. Multiplying by $112\frac{1}{2}$. A careful study of the multipliers discussed in this article so far will contribute to a quick appreciation of the short method of multiplying by $112\frac{1}{2}$. Note in the following illustration the simplicity and ease of the short method as compared with the conventional method.

Conventional Method	Short Method	
174	174 multiplied by 100	= 17400
$\times\ 112\frac{1}{2}$	174 times $12\frac{1}{2}$ ($\frac{1}{8}$ of 17400)	= 2175
87	174 multiplied by $112\frac{1}{2}$	= 19575
348		
174		
174		
19575		

The advantage of the short method is so obvious that comment is hardly necessary. Under the short method only fourteen figures were written down, only one operation (in division) was necessary, and only two numbers had to be added. Under the conventional method twenty-three figures were written down, and four numbers had to be added.

The test for the value of a short-cut, however, is not always how few figures need to be written down in the computation. The time-saving and effort-saving factors and the assurance of accuracy are of greater importance. In the solution by the conventional method four partial products were taken, and we all know from experience that the likelihood of an error occurring in the total is greater when many partial products must be added than when only two lines of figures are added. Furthermore, the likelihood of error is even greater when the partial products, as in solutions by the conventional method, are "angular" products.

1-i. Multiplying by .125. It is worth remembering that 125 is exactly one eighth of 1000, and that .125 is exactly one eighth of 1. Thus 327 multiplied by 125 equals 327000 divided by 8; and 327 multiplied by .125 equals 327 divided by 8. It is much easier to divide by the one digit (8) than to multiply by the three digits (125).

PROBLEMS

★ 1. Without putting pencil to paper and without hesitating for a moment read, from left to right, the product of 5 times $648.32.
Ans. $3241.60.

★ 2. Compute by the process of division the weight of 5 bushels of barley. (One bushel of barley weighs 48 pounds.) *Ans.* 240 pounds.

3. What is the cost of a rug of 15 square yards quoted at $4.62 a square yard? *Ans.* $69.30.

4. If the air express rate between two points is $1.68 per pound, what would the transportation cost be on a shipment weighing 15 pounds? *Ans.* $25.20.

★ 5. At $88.00 an acre what is the value of $7\frac{1}{2}$ acres of land?
Ans. $660.00.

6. If a gallon of cottonseed oil weighs $7\frac{1}{2}$ pounds, what would the weight be of 136 gallons? *Ans.* 1020 pounds.

7. A manufacturer uses a certain type of paper by the square foot but buys it by the square yard. How many square feet will he

obtain from 260 square yards? (One square yard equals 9 square feet.) *Ans.* 2340 square feet.

8. A girl can produce 187 machinery parts in one day. How many might she be expected to produce in 9 days? *Ans.* 1683.

9. A cosmetic manufacturer finds that the net weight of a pint bottle of a newly created product is 18 ounces. Compute the number of ounces that would be necessary to fill one gross of these pint bottles. *Ans.* 2592 ounces.

10. A contractor agrees to complete a job in 28 working days. If his labor cost is $18 a day, what would he have to pay out in labor for the 28 days? *Ans.* $504.00.

★ 11. If a cow gives an average of 23 pounds of milk a day, how many pounds of milk will she give in 11 days? *Ans.* 253 pounds.

★ 12. Compute the total number of square inches in 11 square feet. (One square foot equals 144 square inches.)
Ans. 1584 square inches.

★ 13. If a gallon of molasses weighs $12\frac{1}{2}$ pounds, what would 176 gallons weigh? *Ans.* 2200 pounds.

14. A manufacturer decides to dispose of 3 gross of miscellaneous equipment parts at a flat price of $12\frac{1}{2}$ cents each. What would the total charge amount to? *Ans.* $54.00.

15. A manufacturer produces $112\frac{1}{2}$ dozen units a month at a net profit of $4.80 per dozen. What is his total net profit per month?
Ans. $540.00.

16. Three men put in a total of $112\frac{1}{2}$ hours work on a job. If their rate of pay is $1.36 an hour, what is the amount of their combined earnings? *Ans.* $153.00.

★ 17. Compute the height of a stack of 160 metal plates each of which is .125 inches thick. *Ans.* 20 inches.

18. A manufacturer signs an order for 10 gross of screws at $0.125 each. What will this bill of goods cost him? *Ans.* $180.00.

2. How to Multiply Quickly by 45, 35, 125, 180. With the foregoing devices as a guide, the reader will quickly perceive the time-saving advantages of using short methods for multiplying by these numbers.

2-a. Multiplying by 45. This number is equivalent to 50 minus 5. To multiply by 50 is a simple matter, for 50 is one half of 100. Five, on the other hand, is one tenth of 50. All one need do, then, to multiply by 45 is multiply by 50 and subtract from the product one tenth of the product.

Example 1: Multiply 34 by 45.

Solution: 34 times 50 ($\frac{1}{2}$ of 3400)   = 1700
    − 34 times 5 ($\frac{1}{10}$ of 1700)   =   170

    34 multiplied by 45   = 1530

2-b. Multiplying by 35. Thirty-five is the sum of 25 and 10. The sum of 25 times the multiplicand plus 10 times the multiplicand—two easily computed partial products—is therefore equivalent to the product of 35 times the multiplicand.

Example 2: Multiply 432 by 35.

Solution: 432 times 25 ($\frac{1}{4}$ of 43200)   = 10800
    432 times 10   =   4320

    432 multiplied by 35   = 15120

2-c. Multiplying by 125. In line with the explanation in Art. 1-i, the multiplication of a number by 1000 and the division of the product by 8 is equivalent to multiplying by 125. However, 125 is also equivalent to 100 plus one fourth of 100. When the multiplicand is easily divisible by 4, the latter method is more suitable, particularly because the computation may be made more quickly. The following two illustrations will make this point clear.

Example 3: Multiply 122 by 125.

Solution: 122 times 125 ($\frac{1}{8}$ of 122000) = 15250

Example 4: Multiply 36 by 125.

Solution: 36 times 100 $\quad\quad\quad\quad$ = 3600
36 times 25 ($\frac{1}{4}$ of 3600) = 900

36 multiplied by 125 $\quad$ = 4500

It is obviously easier to compute one fourth of 3600 and add the result to 3600 than to divide 36000 by 8.

2-d. Multiplying by 180. The method recommended here is similar to that used in multiplying by 18. Simply multiply by 200 and deduct from the product one tenth of the product.

Example 5: Multiply 68 by 180.

Solution: $\quad$ 68 times 200 (6800 times 2) = 13600
— 68 times 20 ($\frac{1}{10}$ of 13600) $\quad$ = 1360

68 multiplied by 180 $\quad\quad\quad$ = 12240

PROBLEMS

★ **1.** If the fire insurance rate on the contents of a house is 45 cents per $100, what would the premium amount to on contents valued at $26,000? *Ans.* $117.00.

2. How many revolutions will be made in 45 minutes by a motor whose speed is 2100 rpm (revolutions per minute)? *Ans.* 94,500.

3. Compute the weight of 172 cubic feet of dry elm wood, the average weight of which is 35 pounds per cubic foot.

Ans. 6020 pounds.

4. At the rate of 35 cents per square foot what would it cost to treat a floor 18 feet long and 17 feet wide? *Ans.* $107.10.

5. The express charge on a carton weighing 100 pounds is $2.56. Compute the cost of shipping a carton weighing 125 pounds. (Note that shipments in excess of 100 pounds are charged on a pro rata basis; thus the cost of shipping 150 pounds would be $1\frac{1}{2}$ times $2.56.)
Ans. $3.20.

6. Estimate the cost of 125 bushels of corn at $1.34 per bushel.
Ans. $167.50.

7. If the average weight of a bale of waste cotton is 638 pounds, what would the total weight be of 180 bales? *Ans.* 114,840 pounds.

8. Compute the cost of 180 shares of stock purchased at $13\frac{1}{2}$— that is, at $13.50 per share.   *Ans.* $2430.00.

3. How to Multiply Quickly by Numbers Near 100, as 99, 98, 97, 103; and by Numbers Near 1000, as 999, 998, 997. The method illustrated is obviously the only one that should be used in computing problems of this nature. The author would feel apologetic for including this article, were it not for the fact that this method is not commonly practiced.

Example 1: Multiply 147 by 99.

Solution: 99 = 100 − 1. We therefore multiply 147 by 100 and subtract 147 from the result, thus:

147 times 100	= 14700
− 147	= 147

147 multiplied by 99 = 14553

Example 2: Multiply 1347 by 97.

Solution: 97 = 100 − 3.

1347 times 100	= 134700
− 1347 times 3	= 4041

1347 multiplied by 97 = 130659

Example 3: Multiply 238 by 103.

Solution: Multiply 238 by 100 and add 3 times 238.

238 times 100　　　　= 23800
238 times 3　　　　　=　　714
_____

238 multiplied by 103 = 24514

Example 4: Find the cost of 98 pounds of plastic belting at $1.84 a pound.

Solution:　　$1.84 times 100 = $184.00
　　　　　－ $1.84 times 2　=　　　3.68
_____

　　　　$1.84 times 98　= $180.32

To multiply by numbers near 1000—as 999, 998, 997, etc.—the procedure is the same as in multiplying by numbers near 100, except that instead of multiplying by 100 we multiply by 1000.

PROBLEMS

1. A dry goods dealer has several bolts of cloth whose combined length is 97 yards. What would he receive if the entire quantity brought an average price of $3.40 a yard?　　　　*Ans.* $329.80.

2. What would the dealer receive for the cloth mentioned in the foregoing problem if the combined length equaled 103 yards and the average price received was $2.86 a yard?　　　　*Ans.* $294.58.

★ **3.** Ceylon cinnamon featherings are packed in bales averaging 99 pounds each. What would the total weight be of 340 bales?

Ans. 33,660 pounds.

4. If medium-bold, bleached cardamon seeds average 198 to one ounce, how many seeds would be needed to fill 437 one-ounce containers?　　　　*Ans.* 86,526.

★ **5.** In October, 1958, lamb was selling at $22.00 per 100 pounds. What did this price bring on sales of (a) 999 pounds, (b) 998 pounds, (c) 997 pounds?   *Ans.* (a) $219.78; (b) $219.56; (c) $219.34.

4. A Short Way of Multiplying by Numbers Which Can Be Factored, Such as 24, 32, 56, 64, 121. If you wished to multiply quickly by any of these numbers, would you multiply first by one digit, then by the other? That would not be the shortest method. A speedier way would be to multiply by factors.

The number 24, for example, might be broken up into the factors 8 and 3 (the product of 8 multiplied by 3 being 24). Or it may be broken up into the factors 6 and 4, or 12 and 2. For our purposes the most convenient factors of 32 are 8 and 4; of 56, 8 and 7; of 64, 8 and 8; of 121, 11 and 11.

The following example will serve to illustrate the time-saving significance of multiplication by factors as compared with the conventional method.

Example 1: Multiply 827 by 24.

Solution by the Conventional Method	*Solution by the Short Method*
827	827
× 24	× 8
————	————
3308	6616
1654	× 3
————	————
19848	19848

Observe that under the conventional method eighteen figures had to be set down and the computation involved an operation in addition. Under the short method no addition was necessary, and only fourteen figures were set down. Actually it was not necessary to set down more than nine figures: the partial product 6616, and the final product 19848.

In multiplying by 32 the procedure is the same. To multiply 374 by 32, for instance, we would multiply first by 8, then by 4. Eight times 374 equals 2992, and 2992 multiplied by 4 equals 11968.

The procedure in multiplying by 56, 64 and 121 would be along exactly the same lines.

Example 2: Compute the cost of 64 square feet of Plexiglas at $4.12 per square foot.

Solution: 8 times $4.12 = $ 32.96
            8 times $32.96 = $263.68

PROBLEMS

1. What would it cost to ship a carton weighing 24 pounds by air express from Boston, Massachusetts, to Barcelona, Spain, at the rate of $1.38 per pound?   *Ans.* $33.12.

2. The specific gravity of cork is .24, which means that the weight of cork is .24 times the weight of an equal volume of water. If one cubic foot of water weighs 62.5 pounds, what would the weight be of one cubic foot of cork?   *Ans.* 15 pounds.

3. If the moisture content of anthracite is 3.2%, how much moisture may be expected in 26.5 short tons of anthracite? (A short ton equals 2000 pounds.)   *Ans.* 1696 pounds.

4. If a drum of calcium chloride occupies 8.7 cubic feet of space, how much space would be occupied by 32 drums?

Ans. 278.4 cubic feet.

5. What would it cost to have 73 dozen belts sewn at the rate of 56 cents per dozen?   *Ans.* $40.88.

6. The walls of a building exterior are to be given 2 coats of paint. The total area, excluding the open spaces, is 5600 square feet. If it takes $3.74 worth of paint to apply 2 coats to 100 square feet, what would be the total cost of the paint used on the job?

Ans. $209.44.

7. A pump delivers $18\frac{1}{8}$ gallons of water per stroke. How many gallons will it deliver in 64 strokes?   *Ans.* 1160 gallons.

8. Compute in square feet the area of a yard 137 feet long and 64 feet wide.   *Ans.* 8768 square feet.

9. A foot of $1\frac{5}{8}$-inch diameter wire rope weighs 4.09 pounds. How much would 121 feet weigh?   *Ans.* 494.89 pounds.

10. The labor cost of 4 men employed on a contract job is $6.23 per hour. If it required 121 man-hours to complete the job, what was the total labor cost?   *Ans.* $753.83.

5. A Short Way of Multiplying by Numbers Which Are Divisible by 9, Such as 27, 36, 45, 54, 63, 72, 81. In Art. 1-d we learned that to multiply by 9 it is much simpler to multiply by 10 and subtract from the result one tenth of the result. Thus 34 multiplied by 9 equals 340 minus 34.

The same principle may be applied with equally good effect to numbers which are multiples of 9. To multiply by 27, for instance, we would multiply by 30 and subtract from the result one tenth of the result. Similarly, the multiplier 36 would be changed to 40, 45 would be changed to 50, 54 to 60, and so on.

The object of this method is, of course, to save time and effort by reducing the number of partial products to a minimum. Thus to multiply by 72 we would multiply by only one digit (8) instead of by two digits (2 and 7). Using this number in an example let us multiply 643 by 72, first by the conventional method, then by the short method, and observe the time-saving advantage of the latter method.

Conventional Method	Short Method
643	643
× 72	× 80
———	———
1286	51440
4501	− 5144
———	———
46296	46296

It is much easier to take one tenth of a number than to multiply by any digit, particularly if it is a high number, like 7, 8 or 9.

The use of this method need not necessarily be confined to two-digit multipliers. The multiplier 270 would be treated in exactly the same manner as the multiplier 27, the number 270 being changed to 300 instead of to 30.

PROBLEMS

1. A manufacturer receives an order for 536 boxes. Each box requires the use of 27 square feet of lumber. How much lumber will be used to fill the order?   *Ans.* 14,472 square feet.

2. At the price of 36 cents per yard of film, what would 734 yards cost?   *Ans.* $264.24.

3. Compute the total weight of 34 crates of cauliflower weighing 36 pounds each.   *Ans.* 1224 pounds.

4. If the import duty on a certain product is 45%, how much duty would be payable on a shipment valued at $317.50?

Ans. $142.88.

5. The average weight of loose, broken anthracite is 54 pounds per cubic foot. How many pounds would fill a space of 235 cubic feet?   *Ans.* 12,690 pounds.

6. It takes 6 boys paid at the rate of $1.10 an hour and 4 men paid $1.90 an hour 54 hours to complete the construction of a machine. What is the total labor cost?   *Ans.* $766.80.

7. If the gross weight of a box of spermaceti is 63 pounds, what is the gross weight of 23 boxes? *Ans.* 1449 pounds.

8. Compute the value of 72 yards of material at $2.17 per yard.
Ans. $156.24.

9. At the market quotation of $1.95 per 100 pounds of potatoes, what would 81 sacks cost? (A sack of potatoes weighs 112 pounds.)
Ans. $176.90.

10. Estimate the value of 81 acres of land at $173 per acre.
Ans. $14,013.00.

6. In Multiplication It Is Usually Better to Consider the Larger Number the Multiplicand and the Smaller Number the Multiplier. If we were to compute the problem 3 multiplied by 1700, it is obvious that the simplest procedure would be to multiply 1700 by 3 rather than 3 by 1700. In other words, we should use 3 (the smaller number) rather than 1700 (the larger number) as the multiplier.

The same procedure would be used in computing such problems as 28 times 19; 382 times 29; 483 times 73. It is easier to multiply by two digits than by three, by the digit 1 than by any other digit.

On the other hand, the problem 17 multiplied by 300 would call for a slightly different treatment. Transposition in this instance is not necessary. All we need do here is to multiply 17 by 3 and annex two zeros. Neither would transposition be necessary to compute the problem 18 multiplied by 51. It is very convenient to say, "18 multiplied by half a hundred equals 900, and 18 added equals 918." And in the problem 45 times 111, rather than multiply 111 by 45, we need but jot down the partial products 4500, 450 and 45, and add them. (Or, in solving the last problem, the still shorter method described in Art. 1-f may be used; this would reduce the computation to the sum of 4500 and 495.)

Example: A machine takes candy in a plastic state, then forms, cuts and wraps it at the rate of 600 pieces per minute. At this rate how many pieces of candy can be cut and wrapped in $2\frac{1}{2}$ hours?

Solution: $2\frac{1}{2}$ hours equals 150 minutes.

$$100 \text{ times } 150 = 15{,}000$$
$$600 \text{ times } 150 \text{ (6 times } 15{,}000) = 90{,}000$$

Ans. 90,000 pieces.

The transposition of multiplicand and multiplier is only advisable obviously in certain instances. In computing the product of 87 multiplied by 344, for instance, it would be better to multiply by 344 rather than by 87 for, in the first place, the digit 4 occurs twice in 344 and, secondly, it is easier to multiply by the digits 3 and 4 than by the digits 7 and 8.

PROBLEMS

Having in mind the techniques discussed in the preceding articles, would you transpose the multiplicands and multipliers in any of the following problems? Just answer *yes* or *no*.

1. 9.75 multiplied by 12.5.   *Ans.* No.
2. 24 multiplied by $7\frac{1}{2}$.   *Ans.* No.
3. 15 multiplied by 14.   *Ans.* Yes.
4. 88 multiplied by $112\frac{1}{2}$.   *Ans.* No.
5. 43 multiplied by 700.   *Ans.* No.
6. 180 multiplied by 74.   *Ans.* Yes.
7. 17.5 multiplied by 16.5.   *Ans.* Yes.
8. 37 multiplied by 45.   *Ans.* No.
9. 125 multiplied by 87.   *Ans.* Yes.
10. 99 multiplied by 68.   *Ans.* Yes.

7. Transposing Multiplicand and Multiplier Is Particularly Helpful in Monetary Calculations. To the uninitiated the computation of the problem 25 times 35 cents would probably call for the use of pencil and paper. The average person would, in all likelihood, proceed to multiply 25 by 5, 25 by 30, and add the partial products. This is really unnecessary.

Consider how simple the mental calculation of the aforementioned problem becomes when multiplicand and multiplier are transposed, that is, when the problem 25 times 35 cents is changed to read 35 times 25 cents. The multiplication of 25 cents by 35 resolves itself into the simple problem, "How much is 35 quarters?" Since there are four quarters in a dollar, 35 quarters equals $8\frac{3}{4}$ dollars, or $8.75.

PROBLEMS

Compute the answers to the following problems:

★ 1. 74 cents multiplied by 26.   *Ans.* $19.24.
★ 2. $2.25 multiplied by 88.   *Ans.* $198.00.

8. How to Multiply Quickly and Easily by Numbers Which When the Unit Digit Is Increased to 10 Constitute a Multiple of the Number Added, e.g., 38 Increased to 40, 57 to 60. The method of dealing with these multipliers might be regarded as a refinement of the technique discussed in Art. 5. Familiarity with the speedy way of multiplying by 27, 36, etc., will make an understanding of the method to be discussed here a very simple matter.

Just as the unit digits in the multipliers considered in Art. 5 were increased to 10 (27 increased to 30, 36 to 40, etc.), so the unit digits with which we are concerned here are also increased to 10. Thus 38 is increased to 40, 57 to 60, and so on.

The only difference is in the next step. In increasing to 10 the unit digit of two-figure multipliers divisible by 9 (as for example 27 increased to 30) the tens digit of the new number is exactly the same as the number added to the original multiplier. Here (38 increased to 40, 57 to 60, etc.) the tens digit of the new number is a *multiple* of the number added to the original multiplier—4 being a multiple of 2, 6 a multiple of 3, and so on. Conversely—and this applies equally to the multipliers treated in Art. 5—the number added to the original multiplier is an aliquot part of the increased number—that is, it is exactly divisible into it.

It is plain, therefore, that to multiply by 38, instead of multiplying by 8 and by 3, we might multiply by 40 and subtract from the result one twentieth of the result. And so on.

Example:　Multiply 28 by 38.

Solution:	40 times 28	=	1120
−	2 times 28 ($\frac{1}{20}$ of 1120) =		56
	38 times 28	=	1064

Problems

1. If a ton of soft coal occupies 38 cubic feet, what space will be occupied by 62 tons?　　　　　*Ans.* 2356 cubic feet.

2. If a bushel basket of plums weighs 57 pounds, how many pounds will 73 baskets weigh?　　　　*Ans.* 4161 pounds.

3. A barrel of brewer's pitch occupies 11.7 cubic feet. Compute the amount of space that would be occupied by 37 barrels.

Ans. 432.9 cubic feet.

9. A Short Way of Multiplying by Numbers in Which One Part Is an Exact Multiple of, or Is Exactly Divisible into, the Rest of the Number, e.g., 84, 48, 123, 312, 1938, 3612. A studied observation will reveal an interesting fact about these numbers. Note that in 84, 80 is exactly twenty times the rest of the number (the unit digit 4), and that in 48 the 8 is exactly two tenths of 40; that in 123, 120 is exactly 40 times 3, and that in 312 the 12 is four hundredths of 300.

Observation of relationships of this nature saves time and labor in working problems, as will be seen in the illustrations that follow.

Example 1: Multiply 234 by 84.

Solution: 4 times 234   =   936
        80 times 234 (20 times 936) = 18720
_____

        84 times 234   = 19656

Example 1A: Multiply 234 by 48.

Solution: 40 times 234   =   9360
          8 times 234 ($\frac{2}{10}$ of 9360) =   1872
_____

        48 times 234   = 11232

Example 2: Multiply 431 by 123.

Solution: 3 times 431   =   1293
        120 times 431 (40 times 1293) = 51720
_____

        123 times 431   = 53013

Example 2A: Multiply 431 by 312.

Solution: 300 times 431   = 129300
    12 times 431 ($\frac{4}{100}$ of 129300) =   5172
    _____
    312 times 431   = 134472

Example 3: Multiply 3467 by 1938.

Solution: 1900 times 3 467   = 6587300
    38 times 3467 ($\frac{2}{100}$ of 6587300) =   131746
    _____
    1938 times 3467   = 6719046

Example 3A: Multiply 3467 by 3819.

Solution: 19 times 3467   =   65873
    3800 times 3467 (200 times 65873)   = 13174600
    _____
    3819 times 3467   = 13240473

Example 4: Multiply 1237 by 3612.

Solution: 12 times 1237   =   14844
    3600 times 1237 (300 times 14844)   = 4453200
    _____
    3612 times 1237   = 4468044

Example 4A: Multiply 1237 by 1236.

Solution: 1200 times 1237   = 1484400
    36 times 1237 ($\frac{3}{100}$ of 1484400) =   44532
    _____
    1236 times 1237   = 1528932

Multiply 723.4 by each of the following numbers, using the procedure indicated:

1.   63.   Multiply by 3 and add 20 times the result.
2. 284.   Multiply by 4 and add 70 times the result.
3. 567.   Multiply by 7 and add 80 times the result.
4. 328.   Multiply by 8 and add 40 times the result.
5. 1860.   Multiply by 60 and add 30 times the result.
6. 1470.   Multiply by 70 and add 20 times the result.
7. 642.   Multiply by 600 and add $\frac{7}{100}$ of the result.
8. 756.   Multiply by 700 and add $\frac{8}{100}$ of the result.
9. 936.   Multiply by 900 and add $\frac{4}{100}$ of the result.
10. 1272.   Multiply by 1200 and add $\frac{6}{100}$ of the result.

PROBLEMS

1. Compute the total number of yards contained in 84 pounds of typewriter cambric of which there are 5.06 yards to the pound.

Ans. 425.04 yards.

2. A power hack saw makes 126 strokes per minute. If it worked continually for 2 hours and 3 minutes, how many strokes would it have made in that time?   Ans. 15,498 strokes.

3. If a bushel of wheat makes 315 loaves of bread each weighing 1 pound 2 ounces, how many loaves of this weight can be made with 473 bushels of wheat?   Ans. 148,995 loaves.

4. Compute the value in dollars and cents of 876 Venezuelan bolivars, quoted at 30.15 cents per bolivar.   Ans. $264.11.

5. If the capacity of a U. S. dry barrel is 7056 cubic inches, what would be the cubic inch capacity of 13.75 dry barrels?

Ans. 97,020 cubic inches.

6. What is the amount of a fire insurance premium on a $2,400,000 policy issued at the rate of $0.0426 per $100?

Ans. $1022.40.

7. Convert 387 grains to grams. (To convert grains to grams multiply by .0648.)   Ans. 25.0776 grams.

8. Five cows produced a total of 43,364 pounds of milk during one year. The next year their production increased 12.3%. What was their total production in the second year? Compute the answer to the nearest pound.   Ans. 48,698 pounds.

10. A Short Way of Multiplying by Three-Digit Numbers in Which When Increased to an Even Hundred the Hundreds Digit Is Exactly Divisible into, or Is an Exact Multiple of, the Number Added, e.g., 288, 360, 576, 693, 897. Except for the nature of the numbers to be considered here the method of procedure is essentially the same as that discussed in preceding articles. Here we are going to increase three-digit numbers to an even hundred.

It will be interesting to observe that several numbers which are multiples of a gross lend themselves perfectly to the application of this short-cut method of multiplication. The number 288, for instance, equals 2 gross; 576 equals 4 gross; 720, 5 gross, and so on.

Example 1: Multiply 647 by 288.

Solution: 300 times 647   = 194100
       − 12 times 647 ($\frac{4}{100}$ of 194100) =   7764
_____

   288 times 647   = 186336

Example 2: Multiply \$538.26 by 360.

Solution:
   400 times \$538.26   =\$215,304.00
  − 40 times \$538.26 ($\frac{1}{10}$ of \$215,304.00) =   21,530.40
_____

   360 times \$538.26   =\$193,773.60

Example 3: Multiply $273\frac{1}{6}$ by 576.

Solution: 600 times $273\frac{1}{6}$ (100 times 1639) = 163900
      − 24 times $273\frac{1}{6}$ ($\frac{4}{100}$ of 163900) =   6556
_____

   576 times $273\frac{1}{6}$ = 157344

Note in the foregoing illustration the helpfulness of our imaginative reach when confronted by a multiplicand which contains a fraction. Instead of multiplying by 6, 7 and 5, and then adding the fourth partial product of $\frac{1}{6}$ of 576, we simply subtract from 100 times the product of $273\frac{1}{6}$ multiplied by 6, $\frac{4}{100}$ of the result. In the example that follows the fruitfulness of this method is even more apparent.

Example 4: Multiply $813\frac{1}{7}$ by 693.

Solution: 700 times $813\frac{1}{7}$ (100 times 5692) = 569200
    —   7 times $813\frac{1}{7}$ =   5692

       693 times $813\frac{1}{7}$ = 563508

The illustration that follows is a noteworthy example of the usefulness of the technique discussed in Art. 8.

Example 5: Multiply \$16.33$\frac{1}{3}$ by 897.

Solution:
Second step. 900 times \$16.33$\frac{1}{3}$
               (300 times \$49.00) = \$14,700.00
First step. — 3 times \$16.33$\frac{1}{3}$ =   49.00

        897 times \$16.33$\frac{1}{3}$ = \$14,651.00

Example 6: If a sheet of asbestos mill board 42 by 48 inches weighs 5.82 pounds, how much will 239 sheets of these dimensions weigh?

Solution: 6 times 239   = 1434
      — .18 times 239 ($\frac{3}{100}$ of 1434) =   43.02

      5.82 times 239   = 1390.98
                        Ans. 1390.98 pounds.

Exercises

Multiply 258 by each of the following numbers, using the technique indicated:

1. 297.   Multiply by 300 and subtract $\frac{1}{100}$ of the result.
2. 285.   Multiply by 300 and subtract $\frac{1}{20}$ of the result.
3. 294.   Multiply by 300 and subtract $\frac{2}{100}$ of the result.
4. 296.   Multiply by 400 and subtract $\frac{1}{100}$ of the result.
5. 392.   Multiply by 400 and subtract $\frac{2}{100}$ of the result.
6. 475.   Multiply by 500 and subtract $\frac{5}{100}$ of the result.
7. 594.   Multiply by 600 and subtract $\frac{1}{100}$ of the result.
8. 528.   Multiply by 600 and subtract $\frac{12}{100}$ of the result.
9. 784.   Multiply by 800 and subtract $\frac{2}{100}$ of the result.
10. 873.   Multiply by 900 and subtract $\frac{3}{100}$ of the result.

Problems

1. What would the total net weight be of 138 pint containers of cream containing 28% butter fat, if cream of this butter-fat content weighs 8.37 pounds per gallon? Compute the answer to the nearest pound.   *Ans.* 144 pounds.

2. Find the cost of $3\frac{3}{4}$ dozen units at $2.97 per dozen. *Ans.* $11.14.

3. Steam at $100°$ C. has a weight of 0.598 grams per liter. Compute the weight of 374 liters.   *Ans.* 223.652 grams.

4. A square foot of iron 0.072 inches thick weighs 2.88 pounds. What will 37 square feet weigh?   *Ans.* 106.56 pounds.

5. A barrel of cement weighs 376 pounds. Find the weight of 34 barrels.   *Ans.* 12,784 pounds.

6. If a 4-inch pump has a discharge capacity of 380 gallons per minute, how many gallons would be discharged in 4 hours 17 minutes?   *Ans.* 97,660 gallons.

7. Pure chromium weighs 6.93 grams per cubic centimeter. Compute the weight of 492 cubic centimeters.   *Ans.* 3409.56 grams.

8. A foot of flat bar steel $\frac{5}{16}$ inches thick and 7 inches wide weighs 7.44 pounds. How much will 276 feet weigh?

      Ans. 2053.44 pounds.

CHAPTER II

THE BREAKDOWN METHOD OF MULTIPLICATION

The effectiveness of practically every mathematical short-cut is dependent upon some manner of breakdown, and to a greater or lesser extent each of the short-cuts discussed so far is the result of such a procedure. We have seen, for instance, that to multiply by 45 it is easier to multiply first by 50 and then to subtract one tenth of the result; that it is sometimes easier to multiply by factors of a number than by its digits. In Art. 9 we learned how to multiply by a number like 3612 by computing only two partial products and, in Art. 10, how to reduce the process of multiplying by some three-digit numbers to the point where it was but necessary to compute one partial product and one simple calculation in division.

The first chapter gave us a background for the appreciation of a new and even more interesting track that will open out for us in the four articles that follow. Here we will consider some of the many ramifications of the breakdown method of multiplication. And one of the things we will discover is that it is not necessary, in using short-cuts, to limit ourselves to two-, three- or four-figure numbers, or to two-, three- or four-figure numbers in which one part

27

is an exact multiple of, or is exactly divisible into, the other part.

Inseparably linked with all time- and labor-saving mathematical procedure, a thorough understanding of the breakdown method of multiplication will enable the reader to have a valuable insight into the virtually unlimited possibilities of short-cuts in business mathematics.

It is suggested that the subject matter of this chapter be studied very carefully, in order that the techniques treated in the articles in succeeding chapters may be quickly grasped. An abundance of illustrations will help pave the way toward a clearer understanding of the method and to proficiency in its use.

11. Multiplying by Two- and Three-Figure Numbers, Like 12, 26, 35, 39, 48, 52, 76, 128. The number 12 is a relatively easy number to get along with. But could the reader multiply $3.60 by 12 mentally, without using the uncomfortable process which entails "carrying"? By breaking up 12 into the numbers 10 and 2 the mental computation of the problem becomes remarkably simple: 10 times $3.60 equals $36.00; twice $3.60 is $7.20; $36.00 plus $7.20 equals $43.20.

In multiplying $3.60 by 26 the procedure is even simpler: 25 times $3.60 (one fourth of $360.00) equals $90.00; and $90.00 plus $3.60 equals $93.60.

Example 1: Multiply 28 cents by 35.

Solution: 25 times 28 cents ($\frac{1}{4}$ of $28.00) = $7.00
10 times 28 cents   =   2.80

_____

35 times 28 cents   = $9.80

Example 2: Multiply 73 cents by 39.

Solution: 40 times 73 cents (4 times \$7.30) = \$29.20
   — 1 times 73 cents   =   .73

        39 times 73 cents   = \$28.47

Example 3: Multiply 65 cents by 39.8.

Solution: 40 times 65 cents (4 times \$6.50) = \$26.00
   — .2 times 65 cents ($\frac{1}{5}$ of 65 cents) =   .13

        39.8 times 65 cents   = \$25.87

Example 4: Multiply 38 cents by 52.

Solution: 50 times 38 cents ($\frac{1}{2}$ of \$38.00) = \$19.00
         2 times 38 cents   =   .76

        52 times 38 cents   = \$19.76

Example 5: Multiply 44 cents by 76.

Solution: 75 times 44 cents ($\frac{3}{4}$ of \$44.00) = \$33.00
         1 times 44 cents   =   .44

        76 times 44 cents   = \$33.44

Example 6: Find the cost of 128 units at \$4.76 per hundred.

Solution: 100 at \$4.76 per hundred   = \$4.76
          25 at \$4.76 per hundred ($\frac{1}{4}$ of \$4.76) = 1.19
           3 at \$4.76 per hundred (3 times .047) =   .14

        128 at \$4.76 per hundred   = \$6.09

Example 7: Estimate the value of 436 units at \$1.68 per hundred.

| *Solution:* | 400 at \$1.68 per 100 | = \$6.72 |
| | 40 at \$1.68 per 100 ($\frac{1}{10}$ of \$6.72) = | .67 |

| | 440 at \$1.68 per 100 | = \$7.39 |
| — | 4 at \$1.68 per 100 ($\frac{1}{10}$ of .67) = | .07 |

| | 436 at \$1.68 per 100 | = \$7.32 |

PROBLEMS

★ **1.** If there are 32 teeth per inch in a 12-inch hack saw blade, how many teeth are there in the entire blade? (Which partial products did you add or subtract to arrive at the total?)

Ans. 320 plus 64 = 384

★ **2.** A machine folds and closes 55 cartons per minute. How many cartons will it do in 2 hours 4 minutes? *Ans.* 6820

★ **3.** Iron weighs .26 pounds per cubic inch. Compute the weight of 29 cubic inches of iron. *Ans.* 7.54 pounds

★ **4.** Find the cost of 26 units at \$6.80 per hundred. *Ans.* \$1.77.

5. A workman receiving \$1.12 per hour and entitled to time and a half for all time put in over 40 hours in one week works a total of 46 hours. What did he earn for the week? (Hint: He worked 6 hours overtime, so his pay will be computed on the basis of 49 hours straight time.) *Ans.* \$54.88

12. The Use of the Breakdown Method of Multiplication Is Especially Advantageous in Dealing with Decimal Fractions. The use of decimal numbers, either as multiplicands or as multipliers, frequently necessitates the pointing off of decimal places in the answer. This in itself is quite simple, but there is always the possibility of pointing off the wrong number of places. A safer and shorter method of multiplication is the breakdown method

Take for instance the problem 365 times .37147. Let us compute this, first by the conventional method, then by the breakdown method.

Conventional Method

```
    .37147
       365
    ───────
    185735
    222882
    111441
    ───────
  13558655
```

Since there are five decimal places in the multiplicand, the same number of decimal places must be pointed off in the product. So our answer is 135.58655, or 135.59.

Breakdown Method

300 times .37147 (3 times 37.147) = 111.441
60 times .37147 ($\frac{1}{5}$ of 111.441) = 22.288
5 times .37147 ($\frac{1}{2}$ of 3.7147) =   1.857
──
365 times .37147   = 135.59

Which of the two methods do you think is the shorter and more reliable?

Computed by the conventional method each partial product contains six figures and the total, eight figures, whereas by the breakdown method one partial product contains six figures, another has five, and another, four, and the total but five. Consider also the greater possibility of error in adding the larger partial products and the possibility of pointing off the wrong number of decimal places in the computation by the conventional method, and you will appreciate the advantage of the safe and speedy breakdown method of multiplication.

A study of the procedure in the following illustration will be found interesting and profitable.

Example: Find the cost of 1278 units at $1.86 per hundred.

Solution: 1000 at $1.86 per 100   = $18.60
    250 at $1.86 per 100 ($\frac{1}{4}$ of $18.60) =   4.65
     25 at $1.86 per 100 ($\frac{1}{10}$ of $4.65) =   .465
      3 at $1.86 per 100 (3 times .0186) =   .056

    1278 at $1.86 per 100   = $23.77

Do you see how we arrive at the price per unit (.0186) in the foregoing illustration? We keep moving the decimal point to the left, saying to ourselves, "If the price per hundred is $1.86, the price of ten is .186, and the price per unit is .0186."

A type of problem not so frequently encountered, but important nonetheless, is this: Multiply $2175.25 by .1346286. A quick glance at these figures will indicate that to solve this problem by the conventional method would call for at least six partial products, each containing at least six figures. Done by the breakdown method the computation is simple, quick and easy:

$2000.00 times .1346286 (2 times $134.6286) = $269.257
 100.00 times .1346286   =   13.463
  50.00 times .1346286 ($\frac{1}{2}$ of $13.463)   =   6.732
  25.00 times .1346286 ($\frac{1}{2}$ of $6.732)   =   3.366
   .25 times .1346286 ($\frac{1}{100}$ of $3.366) =   .034

$2175.25 times .1346286   = $292.85

The breakdown method of multiplying dollars and cents has definite time-saving advantages, and the reader is urged to drill himself in the technique; if he has occasion to do any calculating at all, the use of this method will save him many precious minutes, he will have less need for calculating machines, and he will save much mental and nervous energy besides. It would be hopeless to attempt to illustrate all or even any considerable number of the many possible adaptations of the breakdown method, and it is hoped that the many illustrations and problems in this chapter have helped the reader to gain an intimate working knowledge of this very important time-saving process.

PROBLEMS

1. Multiply .479 by 298.   *Ans.* 142.742.

2. How many yards are there in 317.5 pounds of fabric of which there are 8.97 yards to the pound?   *Ans.* 2847.975 yards.

3. A cubic foot of asphaltum weighs 87.3 pounds. Estimate the weight of 26.35 cubic feet. Compute the answer to the nearest pound. (Hint: 87.3 is equivalent to 90 minus 2.7.)
                                         Ans. 2300 pounds.

4. If 1000 feet of $\frac{3}{4}$-inch packing-case strapping weigh 38.2 pounds, what should 843 feet weigh? Compute the answer to the nearest quarter of a pound.   *Ans.* $32\frac{1}{4}$ pounds.

CHAPTER III

THE "DOUBLE-AND-HALVE" METHOD OF MULTIPLICATION

One of the most helpful of all mathematical short-cuts is a device which the author chooses to call the "double-and-halve" method. It is a simple trick, and the wonder is that so many successful businessmen with a mathematical background never think of using it.

The principle of the process is based on the fact that when two factors in a multiplication problem are multiplied and divided, respectively, by the same value, the product is not affected.

The illustrations in this chapter demonstrate the ease and simplicity with which many problems can be computed mentally or with a minimum of pencil and paper work by this uncommonly used method.

13. How to Multiply Mentally and Quickly by $2\frac{1}{2}$, $3\frac{1}{2}$, $4\frac{1}{2}$, $5\frac{1}{2}$. To compute 62 times $2\frac{1}{2}$ all one need do is to multiply half of 62 (31) by twice $2\frac{1}{2}$ (5). With practically no effort at all, it is seen that 5 times 31 equals 155.

The same procedure applies to the multipliers $3\frac{1}{2}$, $4\frac{1}{2}$ and $5\frac{1}{2}$. Thus $3\frac{1}{2}$ times 24 is equivalent to 7 times 12. By the same token $4\frac{1}{2}$ times 16 equals 9 times 8, and $5\frac{1}{2}$ times 126 equals 11 times 63. The last problem, by the way, may recall to the reader's mind the interesting rule explained in Art. 1-f, by which 11 times 63 can be computed in a fraction of a second, and with virtually no possibility of error.

The term "double-and-halve" method was chosen primarily for its descriptive value, and for the reason that factors in a multiplication problem can be changed more easily in this than in any other ratio. However, the value by which multiplicand and multiplier may be multiplied and divided, respectively, need not necessarily be limited to 2; any other value may be used to exactly the same effect. Thus $2\frac{1}{2}$ times 440 would be computed more conveniently by multiplying and dividing the factors, respectively, by 4 instead of by 2, changing the problem to read 10 times 110. Similarly, the factors in the problem $3\frac{1}{2}$ times 330 might be multiplied and divided, respectively, by 3, changing the problem to read $10\frac{1}{2}$ times 110.

Example: A machine for de-airing pottery has a capacity of $3\frac{1}{2}$ tons per hour. At this rate how many tons of pottery can be de-aired by this machine in 14 hours?

Solution: $3\frac{1}{2}$ times 14 is equivalent to 7 times 7, which equals 49. *Ans.* 49 tons.

Problems

★ **1.** When insurance is paid in advance for 3 years the premium is $2\frac{1}{2}$ times the one-year premium. If the premium for one year is $32.24 what would it be for 3 years? *Ans.* $80.60.

★ **2.** Asbestos cement sheets in the $\frac{1}{4}$ inch thickness weigh approximately $2\frac{1}{2}$ pounds per square foot. Compute the weight of each of the following sheets: (a) 42 by 48 inches; (b) 48 by 48 inches; (c) 42 by 96 inches. *Ans.* (a) 35 pounds; (b) 40 pounds; (c) 70 pounds.

★ **3.** If the average daily consumption of corn silage by one sheep is $3\frac{1}{2}$ pounds, how many pounds would 64 sheep consume in 30 days?
Ans. 6720 pounds.

★ **4.** Asbestos board is used for fireproof lining of floors, etc. If a board 42 by 48 inches in the $\frac{3}{64}$ inch thickness weighs $3\frac{1}{2}$ pounds, what would 18 boards weigh?   *Ans.* 63 pounds.

★ **5.** A group of anglers catch a total of 42 codfish which have an average weight of $4\frac{1}{2}$ pounds. Estimate in two seconds the weight of the entire catch.   *Ans.* 189 pounds.

★ **6.** A baked cork used for insulation is supplied in bags of 7 cubic feet capacity. If one cubic foot of this material weighs approximately $4\frac{1}{2}$ pounds, what would the weight be of 22 bags? (Hint: $4\frac{1}{2}$ times 22 is equivalent to 9 times 11.)   *Ans.* 693 pounds. (*Arts.* 1-f, 3)

★ **7.** A machine wraps 5 bouillon cubes in a packet at the rate of 68 packets per minute. At this rate how many packets can be wrapped in $5\frac{1}{2}$ hours?   *Ans.* 22,440 packets.

★ **8.** The huacaya sheep yields a fleece weighing approximately $5\frac{1}{2}$ pounds. On this basis what would the fleece yield be of 162 huacaya sheep?   *Ans.* 891 pounds. (*Art.* 1-f)

14. How to Multiply Mentally and Quickly by Numbers Which Contain Fractions Other Than $\frac{1}{2}$.

We saw in the previous article that multiplication problems in which one of the factors contains the fraction $\frac{1}{2}$ lend themselves very conveniently to computation by the double-and-halve method. This process may be used with equal facility in the case of numbers containing other fractions. Thus the problem of finding the area of a floor 8 feet 4 inches long by 24 feet wide is simplified by multiplying the length by 3 and dividing the width by 3, changing the problem to read 25 feet by 8 feet; and we see at a glance that the answer is 200 square feet. Note that we multiplied and divided respectively by 3 because 3 is also the denominator of the fraction $8\frac{1}{3}$, the equivalent in feet of 8 feet 4 inches.

This technique is just as easy to apply to the fraction $\frac{3}{4}$. A good example is $2\frac{3}{4}$, which is the number of bushels in a hectoliter. To find the number of bushels in 28 hectoliters, for instance, we proceed by changing $2\frac{3}{4}$ into a whole number. The denominator of the fraction being 4, we multiply $2\frac{3}{4}$ by 4 and divide 28 by 4, which gives us the equivalent of 11 times 7. Without any further effort whatever we know that there are 77 bushels in 28 hectoliters.

The same technique may be applied with equally good effect to mixed numbers containing tens and hundreds digits as well as unit digits. Thus to do the problem $317\frac{1}{3}$ times 24 we multiply and divide respectively by 3, obtaining the equivalent of 952 times 8. It is interesting to note that in the solution to this problem it is necessary to write down only four figures, compared with 19 by the conventional method, to say nothing of the greater laboriousness of the latter process.

Problems

★ 1. Estimate the volume in cubic feet of a box of these dimensions: length, 18 feet; width, 12 feet; depth, $7\frac{1}{3}$ feet.
Ans. 1584 cubic feet. (*Art.* 11)

★ 2. Compute the number of feet in $203\frac{1}{3}$ rods. One rod equals $16\frac{1}{2}$ feet. (Hint: 610 times $5\frac{1}{2}$ is equivalent to 305 times 11.)
Ans. 3355 feet.

★ 3. If the coastwise freight rate on coal shipped from New York to Portland, Maine, on quantities of 700 tons or less, is $3.75 per ton, what would it cost to transport 32 tons of coal between these two points?
Ans. $120.00.

★ 4. A water tank for the use of horses and cattle is 8 feet long, 3 feet 3 inches wide, and 2 feet 3 inches deep. How many gallons of water will it hold, filled to a depth of 2 feet? (One cubic foot equals $7\frac{1}{2}$ gallons.)
Ans. 390 gallons.

★ 5. A tank has a capacity of 640 cubic feet. Compute the weight of water filled to three fourths of its depth. (One cubic foot of water weighs $62\frac{1}{2}$ pounds.)
Ans. 30,000 pounds.

★ 6. If there are 6400 2½-ounce tacks to the pound, how many tacks of this size should there be in 4 pounds 2 ounces? (Pencil and paper should be used to write the answer only.) *Ans.* 26,400.

★ 7. A San Francisco insurance salesman is asked by a creamery to estimate the annual premium on a Manufacturer's and Contractor's Liability insurance policy based on an annual payroll of $73,250.00. If the rate in California on insurance of this nature is 8 cents per $100 of payroll, what would the premium amount to? *Ans.* $58.60.

★ 8. A road 16 feet wide and one mile long is filled with aggregate one inch thick. If the quantity of aggregate used on this job is 261 cubic yards, how much would be needed to fill a road 2⅖ miles long and 32 feet wide, one inch thick? *Ans.* 1160 cubic yards.

★ 9. If rails weigh 43⅓ pounds per foot, what would be the weight in tons of the rails used to lay one mile of track? (One mile equals 5280 feet, and one ton equals 2000 pounds.) *Ans.* 114.4 tons.

15. How to Multiply Mentally by 14, 16, 18, 24 and Higher Even Numbers.

The principle of the method discussed in this article is based on the fact that it is easier to multiply mentally by one digit than by two. The whole "secret" to the method, then, is to convert the two-digit multiplier to a single digit. Thus to compute 18 times 54½, 18 is halved and 54½ is doubled. This changes the problem to read 9 times 109, which can be computed in but a fraction of the time it would take to work the original problem by the conventional method.

Here, as in the preceding two articles, it will be seen that two factors in a multiplication problem may be multiplied and divided, respectively, by a number other than 2 to equally good advantage. Changing the aforementioned problem to 3 times 327 instead of to 9 times 109 does not affect the product.

As a matter of fact it makes no difference whether, in

doubling and halving, a factor is changed or the product is changed, so long as the doubling process is offset by the halving process. Thus the problem $12\frac{1}{2}$ times 16 might very conveniently be solved by multiplying $12\frac{1}{2}$ by 8, instead of by 16, and completing the computation by multiplying the product by 2.

Another illustration is $17\frac{1}{2}$ times 28. This problem is equivalent to 35 times 14 or 70 times 7; and we see by inspection that the answer is 490.

Even when the multiplicand is a large number the double-and-halve method may be used to advantage, though the use of pencil and paper may be necessary to some extent. Thus the problem $3481.84 multiplied by 14 would be computed by first multiplying mentally by 2 and writing down the partial product $6963.68, then multiplying this product mentally by 7 and writing down the answer, $48,745.76.

Example: What is the total length of 406 logs, each 16 feet long?

Solution: Revising the problem to read 812 times 8, we see by inspection, without any need for putting pencil to paper, that the answer is 6496, for 8 times 800 equals 6400; 8 times 12 equals 96; and 6400 plus 96 equals 6496.

Ans. 6496 feet.

It is interesting to observe that in some instances the change may be made "in midstream," so to speak; that is, a part of the problem is worked with the figures as originally given, and the rest of the problem is done with changes in the multiplicand and multiplier. An example of such a problem is 48 times $1.03. The solution by this method follows:

| 48 times $1.00 | = $48.00 |
| 48 times .03 (12 times .12 computed mentally) | = 1.44 |

| 48 times $1.03 | = $49.44 |

A noteworthy benefit of the double-and-halve method of multiplication is its use in helping to eliminate the need for pencil and paper when these physical accessories are neither available nor practical to use. On a train journey, in an airplane, when in bed with the lights out, in a conversation, or at a conference where it may be necessary to make a quick computation without the use of pencil and paper, it is a decided advantage to be able to do mentally a problem like 16 times 65 without having to multiply by 6 and carry 3. Using the double-and-halve method, the problem can be readily computed mentally by changing it successively to 8 times 130, 4 times 260, twice 520; and with practically no effort at all, and as easily as counting sheep, the answer 1040 comes to mind. Or take the problem $403\frac{1}{2}$ times 16; by the double-and-halve method we obtain the equivalent of 807 times 8, and without any further effort the answer 6456 becomes obvious. The time-saving advantages and the reduction in the possibility of error of the double-and-halve method of multiplication cannot be overemphasized.

Problems

★ 1. A merchant plans to include in an advertising campaign the use of 1400 booklets at a cost of $6.00 per hundred. Using the double-and-halve method, and taking no more than 2 seconds to do it, compute mentally the total cost of the booklets.   *Ans.* $84.00.

★ 2. A 10-ton Diesel locomotive hauls trains of fourteen 3500-

pound loads ten times daily over a certain distance. How many pounds are hauled by this locomotive in a day?

Ans. 490,000 pounds.

★ 3. A shoe machine sews 60 buttons per minute, feeding and attaching 16 stitches to each button. How many stitches does this machine make in a continuous operation of 1 hour 40 minutes?

Ans. 96,000.

★ 4. A concrete mix in the $1:2\frac{3}{4}:4$ proportion calls for the use of 6.2 sacks of cement for each 100 square feet of area 4 inches thick. If concrete of this mix and thickness is to be laid on floors having a total area of 1800 square feet, how many sacks of cement will be needed to make the mix?   *Ans.* 111.6 sacks.

★ 5. A furrier receives a shipment of skins of which there are to be 18 to the pound. If the net weight of the shipment is 17 pounds, how many skins were received?   *Ans.* 306 skins.

★ 6. Basing your answer on a consumption of 40 pounds of corn silage per head per day, how many pounds of silage may be expected to be consumed by a herd of 14 dairy cows in 24 days?

Ans. 13,440 pounds.

★ 7. Compute the number of bottles that can be washed in three 8-hour days by a machine having a capacity of 600 bottles an hour.

Ans. 14,400.

16. How to Multiply Quickly by 140, 160, 180, 220, 240, 270, 280, 360, etc. Here the method is substantially the same as that described in the preceding article. The only difference is that instead of multiplying and dividing by 2 or by 3, we multiply and divide by 20 or 30, as the case may be, reducing the multiplier to a single-digit number.

Thus 140 times 37 would be changed to 7 times 740; 160 times 129 would become 8 times 2580; 180 times $2.71 would be restated as 9 times $54.20; and the problem 220 times 72 would, by this method, be changed to read 11 times 1440.

The same method would apply to the rest of the multipliers mentioned in this article heading. However, in changing numbers greater than 240 it is advisable to divide and multiply, respectively, by 30 or 40, etc., rather than by 20. Thus 270 times 17 would be changed to 9 times 510, and 360 times 173 might be restated to read 12 times 5190. The problem 280 times 83, on the other hand, might be computed more conveniently by multiplying and dividing, respectively, by 40, changing the problem to read 7 times 3320.

The process of multiplying and dividing factors by 30 or 40 need not necessarily be confined to problems in which the multiplier is greater than 240. It may be used to excellent advantage in converting multipliers like 180 and 160. Thus the problem 180 times $33\frac{1}{3}$ might be changed advantageously by multiplying and dividing, respectively, by 30, making it read 6 times 1000. One hundred and sixty times $21.50 might be changed with good effect to read 4 times $860.00. And a problem like 180 times $16\frac{2}{3}$ can be computed mentally and quickly by changing it to read 3 times 1000.

Note that in the following illustration the multiplication and division by 5 makes the problem calculable mentally in a matter of seconds.

Example: In 1925 the average yield of cotton per acre was 165 pounds. Today the yield is well in excess of 210 pounds. Taking the latter figure as an average yield, how much more cotton would be produced on 2200 acres today than in 1925?

Solution: The difference between 210 pounds and 165 pounds is 45 pounds. 45 times 2200 is equivalent to 9 times 11,000, and we see instantly that the answer is 99,000.

Ans. 99,000 pounds more.

The reader should not lose sight of the prime objective of the double-and-halve method, which is to make possible the mental computation of a large variety of problems and, when mental computation might be a little difficult or hazardous, to shorten the process of computation by reducing the amount of pencil-and-paper work and eliminating entirely the need for addition.

PROBLEMS

★ 1. A seven-hold ship can be loaded at the rate of 140 tons an hour. Estimate the number of tons that can be loaded in $32\frac{1}{2}$ hours.
Ans. 4550 tons.

2. If the gross weight of a wood box of fresh apples is 276 pounds, how much would 160 boxes weigh? *Ans.* 44,160 pounds.

★ 3. A manufacturer announces that he plans to produce a new stove every 20 seconds—that is, 180 an hour. If he is successful in carrying out his plans how many stoves will he be able to produce in a 45-hour week? *Ans.* 8100 stoves.

★ 4. If a generator produces 220 cubic feet of hydrogen per hour, what volume would be produced in 17 hours?
Ans. 3740 cubic feet. (*Art.* 1-f)

★ 5. A perforated metal is made with 240 holes to the square inch. Estimate the number of holes contained in a sheet 18 by 28 inches.
Ans. 120,960 holes. (*Art.* 15)

★ 6. How many pounds of material will be sifted in 9 hours 20 minutes by a turbine sifter having a capacity of 270 pounds per hour? *Ans.* 2520 pounds. (*Art.* 14)

★ 7. The raw material used in the manufacture of leather belting is known as the strap butt, which has an area of approximately $19\frac{1}{4}$ square feet. Estimate the total area of a lot of 280 strap butts.
Ans. 5390 square feet. (*Art.* 14)

★ 8. If on irrigated land, alfalfa yields $8\frac{1}{3}$ tons of dry hay per acre, how much dry hay may be expected from 360 acres of irrigated land? *Ans.* 3000 tons. (*Art.* 14)

CHAPTER IV

MORE TRICKS IN MENTAL ARITHMETIC

Fortified with a knowledge of the breakdown method of multiplication as explained in Chapter II, the reader will readily appreciate the short-cuts considered in the following articles.

17. Many Different Problems in Which the Multiplier Is 12 or a Single Digit, Such as 6, 7 or 9, Can Be Computed Mentally with Very Little Effort. If you had to multiply 34 by 6 mentally would you do it by the conventional method? Would you write down 34, with 6 underneath it, and proceed to multiply 4 by 6, setting down 4 and carrying 2, and so on? This would indeed be an unnecessarily laborious process.

Consider this simpler way: think of the multiplicand as 30 plus 4. Now multiply each of these numbers (30 and 4) separately by 6 and add the products. Six times 30 equals 180; 6 times 4 equals 24; 180 plus 24 equals 204.

Three-digit numbers are no more difficult to manipulate by this method than two-digit numbers. The problem 128 times 7, for instance, would be worked in this way: 7 times 100 equals 700; 7 times 20 equals 140, and 700 plus 140 equals 840; 7 times 8 equals 56, and 840 plus 56 equals 896. That is the *theory* of the method—actually it is unnecessary to say to oneself, audibly or inaudibly, "7 times 20 equals 140," or "7 times 8 equals 56." It would save time and avoid confusion to say merely, "700, plus 140 equals 840, plus 56 equals 896."

Nine is another interesting number in this connection. Here we will find that in some instances it is just as easy to multiply by 10 and then to subtract—first the hundreds, then the tens, and finally the unit digits—as to multiply each digit by 9 and add the partial products. Thus taking the problem 228 times 9, the computations by both methods would be as follows:

Method A: 228 times 10   = 2280
          2280 minus 228   = 2080 minus 28
          2080 minus 28   = 2060 minus 8
          2060 minus 8   = 2052

Method B: 200 times 9   = 1800
          1800 plus 180 (9 times 20) = 1980
          1980 plus 72 (9 times 8)   = 2052

And here, as in many other instances throughout the book, some readers will prefer the first method and others the second.

The multiplier 12 is perhaps the most interesting of all because one can multiply by this number in many different ways. In the case of multiplicands with low digits, as for example 109, 213, 342, the most practical method might be to multiply each digit separately, starting with the hundreds. Thus to multiply 109 by 12 we would say, "1200 and 108 equals 1308." And to multiply 213 by 12 we might say, "2400 and 120 equals 2520, and 36 equals 2556." On the other hand, to multiply 826 by 12, it may be found easier to multiply 825 by 12 (which equals 3300 times 3), and quick as a flash we should note that the answer is 9900 plus 12, or 9912. And if the problem were 185 times 12, it would be very convenient to say, "10 times 185 equals 1850, and 370 (twice 185) equals 2220." Or, since by doubling 185 the multiplicand is reduced to a two-digit number and the multiplier to a one-digit number, we might say, "185 times 12 equals 370 times 6; 300 times 6 equals 1800, and 420 (6 times 70) equals 2220."

Example: Estimate mentally the value of 12 instrument panels at $2.37 each.

Solution: 12 times $2.00   = $24.00
            12 times $0.30 = $3.60; and $24.00 = $27.60
            12 times $0.07 = $0.84; and $27.60 = $28.44
                                                   Ans. $28.44.

The endless variety of ways in which multiplicands and multipliers can be manipulated will be readily apparent. No one method is the best in every instance or the most suitable for all individuals, and it is hoped that a studied concentration on the examples given will help develop the reader's mathematical thinking so he will acquire the instinct of being able to quickly determine the most practical method by which he can most readily compute any type of problem.

PROBLEMS

The following problems should be worked without pencil and paper.

★ 1. Find the cost of 12 yards of cloth at $2.43 per yard.
                                                   Ans. $29.16.

★ 2. How much work, in terms of watt-hours, is done by a 12-

horsepower motor? (One horsepower equals 746 watts. And the work done by one watt in one hour is equivalent to one watt-hour.)
Ans. 8952 watt-hours.

★ **3.** Compute the cost of 6 shirts at $3.43 each. *Ans.* $20.58.

★ **4.** It takes 2.46 cubic yards of concrete to construct an 8-inch-thick concrete floor of 100 square feet. How many cubic yards of concrete will be required to make in the same thickness a floor having an area of 600 square feet? *Ans.* 14.76 cubic yards.

★ **5.** Elevator insurance is usually issued at so much per unit. If the rate for elevators in office and bank buildings is $53.00 per unit per year, what would the premium be for one year on 7 elevators in this classification? *Ans.* $371.00.

★ **6.** One bundle of 500 feet of galvanized pipe $\frac{1}{8}$ inch thick weighs 123 pounds. How much will 7 bundles weigh? *Ans.* 861 pounds.

★ **7.** Shortage of stock makes it necessary for a printer to deliver only 9000 letterheads on an order for 10,000. At the price per thousand of $7.30, what would the 9000 letterheads cost?
Ans. $65.70.

★ **8.** Estimate the value of 9 dozen bracelets at $4.35 per dozen.
Ans. $39.15.

18. How to Multiply Mentally by a Power of 2, e.g., 4, 8, 16, etc.

An especially significant nugget of arithmetical knowledge is the "successive" method of multiplying mentally by a power of 2.

To multiply 73 by 4, for instance, it is not necessary to use the conventional method, multiplying 3 by 4, writing down 2 and carrying 1, and so on. Even if the conventional method were used to obtain the answer mentally, it would have a drawback for, in mental computations which necessitate carrying, errors are likely to occur. A shorter method is to double the multiplicand and keep on doubling the products as many times as the multiplier can be factored by 2, or as many times as may be necessary.

Four, for example, contains the "2 factor" twice; so that the problem 73 times 4 would be calculable mentally in this fashion: twice 73 equals 146, and twice 146 equals 292.

If the multiplier were 8 instead of 4, we would continue the process once more, saying to ourselves, "twice 292 equals 584." And if the multiplier were 16, the answer would be twice 584, or 1168.

Is it not likely, you might ask, to lose track of the number of times the multiplicand is multiplied by 2? Not if the procedure is systematic. A good way to insure this is to restate the problem at each stage of the calculation. Thus taking the problem 29 times 16, we would say, "29 times 16 equals 58 times 8, equals 116 times 4, equals 232 times 2, equals 464."

In many instances the problem becomes easily calculable mentally without breaking the multiplier down to 2. Thus after the problem 35 times 16 has been changed to 70 times 8, the answer becomes evident immediately—8 times 7 equals 56, and annexing a zero supplies the answer, 560. Similarly, $22\frac{1}{2}$ times 16 equals 45 times 8, equals 90 times 4; and we know in a flash that the answer is 360.

Example: Compute mentally the cost of 16 tons of steel scrap at $17.75 per ton.

Solution: 16 at $17.75
           equals 8 at $35.50,
           equals 4 at $71.00,
           equals 2 at $142.00,
           equals $284.00.

Naturally, this method could not be used very conveniently when the multiplicand we start with consists of three or more figures, or with multipliers that are greater than 16 or 32. Nonetheless, it is a significant short-cut which, in addition to saving time, will add pleasure and satisfaction to your mathematical adventures.

PROBLEMS

The following problems should be worked without pencil and paper, and the answers should be written down only after they have been computed mentally.

⋆ 1. What did it cost to ship a 4-pound package from Miami, Florida, to Salinas, Ecuador, at the air express rate of 86 cents a pound? *Ans.* $3.44.

⋆ 2. What is the cost of 8 chairs at $12.65 each? *Ans.* $101.20.

⋆ 3. The peck is a unit of dry measure. It is equal to 16 pints. How many pints are there in 17 pecks? *Ans.* 272 pints.

⋆ 4. Gun metal, a soft bronze, is formed with 16 parts of copper to one of tin. Compute the number of parts of copper that would be necessary to use with 23 parts of tin in the making of this metal.
Ans. 368 parts of copper.

⋆ 5. A workman hired at an hourly rate of $1.17 decides to quit at the end of the fourth day. If he worked a total of 32 hours, how much pay will be coming to him? *Ans.* $37.44.

⋆ 6. A woman's hosiery machine has a capacity of 32 dozen pairs an hour. How many dozen pairs can be produced with this equipment in 37 hours? *Ans.* 1184 dozen pairs.

19. How to Compute Mentally, Multiplication Problems in Which One Factor Is a Small Sum of Money, the Other a Whole Number. It is unfortunate but true that many individuals do not know how to use the decimal system for solving multiplication problems in which one factor is a small sum of money.

In Art. 7 we learned that sometimes the transposition of factors in a multiplication problem makes the product instantly apparent. We saw, for instance, that by changing the problem 25 times 35 cents to read 35 times 25 cents, the answer was immediately obvious. In this article we shall make an attempt to visualize the fractional relationship between $1.00 and amounts under $1.00, and to learn another useful method of dealing with multiplicands having a value of less than a dollar.

Let us begin with a review of a few simple facts. Ninety cents is the equivalent of $1.00 less one tenth of $1.00; 55 cents is half a dollar plus one tenth of half a dollar; 45 cents is half a dollar less one tenth of half a dollar; $1.05 is $1.00 plus one twentieth of $1.00.

If you are not accustomed to working with figures this may seem a little confusing at first. It will probably be much clearer after observing the steps in the following solutions:

Example 1: Multiply 90 cents by 35 mentally.

Solution: 35 times $1.00 = $35.00
— 35 times .10   =   3.50
_____

35 times .90   = $31.50

Example 2: Multiply 55 cents by 46 mentally.

Solution: 46 times .50   = $23.00
46 times .05 ($\frac{1}{10}$ of $23.00) =   2.30
_____

46 times .55   = $25.30

Example 3: Multiply 45 cents by 84.

Solution: 84 times .50   = $42.00
— 84 times .05 ($\frac{1}{10}$ of $42.00) =   4.20
_____

84 times .45   = $37.80

In problems in which the multipliers contain but a few digits, as in the preceding three illustrations, it is comparatively easy to perform the entire computation mentally. With large multipliers the computation may be speeded by writing down the partial products. It would be good practice, though, to learn to add small sums like these mentally.

Here is an easy and interesting example: Multiply 98 cents by 20. In this case either of two methods may be used. This problem is the equivalent of $9.80 multiplied by 2, and without giving it a second thought we see that the answer is $19.60. Or we may take the product of $1.00 multiplied by 20, and subtract the product of 20 times 2 cents—two perfectly simple calculations which should enable one to arrive at the answer to a problem of this kind in a matter of seconds.

Another problem of this nature is 96 cents multiplied by 12. But here it would obviously be simpler to say, "12 times $1.00 equals $12.00; 12 times 4 cents equals .48; $12.00 minus .48 equals $11.52."

Let us take another example: 119 times 98 cents. One hundred and nineteen times $1.00 equals $119.00; 119 times 2 cents equals $2.38; $119.00 minus $2.38 equals $116.62.

Example 4: Estimate the cost of a 52-pound roll of paper at $8\frac{1}{2}$ cents per pound.

Solution: 50 times $8\frac{1}{2}$ cents ($\frac{1}{2}$ of $8.50) = $4.25
    2 times $8\frac{1}{2}$ cents   =   .17
    _____

    52 times $8\frac{1}{2}$ cents   = $4.42

It goes without saying that while the purpose of this discussion is to indicate the ease with which sums under $1.00 may be multiplied mentally, the same method may be used to advantage in the case of sums over $1.00, as demonstrated in the illustration that follows:

Example 5: Multiply $1.05 by 460.

Solution: 460 times $1.00   = $460.00
           460 times .05 ($\frac{1}{20}$ of $460.00) =   23.00

—————————————————————

           460 times $1.05   = $483.00

PROBLEMS

The following problems should be worked without pencil and paper, and the answers should be written down only after they have been computed mentally.

★ 1. 81 times 25 cents.   *Ans.* $20.25.
★ 2. 26 times 48 cents.   *Ans.* $12.48.
★ 3. 36 times 23 cents.   *Ans.* $8.28.
★ 4. 19 times 60 cents.   *Ans.* $11.40.
★ 5. 76 times 42 cents.   *Ans.* $31.92.
★ 6. 88 times 30 cents.   *Ans.* $26.40.
★ 7. 45 times 78 cents.   *Ans.* $35.10.
★ 8. 55 times 46 cents.   *Ans.* $25.30.
★ 9. 69 times 40 cents.   *Ans.* $27.60.
★ 10. 98 times 52 cents.   *Ans.* $50.96.

Using as many as possible of the short-cuts discussed in preceding articles, work the following problems with a minimum of pencil-and-paper work.

11. 9 times $18.36.   *Ans.* $165.24. (*Art.* 1-d)
12. 11 times $4.30.   *Ans.* $47.30.   (*Art.* 1-f)
13. 14 times $48.08.   *Ans.* $673.12. (*Art.* 15)
14. 15 times $8.36.   *Ans.* $125.40. (*Art.* 1-b)

15. 125 times $2.48.   *Ans.* $310.00. (*Art.* 2-c)
16. 104 times $1.63.   *Ans.* $169.52.   (*Art.* 3)
17. 64 times $1.16.   *Ans.* $74.24.   (*Art.* 4)
18. 72 times $3.11.   *Ans.* $223.92.   (*Art.* 4)

20. Seemingly Difficult Multiplication Problems Can Be Solved with Surprisingly Little Paper Work. In the preceding article we learned how to compute mentally and with a minimum of effort such problems as 35 times 90 cents, 46 times 55 cents, etc. Here we shall learn how to compute more difficult problems in a fraction of the time ordinarily taken, with a minimum of pencil-and-paper work, and with reasonable assurance of accuracy.

Taking the problem 65 cents multiplied by 44, observe that the digits in the multiplier are alike. It is not difficult to multiply 65 cents by 4 mentally; twice 65 cents equals $1.30, and twice $1.30 equals $2.60. Now if 4 times 65 cents equals $2.60, 40 times 65 cents equals 10 times $2.60, or $26.00. Adding $2.60 and $26.00 gives us our answer, $28.60. The only figures we needed to write down, if any, were $2.60 and $26.00. We did not need to write down their sum, for these simple values can be added mentally with little difficulty.

Now see how easy it is to do the problem 35 cents multiplied by 4.4 mentally. Twice 35 cents equals 70 cents; therefore, 4 times 35 cents equals $1.40. Now if 4 times 35 cents equals $1.40, .4 times 35 cents equals one tenth of $1.40, or 14 cents. All we need to do now is add .14 to $1.40, and we have the answer, $1.54. All the figures we needed to write down, if any, were $1.40 and .14.

Here is an interesting example: 5.9 times 35 cents. Remember what we did when we multiplied by 9 (Art. 1-d); we found it easier to multiply first by 10 and then subtract one tenth of the result. Using this method here, we multiply 35 cents by 6, which gives us $2.10, and subtract one tenth of 35 cents. The only figures we need to write down, if any, are $2.10 and .03 or .04, a total of five figures.

Another typical illustration is 1804 times $0.489. Notice that .489 is the equivalent of .50 minus .011. The computation would be as follows:

$0.50 multiplied by 1804 ($\frac{1}{2}$ of $1804.00)	= $902.00
— $0.011 multiplied by 1804 ($18.04 plus $1.80) =	19.84
$0.489 multiplied by 1804	= $882.16

This solution required no multiplying at all. We simply worked with decimal points, which is much simpler than multiplying 1804 by 9, then by 8, and finally by 4, and then adding the three partial products to obtain the answer.

The problem 225 times $0.224 is interesting for a different reason. Here we have the choice of two methods:

Method A: 200 times $0.224 (twice $22.40) =	$44.80
25 times $0.224 ($\frac{1}{4}$ of $22.40) =	5.60
225 times $0.224	= $50.40

Method B: 225 times $0.20 ($\frac{1}{5}$ of 225.00) =	$45.00
225 times $0.02 ($\frac{1}{10}$ of 45.00) =	4.50
225 times $0.004 ($\frac{1}{5}$ of 4.50) =	.90
225 times $0.224	= $50.40

Method A is, of course, the shorter.

In the example 5.2 times 55 cents we also have two choices of computation. One choice is to multiply 50 cents by 5.2, and add one tenth of the product; the other is to multiply 55 cents by 5 and add .2 (one fifth) of 55 cents.

Here is a type of problem which occurs frequently in business: 60 cents multiplied by 39.9. Notice that the multiplier is short by .1 of making it the nice round number 40. The quickest method of computation, therefore, would be:

40	times \$0.60 (4 times \$6.00)	= \$24.00
− .1 times \$0.60		= .06
39.9 times \$0.60		= \$23.94

A good illustration of how unnecessary it is at times to use the conventional method of multiplication is the problem 16 times \$8.03. We have here two simple little problems in one: 16 times \$8.00, and 16 times \$0.03. Both problems can be computed mentally with ease, so why go to the trouble of setting down multiplicand and multiplier, writing down, in all, five lines of figures? Sixteen times \$8.00 equals \$128.00; 16 times \$0.03 equals \$0.48; total \$128.48. (To compute 16 times 8 mentally, we simply take 8 times 8, and double the result.)

An unusually interesting example of the little need for paper work in computing many problems is demonstrated by the following: The Agricultural Census of 1945 (preliminary) shows West Virginia as having 99,128 farms averaging 88.4 acres in size. Now to compute the total farm acreage we can multiply the number of farms by the number of acres, or vice versa. Note that either method can be worked by the technique discussed in Art. 9, as illustrated:

Method A: 99,128 multiplied by 88.4.

$$\begin{array}{r} 99128 \\ 88.4 \\ \hline \end{array}$$

First partial product	39651.2
Second partial product	
(20 times 1st product)	793024
Third partial product	793024

$$\begin{array}{r} \hline 8762915.2 \end{array}$$

Ans. 8,762,915.2 acres.

Method B: 88.4 multiplied by 99,128.

100,000 times 88.4		= 8,840,000
− 872 times 88.4		
800 times 88.4	= 70720	
72 times 88.4 ($\frac{9}{100}$ of		
70720)	= 6364.8	

$$= \quad 77,084.8$$

99,128 times 88.4   = 8,762,915.2

Ans. 8,762,915.2 acres.

Problems

Problems 1 to 6 should be worked without computing more than two partial products in each instance.

1. 164 times $2.74.	*Ans.* $449.36.	(*Art.* 9)
2. 325 times $16.50.	*Ans.* $5362.50.	(*Art.* 9)
3. $52\frac{1}{2}$ times $0.0288. (Hint: 5 is twice $2\frac{1}{2}$.)		
	Ans. $1.51.	(*Art.* 9)
4. 39.7 times $1.23.	*Ans.* $48.83.	(*Art.* 11)

5. $51\frac{1}{4}$ times $0.32.   *Ans.* $16.40   (*Art.* 9)

6. $47\frac{1}{2}$ times $4.86.   *Ans.* $230.85.   (*Art.* 9)

7. Using the short-cut method for multiplying by 27, compute the cost of a mailing list of 13,500 names at $13.50 per thousand. (Hint: Half of 13,500 is equivalent to $6\frac{3}{4}$ thousand.)

Ans. $182.25. (*Art.* 5)

The following problems should be worked without pencil and paper, and the answers should be written down only after they have been computed mentally.

★ 8. If 26-inch duck fabric weighs 16.55 ounces per yard, how much should 32 yards weigh? (Hint: If one yard weighs 16.55 ounces, 16 yards should weigh 16.55 pounds.)   *Ans.* 33.1 pounds.

★ 9. Formaldehyde weighs 8.2 pounds per gallon. Estimate the weight of the contents of 24 pint bottles of this compound.

Ans. 24.6 pounds.

★ 10. If one pound of butter fat makes $1\frac{1}{6}$ pounds of butter, how many pounds of butter can be made from 37 pounds of butter fat?

Ans. $43\frac{1}{6}$ pounds.

★ 11. Compute the amount of wages due a workman for 39 hours at $1.24 an hour.   *Ans.* $48.36. (*Art.* 11)

21. In Computations Requiring Paper Work, Multiplicand and Multiplier Need Not Always Be Written Down. Several times in the preceding pages it was pointed out that in computing many different types of multiplication problems it was unnecessary to write down the multiplicand and the multiplier.

Most of us are in the habit of writing down the multiplicand and, under the multiplicand, the multiplier, as though we were writing an examination paper and wanted to satisfy the examiner that we knew what we were doing. In a great many instances this copying of factors is entirely unnecessary, particularly when the factors are easily observable. Let us say that we were to compute the amount of a sale comprising 478 units at 34 cents each.

Both numbers, 478 and 34, are already before our eyes, either on a memo or on some kind of business form. It would, therefore, be a waste of time to copy these numbers on a scratch pad. Why not proceed with the computation using the figures that are already before us, writing down nothing more than the product of 4 times 478 and 30 times 478?

Example: A manufacturer rents a loft 127 feet long by 28 feet wide. What is the total floor space of the loft?

Solution: 125 times 28 ($\frac{1}{8}$ of 28000) = 3500

         2 times 28   =   56

_____

     127 times 28   = 3556

                          Ans. 3556 square feet.

In the foregoing problem it was even unnecessary to write down 3500 and 56, for $\frac{1}{8}$ is equivalent to $\frac{1}{2}$ of $\frac{1}{4}$, and since $\frac{1}{4}$ of 28,000 equals 7000, $\frac{1}{8}$ of 28,000 equals 3500; and 3500 plus twice 28 equals 3556.

The time- and energy-saving advantages of eliminating this unnecessary appendage from calculations are especially important to those who continually work with figures, and the reader is urged not to underestimate the value of this significant, although uncommonly practiced, short-cut.

Problems

The following problems should be worked without pencil and paper, and the answers should be written down only after they have been computed mentally.

   ★ **1.** 25 gallons at $1.96 a gallon.   *Ans.* $49.00.   (*Art.* 2)

   ★ **2.** $7\frac{1}{4}$ hours at $1.60 an hour.   *Ans.* $11.60.   (*Art.* 14)

★ 3. 27 times 23.   *Ans.* 621.   (*Art.* 5)
★ 4. 48 at 26¼ cents each.   *Ans.* $12.60.   (*Art.* 14)
★ 5. 29 times 16.   *Ans.* 464.   (*Art.* 11)
★ 6. 7½ dozen at $4.80 a dozen.   *Ans.* $36.00.   (*Art.* 1-c)
★ 7. 98 at 14 cents each.   *Ans.* $13.72.   (*Arl.* 3)
★ 8. 36 times $15.25.   *Ans.* $549.00.   (*Arts.* 14, 1-d)
★ 9. 104 times $23.00.   *Ans.* $2392.00. (*Art.* 3)

Compute the answers to the following problems with a minimum of pencil-and-paper work and without writing down the multiplicands and multipliers.

10. The area in square feet of a room 22 feet 2 inches wide by 24 feet long.   *Ans.* 532 square feet. (*Art.* 2)

11. The total weight of 33 bales of cinnamon sticks, each bale weighing 112 pounds.   *Ans.* 3696 pounds. (*Art.* 1-f)

12. The cost of treating a floor having an area of 450 square feet, at $1.30 per square foot.   *Ans.* $585.00. (*Arts.* 2-a, 5)

13. The weight of 96 cubic feet of water, the weight of one cubic foot of water being 62½ pounds.   *Ans.* 6000 pounds. (*Art.* 3)

14. The commission earned by a broker on 167 units at $3.15 a unit.   *Ans.* $526.05. (*Art.* 9)

15. The number of cubic feet of space occupied by 17½ cords of wood. (A cord of wood equals 128 cubic feet.)
                    Ans. 2240 cubic feet. (*Arts.* 11, 13)

16. At 4.7 yards of 36½-inch-wide print cloth to the pound, the number of yards in 19 pounds.   *Ans.* 89.3 yards. (*Art.* 11)

17. The weight of 7⅓ cubic feet of Portland cement. (One cubic foot of Portland cement weighs 183 pounds.)
                    Ans. 1342 pounds. (*Arts.* 1-f, 14)

22. How to Compute Mentally Costs, Invoice Extensions, etc., When the Price or Rate Given Is per 100 or per 1000.

Ask the average person to compute *mentally* the value of 9 articles priced at $26.00 per hundred or the value of 23 articles at $20.00 per thousand, and the chances are he may prefer to walk a mile.

Yet nothing could be simpler.

To solve the first problem we need but to determine the price per unit, and this much can be done without performing any calculation whatever; the decimal point is simply moved two places to the left. So that instead of reading $26.00 per hundred we read 26 cents each. Nine times 26 cents is the equivalent of 10 times 26 cents minus 26 cents, which equals $2.34, all of which could be done mentally.

In our second problem, 23 at $20.00 per thousand, the price is equivalent to $2.00 per hundred. Two dollars per hundred is 2 cents each, and 23 times 2 cents equals 46 cents. And this problem, too, could be computed mentally in less time than it takes to pick up a pencil.

Let us try a slightly more difficult problem: 38 at $35.00 per thousand. This is the same as $3.50 per hundred, which is $3\frac{1}{2}$ cents each. Our problem now becomes 38 times $3\frac{1}{2}$ cents, which, by the "double-and-halve" method (Chapter III), may be restated as 19 times 7 cents. We know in a flash that 20 times 7 cents equals $1.40, and subtracting 7 cents supplies the answer, $1.33.

Example: An advertisement announces the availability of braid at $0.88 per 100 yards. Estimate mentally the cost of 10,250 yards of this material.

Solution: 10,000 yards at $0.88 per 100 yards
                    (100 times $0.88)   = $88.00
              250 yards at $0.88 per 100 yards
                    ($2\frac{1}{2}$ times $0.88, or 10
                    times $0.22)   =   2.20
_____

10,250 yards at $0.88 per 100 yards = $90.20

PROBLEMS

★ 1. At the market quotation of $6.76 per 100 pounds, what is the value of 203 pounds? *Ans.* $13.72. (*Art.* 3)

2. At the wholesale price of $3.46 per 100 pounds, how much is 390 pounds of an ingredient worth? *Ans.* $13.49. (*Art.* 11)

3. In June, 1946, lambs were quoted at $16.75 per 100 pounds. Estimate the cost of 408 pounds. *Ans.* $68.34. (*Art.* 3)

4. Compute the cost of 4 dozen oilers at $13.10 per 100.

Ans. $6.29. (*Art.* 11)

5. One hundred feet of asphalt-felt joints, 4 inches wide and $\frac{3}{4}$ inch thick, weigh 140 pounds. Find the weight of 126 feet.

Ans. 176.4 pounds. (*Art.* 11)

6. At $2.80 per 1000 yards, what is the cost of 216 yards of ribbon? *Ans.* $0.61. (*Art.* 9)

7. Compute the value of (a) 2075 board feet of lumber at $40.07 per 1000, and (b) 1160 board feet at $46.03 per 1000.

Ans. (a) $83.14; (b) $53.39. (*Art.* 11)

8. What would 1508 common bricks cost at $18.20 per 1000?

Ans. $27.44. (*Art.* 11)

9. One thousand sheets of 16 substance writing paper, 22 by 34 inches, weigh 64 pounds. An advertising campaign calls for the use of 1125 sheets of this stock, including the quantity allowed for waste. What should the net weight of the purchase be?

Ans. 72 pounds. (*Art.* 2-c)

10. If it takes 8.5 hours to glue by hand the covers to 1000 96-page sewed books, size 12 by 9 inches, how long would it take to glue the covers to 240 of these books? *Ans.* 2.04 hours. (*Art.* 11)

23. How to Compute Mentally Little Problems in Which the Price per Unit Contains Several Decimal Places. The decimal point needlessly confuses many individuals who are otherwise good at figures.

Consider the problem $0.331 multiplied by 40. In Chapter III we learned that when factors in a multiplication problem are multiplied and divided, respectively, by the same number, the product is not affected. What would be simpler, then, than to reduce the multiplier in this problem to a single-digit number? By dividing 40 by 10 and multiplying $0.331 by 10 our problem becomes 4 times $3.31. Applying the method described in Art. 17, we can compute this problem mentally as follows: 4 times $3.00 equals $12.00; 4 times $0.30 equals $1.20; and 4 times $0.01 equals $0.04. The mental computation and addition of these three little partial products should be virtually effortless.

An additional advantage of reducing the multiplier to a single-digit number in a problem of this nature is that it makes possible at a glance an approximation of the answer. In the problem in the preceding paragraph, for instance, we can see instantly that the answer will be greater than $12.00 but less than $16.00.

In the problem 36 times $1.0275, however, it is not necessary to convert the multiplier to a single-digit number. A better method of procedure would be as follows:

36 times $1.00	= $36.00
36 times $0.025 (18 times 5 cents) =	.90
36 times $0.0025 ($\frac{1}{10}$ of .90) =	.09
36 times $1.0275	= $36.99

The above illustration is, of course, for the purpose of explanation only. With a little practice the mental computation of such a problem should be a comparatively simple matter.

A problem of a different type is $0.346 multiplied by 7. Here the reader's attention is again called to the method discussed in Art. 17, namely, that in mental multiplication it is useful to think of some numbers as a group of separate numbers. Instead of multiplying $0.346 by 7 by the conventional method, which would make it necessary to remember the last figure of each partial product and carry the rest of the product, we make three separate little computations, adding one computation to the other as it is made. Our problem would, therefore, be computed as follows: 7 times $0.30 ($2.10) plus 7 times $0.04 ($0.28) equals $2.38; plus 7 times $0.006 ($0.04) equals $2.42. It is really as simple as that, and the fact that your interest has carried you to this point is a good indication that you will find it so.

PROBLEMS

★ 1. How much would a dealer have to pay for 70 pounds of hide at $0.104 per pound?   *Ans.* $7.28.

2. Find the cost of 640 yards of printcloths at $0.1415 per yard.
Ans. $90.56.

★ 3. What is the worth of 49 gallons of gas at the market quotation of $0.1612 per gallon?   *Ans.* $7.90. (*Art.* 11)

4. Compute the value of 360 pounds of flavoring at $0.1905 per pound.   *Ans.* $68.58. (*Art.* 5)

★ 5. How much is 7 pounds of zinc alloy worth at $0.0869 per pound?   *Ans.* $0.61.

6. The cost of a factory operation is $0.1825 per unit. If the work is turned over to a contractor who can supply the units at 14 cents each, how much would the manufacturer save on 25 gross?
Ans. $153.00.

★ 7. A factory inspector finds that 7 in every 100 parts used in the production of an office device are defective. If 2500 of these parts were purchased at $0.0432 each, how much credit will the purchaser be entitled to upon the return of the defective parts?
Ans. $7.56. (*Art.* 9)

CHAPTER V

MORE SHORT-CUTS IN MULTIPLICATION

This chapter presents a miscellaneous collection of short-cuts which are more or less independent of the rest of the material in this book. A cursory examination of the following articles will indicate that a large variety of problems, in the solution of which much valuable time is ordinarily wasted, can be computed with surprising rapidity. The methods outlined are more easily illustrated than described.

24. How to Square Numbers Ending in 5. Disregard for a moment the unit digit 5. Add 1 to the rest of the number in the multiplicand; multiply the result by the rest of the number in the multiplier, and consider the product as hundreds. Now add the square of the unit digit 5.

Example 1: Square 35.

Solution: 3 times 4 equals 12; 100 times 12 = 1200
5 times 5   =   25
_____
35 times 35   = 1225

Example 2: Square 185.

Solution: 18 times 19 equals 342; 100 times 342 = 34200
        5 times 5   =   25

_____

185 times 185   = 34225

To square a number which ends with a zero but whose last digit is 5, disregard the zero and annex two zeros to the result, as shown in the illustration that follows:

Example 3: A waterproofing product adapted for application to wood and metal surfaces covers approximately 450 square feet per gallon. Find the approximate number of square feet that would be covered by 450 gallons of this material.

Solution: 4 times 5 equals 20; 100 times 20 =   2,000
          5 times 5   =   25

_____

45 times 45   =   2,025
450 times 450   = 202,500
        Ans. Approximately 202,500 square feet.

It is interesting to note that for every zero after the 5 in the number to be squared, two zeros are annexed to the result. Thus to square 4500, four zeros would be annexed to the product of 45 times 45; to square 85,000, six zeros would be annexed to the product of 85 times 85; and so on.

PROBLEMS

★ **1.** Compute in square feet the area of a room 25 feet by 25 feet.
                                   Ans. 625 square feet.
  2. Find the area of a circle whose radius is 35 inches. (The formula for finding the area of a circle is πr^2, π being equal to 3.1416,

and r^2 meaning radius squared. The radius is a straight line extending from the center of a circle to the circumference. The answer to this problem will therefore be arrived at by finding the product of 3.1416 times 35 times 35 inches.)   *Ans.* 3848.46 square inches.

3. Compute the area of a sphere whose diameter is 55 inches. (The formula for finding the area of a sphere is πD^2. D^2 means diameter squared. The diameter is the length of a straight line through the center of an object from side to side.)

Ans. 9503.34 square inches.

4. Estimate the area of a cylinder having a radius of 6.5 inches and a height of 8 inches. (The formula for finding the area of a cylinder is $2\pi r^2$ plus $2\pi rh$—h meaning height or length. The answer to this problem therefore will be obtained by adding two products: the product of 2 times 3.1416 times 6.5 times 6.5 inches plus the product of 2 times 3.1416 times 6.5 times 8 inches.)

Ans. 592.1916 square inches.

5. Estimate the volume of a cylinder having a radius of 7.5 inches and a height of 9 inches. (The formula for finding the volume of a cylinder is $\pi r^2 h$.)   *Ans.* 1590.435 cubic inches.

25. How to Square Numbers Containing the Fraction $\frac{1}{2}$.
Add 1 to the whole number in the multiplicand and multiply the result by the whole number in the multiplier. Now add the square of the fraction $\frac{1}{2}$.

Example 1: Square $6\frac{1}{2}$.

Solution: 6 times 7 $= 42$
$\frac{1}{2}$ times $\frac{1}{2}$ $= \frac{1}{4}$

$6\frac{1}{2}$ times $6\frac{1}{2} = 42\frac{1}{4}$

Example 2: Square $17\frac{1}{2}$.

Solution: 17 times 18 $= 306$
$\frac{1}{2}$ times $\frac{1}{2}$ $= \frac{1}{4}$

$17\frac{1}{2}$ times $17\frac{1}{2}$ $= 306\frac{1}{4}$

Example 3: What would the import duty amount to on a shipment of sheep's-wool sponges valued at $2250.00, at the rate of $22\frac{1}{2}\%$? (Note that $22\frac{1}{2}\%$ of $2250.00 is equivalent to $22\frac{1}{2}$ times $22.50.)

Solution:

22 times 23 (2 times 253)   = 506

$\frac{1}{2}$ times $\frac{1}{2}$ = $\frac{1}{4}$

$22\frac{1}{2}$ times $22\frac{1}{2}$ = $506\frac{1}{4}$

Ans. $506.25.

Problems

★ **1.** How many square yards are there in a square rod? (One rod equals $5\frac{1}{2}$ yards.)   *Ans.* $30\frac{1}{4}$ square yards.

2. How many square feet are there in a square rod? (One rod equals $16\frac{1}{2}$ feet.)   *Ans.* $272\frac{1}{4}$ square feet. (*Art.* 15)

3. From a sheet of asbestos measuring 4 feet by 8 feet, fifty equal squares of $9\frac{1}{2}$ by $9\frac{1}{2}$ inches are cut. Assuming that there is no waste in cutting, how many square inches of the original sheet will remain?   *Ans.* $95\frac{1}{2}$ square inches. (*Art.* 4)

4. Find the area of a hexagon whose diameter is $8\frac{1}{2}$ inches. (A hexagon is a 6-sided figure all of whose angles are equal. To find the area of a hexagon the square of the diameter is multiplied by 0.866.)   *Ans.* 62.5685 square inches.

★ **5.** In a right triangle (a triangle in which one of the angles is a right angle—that is, 90 degrees) the square of the hypotenuse (the side opposite the right angle) is equal to the sum of the squares of the other two sides. If one of the two sides is $4\frac{1}{2}$ feet long, and the other $6\frac{1}{2}$ feet, what is the area of the square of the hypotenuse?   *Ans.* $62\frac{1}{2}$ square feet.

26. How to Find the Product of Two Factors When the Sum of the Unit Digits Is 10 and the Rest of the Number Is the Same in Both Factors.

The rule here is the same as when squaring a number ending in 5 (Art. 24) except that, instead of squaring the unit digit 5, one unit digit is multiplied by the other unit digit.

Example 1: Multiply 86 by 84.

Solution: 8 times 9 equals 72; 100 times 72 = 7200
            4 times 6   =   24
            _____
            86 times 84   = 7224

Example 2: Multiply 41 by 49.

Solution: 4 times 5 equals 20; 100 times 20 = 2000
            9 times 1   =   9
            _____
            41 times 49   = 2009

Example 3: Multiply 237 by 233.

Solution: 23 times 24 equals 552; 100 times 552 = 55200
            3 times 7   =   21
            _____
            237 times 233   = 55221

Example 4: Compute mentally the area in square inches of a sheet of asbestos mill board 42 by 48 inches.

Solution: 4 times 5 equals 20; 100 times 20 = 2000
            2 times 8   =   16
            _____
            42 times 48   = 2016
                        Ans. 2016 square inches.

Problems

★ 1. Compute the number of cubic feet in 23 cubic yards. (One cubic yard equals 27 cubic feet.)   *Ans.* 621 cubic feet.

★ 2. If a chest of tea weighs 84 pounds, how much will 86 chests weigh?   *Ans.* 7224 pounds.

★ 3. There are 38 feet of 3-strand Manila rope $\frac{5}{16}$ inch in diameter to the pound. Compute the number of feet that would be represented by 32 pounds.   *Ans.* 1216 feet.

★ 4. What would the total weight be of 53 cartons of precipitated chalk, each having a gross weight of 57 pounds?

Ans. 3021 pounds.

5. If there are 76 strips of an asphalt roof shingle to the square, how many strips would be required to cover 7400 square feet of roof surface? (The word "square," as used in the building industry, denotes 100 square feet.)   *Ans.* 5624 strips.

6. The gross weight of a barrel of buckwheat is 217 pounds. Compute the gross weight of 213 barrels.

Ans. 46,221 pounds. (*Art.* 1-f)

★ 7. The cuadra is a unit of measurement used in Uruguay. The American equivalent is 1.82 acres. Estimate the number of acres in 188 cuadras.   *Ans.* 342.16 acres. (*Art.* 1-e)

8. What is the value of 812 pounds of lead at the wholesale price of $0.0818 per pound?   *Ans.* $66.42.

9. A machine operated by a single individual can turn out 146 springs per hour. How many springs will be turned out by 4 machines in one week, if each of the 4 operators works a total of 36 hours per week?   *Ans.* 21,024 springs. (*Art.* 15)

★ 10. A coal-crushing machine has a capacity of 113 tons per hour. How many tons of coal can be crushed in 3 weeks if the machine is operated for 39 hours each week?   *Ans.* 13,221 tons. (*Art.* 1-f)

27. How to Find the Product of Two Factors, Each Containing a Fraction, in Which the Whole Numbers Are Alike and the Sum of the Fractions Is 1. Add 1 to the whole number in the multiplicand; multiply the result by the whole number in the multiplier; then add the product of the fractions.

Example 1: Multiply $9\frac{1}{4}$ by $9\frac{3}{4}$.

Solution: 9 times 10   = 90

$\quad\quad\quad\quad \frac{1}{4}$ times $\frac{3}{4}$ = $\frac{3}{16}$

_____

$9\frac{1}{4}$ times $9\frac{3}{4}$ = $90\frac{3}{16}$

Example 2: Multiply $4\frac{1}{3}$ by $4\frac{2}{3}$.

Solution: 4 times 5 $\quad = 20$

$\qquad \frac{1}{3}$ times $\frac{2}{3}$ $\quad = \quad \frac{2}{9}$

_____

$4\frac{1}{3}$ times $4\frac{2}{3}$ $= 20\frac{2}{9}$

Example 3: Multiply $8\frac{3}{7}$ by $8\frac{4}{7}$.

Solution: 8 times 9 $\quad = 72$

$\qquad \frac{3}{7}$ times $\frac{4}{7}$ $\quad = \quad \frac{12}{49}$

_____

$8\frac{3}{7}$ times $8\frac{4}{7}$ $= 72\frac{12}{49}$

Example 4: If $1\frac{1}{5}$ gallons of coconut oil can be obtained from 25 pounds of copra, how many gallons of the oil would be yielded by 45 pounds of copra? (Note that 45 pounds is equivalent to $1\frac{4}{5}$ times 25 pounds.)

Solution: 1 multiplied by 2 $\quad = 2$

$\qquad \frac{1}{5}$ multiplied by $\frac{4}{5}$ $= \frac{4}{25}$

_____

$1\frac{1}{5}$ times $1\frac{4}{5}$ $\qquad = 2\frac{4}{25}$

$\qquad\qquad\qquad\qquad\qquad$ *Ans.* $2\frac{4}{25}$ gallons.

Problems

★ **1.** If a girl can pack $3\frac{2}{3}$ gross units in one hour, how many gross units might she be expected to pack in 3 hours 20 minutes?

$\qquad\qquad\qquad\qquad\qquad\qquad$ *Ans.* $12\frac{2}{9}$ gross units.

★ **2.** A chemist can produce in one hour a sufficient quantity of a liquid preparation to fill 31 quart bottles. At this rate how many gallons of the material could be produced in $7\frac{1}{4}$ hours? (Hint: 31 quarts equal $7\frac{3}{4}$ gallons.) $\qquad\qquad$ *Ans.* $56\frac{3}{16}$ gallons.

★ **3.** Compute the cost of $8\frac{2}{5}$ yards of material costing $8.60 a yard. (Hint: $8.60 equals $8\frac{3}{5}$.) $\qquad\qquad$ *Ans.* $72.24.

★ **4.** Compute the total yardage of $9\frac{1}{6}$ lengths of material, each measuring $9\frac{5}{6}$ yards. $\qquad\qquad$ *Ans.* 90 yards 5 inches.

★ 5. If $6\frac{1}{4}$ sacks of Portland cement are required to make one cubic yard of a $1:2\frac{1}{4}:3$ mix concrete, how many sacks of Portland cement will be needed to make $6\frac{3}{4}$ cubic yards of concrete of this mix?   *Ans.* $42\frac{3}{16}$ sacks.

★ 6. How many acres are there in a piece of land $4\frac{5}{8}$ miles long by $4\frac{3}{8}$ miles wide? (One square mile equals 640 acres.)

Ans. 12,950 acres.

28. How to Find the Product of Factors Ending with Zeros. Eliminate the zeros after the last significant figure in each factor, compute the problem with the remaining figures, then annex to the product as many zeros as were eliminated.

Example 1: Multiply 2300 by 350.

Solution: Eliminate the three zeros, and multiply 35 by 23.

23 times 25 ($\frac{1}{4}$ of 2300) = 575
23 times 10   = 230

---

23 multiplied by 35   = 805
Annexing three zeros, we arrive at the answer, 805000.

Example 2: Multiply 16040 by 1020.

Solution: Note that we eliminate only those zeros *after the last significant figure.*

1604 times 100   = 160400
1604 times 2   =   3208

1604 multiplied by 102 = 163608
Annexing two zeros, we arrive at the answer, 16,360,800.

Example 3: How many apples can be pared and cored in 30 hours by a machine operating at a speed of 2400 apples an hour?

Solution: 3 times 24 = 72

Annexing three zeros gives us 72,000.

Ans. 72,000 apples.

PROBLEMS

⋆ **1.** Estimate the total weight of 120 Indian bales of cotton having an average weight of 600 pounds.   *Ans.* 72,000 pounds.

⋆ **2.** Compute the number of square rods in 30 acres. (One acre equals 160 square rods.)   *Ans.* 4800 square rods.

⋆ **3.** If a power excavating bucket can handle 800 cubic yards per hour, what volume would be moved in 60 hours?

Ans. 48,000 cubic yards.

⋆ **4.** A full coil of $\frac{3}{8}$ inch diameter Manila rope weighs 60 pounds. Estimate the weight of 330 coils.   *Ans.* 19,800 pounds.

⋆ **5.** If there are 520 whole black peppercorns to the ounce, how many would there be in 10 pounds?   *Ans.* 83,200. (*Art.* 15)

⋆ **6.** What is the capacity in cubic feet of a ditch 20 feet deep, 8 feet wide and 200 feet long?   *Ans.* 32,000 cubic feet.

⋆ **7.** A cord of wood yields about 1500 pounds of excelsior. How many pounds of excelsior could be obtained from 260 cords?

Ans. 390,000 pounds. (*Art.* 1-b)

⋆ **8.** If granite weighs 170 pounds per cubic foot, how much will 320 cubic feet weigh?   *Ans.* 54,400 pounds.

⋆ **9.** Compute the number of pounds in 40 long tons. (A long ton equals 2240 pounds.)   *Ans.* 89,600 pounds.

⋆ **10.** An unskilled workman can cut 35 squares in one hour. If 5 men of equal capacity are hired to do this work, how many squares should be ready at the end of four 40-hour weeks?   *Ans.* 28,000.

29. How to Multiply Quickly by $\frac{3}{4}$. The conventional method of multiplying by $\frac{3}{4}$ is to multiply by 3 and divide by 4. A much simpler method is to take half of the multiplicand and add to it half of the half.

Example 1: Multiply 84 by $\frac{3}{4}$.

Solution: $\frac{1}{2}$ of 84 $\qquad\qquad = 42$
$\frac{1}{4}$ of 84 ($\frac{1}{2}$ of 42) $= 21$

$\frac{3}{4}$ of 84 $\qquad\qquad = 63$

Example 2: Compute the cost of 170 shares at $11.75 per share.

Solution: 17 times $11.00 $\qquad\qquad\qquad = \$\ 187.00$
17 times $0.50 ($\frac{1}{2}$ of $17.00) $\quad = \qquad 8.50$
17 times $0.25 ($\frac{1}{2}$ of $8.50) $\quad\ = \qquad 4.25$

17 times $11.75 $\qquad\qquad\qquad\quad = \$\ 199.75$
170 times $11.75 (10 times $199.75) $= \$1997.50$
Ans. $1997.50.

PROBLEMS

★ **1.** Find the cost of $\frac{3}{4}$ gross of screws at $9.60 a gross.
Ans. $7.20.

★ **2.** What is the value of $\frac{3}{4}$ yard of fabric at $2.60 a yard?
Ans. $1.95.

★ **3.** Compute the amount due a workman for $\frac{3}{4}$ hour at $1.40 an hour. *Ans.* $1.05.

★ **4.** Compute the amount due an employee for 30 hours of work at $63.60 per 40-hour week. *Ans.* $47.70.

★ **5.** What should a grocer charge for 9 eggs at 75 cents a dozen?
Ans. $0.57.

★ **6.** What is the worth of 75 machine parts at $4.30 per hundred?
Ans. $3.23.

★ **7.** How much should a jobber charge for 750 units at $16.00 per thousand? *Ans.* $12.00.

★ **8.** How many square inches are there in $\frac{3}{4}$ of a square foot? (One square foot equals 144 square inches.) *Ans.* 108 square inches.

★ **9.** How many pounds are there in $\frac{3}{4}$ of a metric ton? (A metric ton equals 2205 pounds.) *Ans.* $1653\frac{3}{4}$ pounds.

★ **10.** State the equivalent in yards of $\frac{3}{4}$ of a mile. (A mile equals 1760 yards.)   *Ans.* 1320 yards.

★ **11.** Compute the weight of 750 board feet of American Elm. (One thousand board feet of American Elm weigh 2920 pounds and, should the reader be interested to know, a board foot is the equivalent of one square foot one inch thick.)   *Ans.* 2190 pounds.

★ **12.** What is the expired amount of an annual insurance premium costing $37.00, nine months after the insurance has been in force?
Ans. $27.75.

30. How to Multiply by a Number Containing a Fraction. First step: multiply by the whole number. Second step: if it is seen that the multiplicand is exactly divisible by the denominator of the fraction, divide by the denominator and multiply the result by the numerator. If exact divisibility is not possible, or if a quick glance does not reveal the possibility, multiply by the numerator, then divide the result by the denominator. Now add the results obtained in the two steps.

Example 1: Multiply 243 by $3\frac{7}{9}$.

Solution: 243 times 3   = 729
243 divided by 9 equals 27; 27 times 7 = 189

---

243 times $3\frac{7}{9}$ = 918

Example 2: Multiply 142 by $4\frac{3}{11}$.

Solution: (Note that in this illustration the second plan is followed in multiplying by the fraction.)
142 times 4   = 568
142 times 3 equals 426; 426
    divided by 11   = $38\frac{8}{11}$

---

142 times $4\frac{3}{11}$ = $606\frac{8}{11}$

Although the aforementioned rule applies to fractions of any denominator, the breakdown method often is very useful in problems of this kind. The problem in the following illustration is typical:

Example 3: Multiply 378 by $6\frac{4}{7}$.

Solution: 378 times 6 $= 2268$

378 times $\dfrac{3\frac{1}{2}}{7}$ ($\frac{1}{2}$ of 378) $=$ 189

378 times $\dfrac{\frac{1}{2}}{7}$ ($\frac{1}{7}$ of 189) $=$ 27

---

378 times $6\frac{4}{7}$ $= 2484$

Example 4: Convert $7\frac{5}{8}$ long tons to pounds. A long ton equals 2240 pounds.

Solution: 7 times 2240 $= 15,680$

$\frac{4}{8}$ of 2240 ($\frac{1}{2}$ of 2240) $= 1,120$

$\frac{1}{8}$ of 2240 ($\frac{1}{4}$ of 1120) $=$ 280

$7\frac{5}{8}$ times 2240 $= 17,080$

Ans. 17,080 pounds.

Problems

Note that in Problems 1 to 6 the multiplicand is exactly divisible by the denominator in the fraction. This makes it more practical to divide first the multiplicand by the denominator and then to multiply the result by the numerator. In Problems 7 to 10, on the other hand, divisibility is not exact, so here the reverse procedure is preferable—that is, to multiply first by the numerator and then to divide the result by the denominator.

1. Compute the total number of units in $6\frac{2}{3}$ gross.

Ans. 896. (*Art.* 14)

2. One cubic inch of platinum weighs 11.28 troy ounces. How many troy ounces will $7\frac{2}{3}$ cubic inches weigh?

Ans. 86.48 troy ounces.

3. Convert $5\frac{2}{3}$ pounds to kilograms. (One pound equals 0.4536 kilograms.) *Ans.* 2.5704 kilograms.

4. A 20-foot-diameter cast-in-place silo requires 78 vertical reinforcing bars, each 14 feet 8 inches long. Compute the total length of the bars. *Ans.* 1144 feet. (*Art.* 14)

5. The net weight of a box of 90-pound, 10-by-20 inch, tin-plate sheets is 129 pounds. If there are 225 sheets to the box, what should the total net weight be of the contents of two boxes and 100 loose sheets? (Hint: 100 sheets equals $\frac{4}{9}$ of 225 sheets.)

Ans. $315\frac{1}{3}$ pounds.

6. There are 231 cubic inches in one gallon. Estimate the number of cubic inches in $7\frac{4}{11}$ gallons. *Ans.* 170 cubic inches.

7. Compute the value of $16\frac{2}{3}$ yards of material at $4.14 a yard. (Hint: $16\frac{2}{3}$ is exactly one sixth of 100.) *Ans.* $69.00.

8. If a bar of steel weighs 1 pound 6 ounces per foot of its length, what will 29 feet weigh? *Ans.* 39 pounds 14 ounces.

9. How much will $38\frac{4}{9}$ square feet of leather cost at $0.536 per square foot? *Ans.* $20.61.

10. One cubic foot of water weighs $62\frac{1}{2}$ pounds. Estimate the weight of $6\frac{7}{10}$ cubic feet. *Ans.* 418.75 pounds.

CHAPTER VI

ALIQUOT PARTS

No study of business mathematics would be complete without due consideration to the subject of aliquot parts.

With the techniques of the breakdown method of multiplication (Chapter II) and the double-and-halve method (Chapter III) as a background, a knowledge of aliquot parts will enable the reader to solve many different problems involving decimals and fractions speedily and with interesting results. The three subjects—the breakdown method, the double-and-halve method, and aliquot parts —necessarily overlap each other, and if the reader feels he has not thoroughly mastered the techniques of the first two methods he is urged to review them.

In this chapter frequent use will be made of the decimal point, and it would be well for readers who do not feel thoroughly at home in dealing with decimals to glance through the pages of Chapter XVI before proceeding with the study of the articles that follow.

31. The Significance of Decimal Fractions Like .25, .12$\frac{1}{2}$, .37$\frac{1}{2}$, .62$\frac{1}{2}$ and Their Variations. "Aliquot," as defined in Funk & Wagnalls Dictionary, means "contained in something else an exact number of times: said of a part or division: as, 6 is an aliquot part of 12 and 18."

Having in mind this definition, it is easy to understand

that 25 cents is an aliquot part of a dollar—it is one fourth of a dollar; so is $12\frac{1}{2}$ cents an aliquot part of a dollar—it is one eighth; and $6\frac{1}{4}$ cents, which is one half of $12\frac{1}{2}$ cents, is one sixteenth of a dollar. Each of these values is contained in one dollar an exact number of times. The value $37\frac{1}{2}$ cents, on the other hand, is not strictly an aliquot part of a dollar, but $12\frac{1}{2}$ cents (which is one third of $37\frac{1}{2}$ cents) is. And so for practical purposes we may extend our definition to include values such as $37\frac{1}{2}$ cents too.

Thus if we wish to find the product of 36 times 25 cents, we need but to multiply 36 by $\frac{1}{4}$ and consider the answer as dollars. To find the product of 24 times $12\frac{1}{2}$ cents, we would multiply 24 by $\frac{1}{8}$. Similarly, to multiply $6\frac{1}{4}$ cents by 32, we would restate the problem to read $\frac{1}{16}$ dollar multiplied by 32, and promptly we should know that the answer is $2.00.

All of us know that $33\frac{1}{3}$ is exactly one third of 100 or, stated another way, 100 times one third. So that to multiply 138 by $33\frac{1}{3}$ we need but to annex two zeros to 138 and divide the result (13800) by 3.

And since $66\frac{2}{3}$ is exactly twice $33\frac{1}{3}$, we should find the product of a number times $66\frac{2}{3}$ by first finding the product of the number times $33\frac{1}{3}$ and then multiplying the result by 2.

Example 1: Find the product of 384 times $12\frac{1}{2}$ cents.

Solution: 384 times $12\frac{1}{2}$ cents ($\frac{1}{8}$ of $384.00) = $48.00

Example 2: Multiply 160 by $6\frac{1}{4}$ cents.

Solution: 160 times $12\frac{1}{2}$ cents ($\frac{1}{8}$ of $160.00) = $20.00

---

160 times $6\frac{1}{4}$ cents ($\frac{1}{2}$ of $20.00) = $10.00

Example 3: Multiply 135 by $62\frac{1}{2}$ cents.

Solution: (Note that $62\frac{1}{2}$ cents is the sum of 50 cents plus $12\frac{1}{2}$ cents.)

135 times 50 cents ($\frac{1}{2}$ of $135.00) = \$67.50

135 times $12\frac{1}{2}$ cents ($\frac{1}{8}$ of \$135.00
  or $\frac{1}{4}$ of \$67.50) = $16.87\frac{1}{2}$

---

135 times $62\frac{1}{2}$ cents = \$84.38

Thus far we have dealt with numbers which are aliquot parts of a dollar or, we might say, aliquot parts of 100. Similarly, an understanding of aliquot parts is virtually essential in dealing with percentages. Suppose, for instance, you wanted to calculate $8\frac{1}{3}$ per cent of a number. Even without remembering that $8\frac{1}{3}$ is exactly one twelfth of 100, experience with numbers will enable you to quickly determine that $8\frac{1}{3}$ is one third of 25, and therefore one twelfth of 100; that $16\frac{2}{3}$ is one half of $33\frac{1}{3}$ and therefore one sixth of 100, and so on.

PROBLEMS

Write the decimal equivalents of the following fractions:

1. $3\frac{5}{8}$ *Ans.* $3.62\frac{1}{2}$.
2. $4\frac{2}{3}$ *Ans.* $4.66\frac{2}{3}$.
3. $18\frac{1}{5}$ *Ans.* 18.2.
4. $13\frac{1}{12}$ *Ans.* $13.08\frac{1}{3}$.
5. $7\frac{1}{3}$ *Ans.* $7.33\frac{1}{3}$.
6. $31\frac{3}{8}$ *Ans.* $31.37\frac{1}{2}$.
7. $162\frac{3}{5}$ *Ans.* 162.6.
8. $9\frac{5}{6}$ *Ans.* $9.83\frac{1}{3}$.

Compute the answers to the following problems with a minimum of pencil-and-paper work.

9. How much cord would be required to obtain 136 pieces, each of which is to be $4.37\frac{1}{2}$ inches long?   *Ans.* 595 inches.

10. If a bottle of liquid contains $\frac{4}{5}$ of a quart, how many quarts would be necessary to fill 186 bottles? Give your answer in decimal form. *Ans.* 148.8 quarts.

11. As a result of competition a manufacturer offers a discount of $66\frac{2}{3}\%$ from his list prices. His customers, in other words, will pay only $33\frac{1}{3}\%$. On this basis what would a purchaser have to pay for a bill of goods which, at the list price, would have amounted to $273.90? *Ans.* $91.30.

32. How to Multiply by Near-Aliquot Numbers Like $.11\frac{1}{2}$, $.13\frac{1}{2}$, $.22\frac{1}{2}$, $.27\frac{1}{2}$, etc.

Except for the nature of the numbers to be considered here, the method of procedure is essentially the same as that discussed in preceding articles. For example, to multiply 440 by $.11\frac{1}{2}$ we would multiply 440 by $.12\frac{1}{2}$ (or $\frac{1}{8}$), which is 55, and subtract .01 of 440, which is 4.4, obtaining the total of 50.6.

The same method would apply to the rest of the multipliers in this article heading. Thus $.13\frac{1}{2}$ might be restated as $.12\frac{1}{2}$ plus .01; $.22\frac{1}{2}$ as .25 minus $.02\frac{1}{2}$ (one tenth of .25); and $.27\frac{1}{2}$ as .25 plus $.02\frac{1}{2}$.

Our study of aliquot parts thus far has been concentrated on fractions. The technique, however, is not altered one bit when the multiplier, for instance, is $27\frac{1}{2}$ instead of $.27\frac{1}{2}$. The result of multiplying $27\frac{1}{2}$ is simply 100 times the result obtained in multiplying the same number by $.27\frac{1}{2}$.

Problems I

Compute the answers to the following:

⋆ **1.** 88 times $.11\frac{1}{2}$ *Ans.* 10.12.
⋆ **2.** 60 times $.13\frac{1}{3}$ *Ans.* 8. (*Art.* 14)
⋆ **3.** 72 times $.13\frac{1}{2}$ *Ans.* 9.72.
⋆ **4.** 96 times $.22\frac{1}{2}$ *Ans.* 21.6.
⋆ **5.** $23\frac{1}{3}$ times 36   *Ans.* 840.
  6. $27\frac{1}{2}$ times $23.00   *Ans.* $632.50.

Equally interesting results can be obtained with the near-aliquot fractions in the following problems:

7. A formula for making 100 pounds of parchment red ink calls for the use of 8 pounds of varnish. If it is desired to make only $38\frac{1}{2}$ pounds of this ink how much varnish will be required? Compute the answer to the nearest hundredth.   *Ans.* 3.08 pounds.

★ 8. Of one variety of corner beads, used in the building industry, 1000 lineal feet weigh 320 pounds. How much will 1625 lineal feet weigh?   *Ans.* 520 pounds.

PROBLEMS II

Design a form headed as in the specimen tabulation shown below, and, in the manner indicated in this specimen, show how you would use your knowledge of aliquot parts and the breakdown method of multiplication (Chapter II) to multiply by each of the following numbers. For example, to show how you would multiply by 9.3, write .3 in the plus section of the column headed "First Step," and 30 in the plus section of the column headed "Second Step." And so on.

SPECIMEN TABULATION

To Multiply by	First Step		Second Step	
	Add or Subtract, as the Case May Be, the Multiplicand Times the Number Indicated Here		Add or Subtract, as the Case May Be, the Product Obtained in the First Step, Times the Number Indicated Here	
	Add	Subtract	Add	Subtract
9.3	.3		30	
19.8	20			$\frac{1}{100}$
11.8		.2	60	

★ 1. 3.18.   *Ans.* 3 plus $\frac{6}{100}$ of 3.
★ 2. 14.7.   *Ans.* Subtract .3 and add 50 times .3.
★ 3. 16.2.   *Ans.* .2 plus 80 times .2.
★ 4. 21.6.   *Ans.* 20 plus $\frac{8}{100}$ of 20.
★ 5. 9.6.   *Ans.* 10 minus $\frac{4}{100}$ of 10.
★ 6. 5.4.   *Ans.* 6 minus $\frac{1}{10}$ of 6.
★ 7. 16.8.   *Ans.* .8 plus 20 times .8.
★ 8. 18.6.   *Ans.* .6 plus 30 times .6.
★ 9. 11.4.   *Ans* Subtract .6 and add 20 times .6.
★ 10. 7.6.   *Ans.* Subtract .4 and add 20 times .4.
★ 11. 15.6.   *Ans.* Subtract .4 and add 40 times .4.
★ 12. 45.9.   *Ans.* 46 minus .1.
★ 13. 32.7.   *Ans.* Subtract .3 and add 110 times .3.
★ 14. 92.7.   *Ans.* Subtract .3 and add 310 times .3.
★ 15. 5.97.   *Ans.* Subtract .03 and add 200 times .03.
★ 16. 39.8.   *Ans.* Subtract .2 and add 200 times .2.
★ 17. 23.8.   *Ans.* Subtract .2 and add 120 times .2.
★ 18. 47.4.   *Ans.* Subtract .6 and add 80 times .6.
★ 19. 69.3.   *Ans.* Subtract .7 and add 100 times .7.
★ 20. 23.4.   *Ans.* Subtract .6 and add 40 times .6.

CHAPTER VII

PERCENTAGES AND DISCOUNTS

A consideration of aliquot parts is logically followed by a study of percentages and discounts, for in the arithmetic of business no other problems occur more frequently, and in no other problems is the rapid speed of computation made possible by a knowledge of aliquot parts better exemplified.

Readers who, in the preceding chapters, found the slightest difficulty understanding the illustrations which involved the decimal point are advised to study Chapter XVI before proceeding further. This study will enable the reader to benefit fully from the techniques described in the following articles.

33. Quick Ways of Deducting the Per-Cent Rates of 20, 30, 40, 60, 70, 80 and 90. Time and again the author has seen the simplest per cents computed the long way, when much time and labor might have been saved by the use of a short-cut.

Take, for instance, the problem $300.00 less 20 per cent. Here is how this is commonly computed:

Long Way

$$\begin{array}{r} \$300.00 \\ 20\% \quad 60.00 \\ \hline \$240.00 \end{array}$$

The above method is needlessly long. It calls for two operations: the calculation of 20 per cent of the base and the subtraction of the percentage from the base. Two operations are really unnecessary, for this reason: the discount, we are told, is 20 per cent, and so the *net* amount, or the figure we wish to arrive at, is 80 per cent (100 minus 20 equals 80) of $300.00. Our problem, therefore, can be solved in *one* operation by calculating 80 per cent of $300.00. And what could be simpler? Eighty per cent of *one* hundred dollars is $80.00; therefore 80 per cent of *three* hundred dollars equals three times $80.00, or $240.00. No need for any subtraction, and no need to use pencil and paper.

If the base had been $324.60 instead of $300.00, the solution would be no more difficult. Eighty per cent is the equivalent of eight tenths; so that all we need do is divide $324.60 by 10 and multiply the quotient ($32.46) by 8, which can be done mentally and effortlessly. There is no need to write down $324.60 and 80 per cent. A mental picture of the changed position of the decimal point makes it a comparatively simple matter to multiply by 8 and write the answer, $259.68, directly into the record or document concerned without using any scratch paper whatever.

In any problem involving the deduction of a per cent like 20, 30, 40, 60, 70 or 80, the thing to do, therefore, is to determine the per cent that is *payable* and then multiply the gross amount by that per cent.

Example 1: Compute $736.00 less 30%.

Solution: $736.00 less 30% is equivalent to 70% of
$736.00, or $\frac{7}{10}$ of $736.00.

$\frac{1}{10}$ of $736.00   = $ 73.60

_____

$\frac{7}{10}$ of $736.00 (7 times $73.60) = $515.20

Example 2: Compute $89.40 less 60%.

Solution: $89.40 less 60% is equivalent to 40% of $89.40,
or $\frac{4}{10}$ of $89.40.

$\frac{1}{10}$ of $89.40   = $ 8.94

_____

$\frac{4}{10}$ of $89.40 (4 times $8.94) = $35.76

With the per-cent rates of 10 and 90 the procedure is
even simpler. In calculating $18.60 less 10 per cent, for
instance, there is really no calculating to do at all; from
$18.60 we merely deduct one tenth ($1.86). On the other
hand, problems which call for the deduction of 90 per cent
are the simplest of all percentage problems, for their solution does not call for deductions or computations of any
kind; the decimal point is simply moved one place to the
left, and the resulting number constitutes the answer.
Thus $143.00 less 90 per cent equals $14.30.

PROBLEMS

1. Compute the net amount due on a bill for $84.60 less a dis-
count of 20%.   *Ans.* $67.68.
2. The list price of a mechanical testing device is $185.00. If
the purchaser is offered a trade-in allowance of 30% for his old
machine, how much will the new machine cost him in exchange?
                                                  Ans $129.50.

⋆ **3.** If a 650-pound steer lost 40% of its weight in dressing, what was the weight of the carcass? *Ans.* 390 pounds.

4. The elimination of waste motion and other unnecessary time-consuming factors in a production plant enabled a manufacturer to announce a 60% discount off list prices. On this basis how much would a customer have to pay on a purchase which, at the list price, amounts to $318.40? *Ans.* $127.36.

⋆ **5.** The 80% co-insurance clause is a stipulation in many fire insurance policies which provides for full payment of damage if the property is insured for 80% of its value and the damage does not exceed the face value of the policy. In other words, if property valued at $76,000 and insured for 80% of its value was damaged to the extent of $10,000, the company would pay the full amount of the damage. Compute the loss sustained by the owner of property valued at $43,000, completely destroyed by fire, and insured for only 80% of its value. *Ans.* $8600.00.

⋆ **6.** A manufacturer is forced by a strike to lay off 90% of his help. If he had 230 employees on his payroll before the strike, what was the extent of his skeleton force? *Ans.* 23.

34. Quick Ways of Calculating the Per-Cent Rates of $32\frac{1}{2}$, $37\frac{1}{2}$, $42\frac{1}{2}$, $47\frac{1}{2}$, $52\frac{1}{2}$, $57\frac{1}{2}$, $62\frac{1}{2}$ and $67\frac{1}{2}$. If the reader has studied carefully the chapter entitled "Aliquot Parts," he will appreciate the interesting way in which many different per-cent rates lend themselves to short-cut calculation.

Let us take two problems for each of four different rates—one in which we are to find only the percentage, the other in which the net amount is required—and observe the simplicity and rapidity of their solution by a method based on our combined knowledge of aliquot parts and the breakdown method of multiplication. In the case of five of these problems, an alternative method of computation will be indicated, and it is suggested that the reader acquire the habit of computing the answer by one method and proving it by the other method.

Example 1: Find $32\frac{1}{2}\%$ of \$180.00.

Solution:

Method A:

25% of \$180.00 ($\frac{1}{4}$ of \$180.00)	=	\$45.00
5% ($\frac{1}{5}$ of \$45.00)	=	9.00
$2\frac{1}{2}\%$ ($\frac{1}{2}$ of \$9.00)	=	4.50
$32\frac{1}{2}\%$ of \$180.00	=	\$58.50

Method B:

30% of \$180.00 (3 times \$18.00)	=	\$54.00
$2\frac{1}{2}\%$ ($\frac{1}{40}$ of \$180.00 or $\frac{1}{4}$ of \$18.00)	=	4.50
$32\frac{1}{2}\%$ of \$180.00	=	\$58.50

Example 1A: What is the net amount of a sale amounting to \$180.00 on which a discount of $32\frac{1}{2}\%$ is allowable?

Solution: The answer will be $67\frac{1}{2}\%$ of \$180.00.

Method A:

50% of \$180.00 ($\frac{1}{2}$ of \$180.00)	=	\$ 90.00
$12\frac{1}{2}\%$ ($\frac{1}{4}$ of \$90.00)	=	22.50
5% ($\frac{1}{10}$ of \$90.00)	=	9.00
$67\frac{1}{2}\%$ of \$180.00	=	\$121.50

Method B:

60% of \$180.00 (6 times \$18.00)	=	\$108.00
6% ($\frac{1}{10}$ of \$108.00)	=	10.80
$1\frac{1}{2}\%$ ($\frac{1}{4}$ of \$10.80)	=	2.70
$67\frac{1}{2}\%$ of \$180.00	=	\$121.50

Example 2: Find $37\frac{1}{2}\%$ of $426.00.

Solution:

Method A:

$$25\% \text{ of } \$426.00 \ (\tfrac{1}{4} \text{ of } \$426.00) = \$106.50$$
$$12\tfrac{1}{2}\% \ (\tfrac{1}{2} \text{ of } \$106.50) \qquad\quad = \quad\ 53.25$$

$$37\tfrac{1}{2}\% \text{ of } \$426.00 \qquad\qquad\quad = \$159.75$$

Method B:

$$12\tfrac{1}{2}\% \text{ of } \$426.00 \ (\tfrac{1}{8} \text{ of } \$426.00) = \$\ 53.25$$

$$37\tfrac{1}{2}\% \ (3 \text{ times } \$53.25) \qquad\quad = \$159.75$$

Example 2A: What is the net amount payable on a purchase of $426.00 less $37\frac{1}{2}\%$?

Solution: The answer will be $62\frac{1}{2}\%$ of $426.00.

Method A:

$$50\% \text{ of } \$426.00 \ (\tfrac{1}{2} \text{ of } \$426.00) = \$213.00$$
$$12\tfrac{1}{2}\% \ (\tfrac{1}{4} \text{ of } \$213.00) \qquad\quad = \quad\ 53.25$$

$$62\tfrac{1}{2}\% \text{ of } \$426.00 \qquad\qquad\quad = \$266.25$$

Method B:

$$12\tfrac{1}{2}\% \text{ of } \$426.00 \ (\tfrac{1}{8} \text{ of } \$426.00) = \$\ 53.25$$

$$62\tfrac{1}{2}\% \ (5 \text{ times } \$53.25) \qquad\quad = \$266.25$$

Example 3: Find $42\frac{1}{2}\%$ of \$826.00.

Solution:

Method A:

25% of \$826.00 ($\frac{1}{4}$ of \$826.00)	=	\$206.50
$12\frac{1}{2}\%$ ($\frac{1}{2}$ of \$206.50)	=	103.25
5% ($\frac{1}{5}$ of \$206.50)	=	41.30

$42\frac{1}{2}\%$ of \$826.00   = \$351.05

Method B:

40% of \$826.00 (4 times \$82.60)	=	\$330.40
$2\frac{1}{2}\%$ ($\frac{1}{40}$ of \$826.00 or $\frac{1}{4}$ of \$82.60)	=	20.65

$42\frac{1}{2}\%$ of \$826.00   = \$351.05

Example 3A: Compute the net amount of a sale amounting to \$826.00 less $42\frac{1}{2}\%$.

Solution: The answer will be $57\frac{1}{2}\%$ of \$826.00.

50% of \$826.00 ($\frac{1}{2}$ of \$826.00)	=	\$413.00
5% ($\frac{1}{10}$ of \$413.00)	=	41.30
$2\frac{1}{2}\%$ ($\frac{1}{2}$ of \$41.30)	=	20.65

$57\frac{1}{2}\%$ of \$826.00   = \$474.95

Example 4: Find $47\frac{1}{2}\%$ of \$785.00.

Solution: Notice that here we *deduct* $2\frac{1}{2}\%$ from 50%.

50% of \$785.00 ($\frac{1}{2}$ of \$785.00)	=	\$392.50
$-\ 2\frac{1}{2}\%$ ($\frac{1}{20}$ of \$392.50 or $\frac{1}{2}$ of \$39.25)	=	19.62

$47\frac{1}{2}\%$ of \$785.00   = \$372.88

Example 4A: Show the net amount of a sale amounting to $785.00 less $47\frac{1}{2}\%$.

Solution: The answer will be $52\frac{1}{2}\%$ of $785.00.

50% of $785.00 ($\frac{1}{2}$ of $785.00)	= $392.50
$2\frac{1}{2}\%$ ($\frac{1}{20}$ of $392.50 or $\frac{1}{2}$ of $39.25) =	19.62
$52\frac{1}{2}\%$ of $785.00	= $412.12

The reader will do well not to leave this article until he has mastered it since the technique illustrated is one of the most interesting and important short-cut techniques in business arithmetic.

Problems

Compute the odd-numbered problems by Method A, illustrated in the text, and the even-numbered problems by Method B.

1. In a survey it was found that 12% of the farms being sold were held for less than two years and that the typical resale profit was 30 to 35%. Using the mean per-cent rate of $32\frac{1}{2}\%$ how much profit would have been made on the sale of a farm purchased two years previously for $28,500? *Ans.* $9,262.50.

2. A bill for $82.70 is subject to a discount of $32\frac{1}{2}\%$. What is the net amount due? *Ans.* $55.82.

3. If the import duty on cotton collar stiffeners is $37\frac{1}{2}\%$, what would the duty amount to on an importation valued at $174.36? *Ans.* $65.39.

4. A flaw in a manufacturing process of a fabric entitled a dealer to an allowance of $37\frac{1}{2}\%$. If the fabric in question was billed at $379.40, how much will the dealer be expected to pay in full settlement? *Ans.* $237.13.

5. A jobber's gross profit on an item is $42\frac{1}{2}\%$. If his cost per unit is $16.00, how much gross profit will he make on a sale of 214 units? *Ans.* $1455.20. (*Art.* 9)

6. A job lot of merchandise is purchased at a discount of $42\frac{1}{2}\%$. The merchandise consisted of 120 gross springs at $3.00 a gross and 200 screws at $2.00 per hundred. Compute the net amount of the purchase. *Ans.* $209.30.

7. The substitution of lower-priced materials in the production of an upholstered chair enabled a manufacturer to sell at $47\frac{1}{2}\%$ less than the higher-priced product, which cost $128.00. What was the price of the cheaper chair? *Ans.* $67.20.

8. A businessman's study of reports leads him to expect that his sales for the year will be $52\frac{1}{2}\%$ higher than in the previous year. If his previous year's sales amounted to $146,700, how much business does he expect to do in the current year? *Ans.* $223,717.50.

9. A meat shortage coupled with a fire loss reduced a butcher's profits so that his income for the year was $57\frac{1}{2}\%$ of his $6472.00 income the previous year. Estimate his profit. *Ans.* $3721.40.

10. An improvement in the packaging design of a company's product resulted in an increase in sales of $62\frac{1}{2}\%$. Everything else being equal, how much business might the company expect to do in a 3-month period as a result of this improvement if in the corresponding period of the previous year its sales amounted to $17,188.00?
Ans. $27,930.50.

★ 11. A liquid preparation of heavy consistency contains $62\frac{1}{2}\%$ water by volume. If a tank is filled to three fourths of its capacity of 128 cubic feet with a batch of the finished material, how much space is occupied by the materials other than water?
Ans. 36 cubic feet.

12. An experiment by a community organization showed that an extension of its cultural activities increased its income by $67\frac{1}{2}\%$. If the quarterly income had previously been $138.40, how much of a quarterly income will the organization expect in the future as a result of this innovation? *Ans.* $231.82.

13. Neglected pruning of a company's mailing list resulted in a wasted expense of $67\frac{1}{2}$ cents of every dollar spent in an advertising campaign. The cost of the campaign was $836.50. Compute the amount that would have sufficed to do this advertising if the mailing list has been kept up to date. *Ans.* $271.86.

35. Calculating Percentages When the Base Is an Aliquot Part of $100, $1000, etc. When the base is an aliquot part of $100, $1000, etc., the transposition of the values simplifies the problem. Thus 14 per cent of $50.00

is equivalent to 50 per cent of $14.00, which is $7.00; $32\frac{1}{4}$ per cent of $25.00 is the same as 25 per cent of $32.25, which is $8.06; $11\frac{3}{4}$ per cent of $37.50 produces the same answer as $37\frac{1}{2}$ per cent of $11.75, which is $4.41; and $18\frac{1}{2}$ per cent of $750.00 is equivalent to 750 per cent of $18.50, or $7\frac{1}{2}$ times $18.50, which is $138.75.

The computation of per cents of multiples of $100 is, of course, very simple. The per-cent rate is simply multiplied by the multiple of $100. Sixty-three per cent of $700.00 is equivalent to $63.00 multiplied by 7; 43 per cent of $1100.00 produces the same result as $43.00 multiplied by 11. And so on.

PROBLEMS

The computation of these problems without pencil and paper should be found a comparatively simple matter.

★ 1. 23% of $50.00.		*Ans.* $11.50.
★ 2. 32% of $27.50.		*Ans.* $8.80.
★ 3. 16% of $37.50.		*Ans.* $6.00.
★ 4. 8.8% of $62.50.		*Ans.* $5.50.
★ 5. 24.16% of $75.00.		*Ans.* $18.12.
★ 6. 48% of $225.00.		*Ans.* $108.00.
★ 7. 72.98% of $50.00.		*Ans.* $36.49.
★ 8. 12.84% of $25.00.		*Ans.* $3.21.
★ 9. 55% of $120.00.		*Ans.* $66.00.
★ 10. 44% of $175.00.		*Ans.* $77.00.

Only the partial products and the answers are to be written down in working the following problems.

11. 36.82% of $150.00.		*Ans.* $55.23.
12. 16.72% of $387.50.		*Ans.* $64.79.
13. 64% of $412.50.		*Ans.* $264.00.
14. 72% of $227.50.		*Ans.* $163.80.
15. 40.56% of $662.50.		*Ans.* $268.71.
16. 15.8% of $520.00.		*Ans.* $82.16.

17. 84.24% of $525.00.		*Ans.* $442.26.
18. 8.96% of $737.50.		*Ans.* $66.08.
19. 3.74% of $650.00.		*Ans.* $24.31.
20. 34.3% of $810.00.		*Ans.* $277.83.

36. A Good Way to Check Per-Cent Computations. A good way to prove the result of a per-cent computation might be described as the "minus" method. To prove, for instance, the result of $37\frac{1}{2}$ per cent of any sum, we might deduct $62\frac{1}{2}$ per cent from the original sum (100 minus $37\frac{1}{2}$ equals $62\frac{1}{2}$). The result of $47\frac{1}{2}$ per cent of any sum might be proved by deducting $52\frac{1}{2}$ per cent from the original sum. And so on.

Or, as indicated in some of the illustrations in Art. 34, the rate per cent may be subdivided in two different ways, a separate computation being made for each of the two sets of figures. Thus $32\frac{1}{2}$ per cent might be divided up into 25, 5 and $2\frac{1}{2}$ per cent; or into 30 and $2\frac{1}{2}$ per cent.

Problems

Prove by the "minus" method the given answers to the following problems.

1. $32\frac{1}{2}$% of $46.40 equals $15.08.
2. $37\frac{1}{2}$% of $48.96 equals $18.36.
3. $42\frac{1}{2}$% of $423.60 equals $180.03.
4. $47\frac{1}{2}$% of $365.20 equals $173.47.
5. $52\frac{1}{2}$% of $286.40 equals $150.36.
6. $57\frac{1}{2}$% of $480.80 equals $276.46.
7. $62\frac{1}{2}$% of $153.36 equals $95.85.
8. $67\frac{1}{2}$% of $1468.40 equals $991.17.

37. Computing the Net Amount When a Sum Is Subject to Two or More Successive Discounts. Many businessmen mistakenly believe that the sequence in which two or more discounts are deducted makes a difference. Of course, it does *not* make any difference.

Example 1: Find the net amount of a bill for $650.00 subject to the successive discount rates of 20%, 10% and 5%.

Solution A: In this solution the discounts are deducted in the order in which they are stated in the problem.

$650.00 less 20% = $520.00
520.00 less 10% =   468.00
468.00 less 5% =   444.60

Ans. $444.60.

Solution B: In this solution the discounts are deducted in a different order.

$650.00 less 10% = $585.00
585.00 less 5% =   555.75
555.75 less 20% =   444.60

Ans. $444.60.

Note that in both solutions the answers are identical. The reason is that in any multiplication problem the order in which the values are arranged is immaterial. Percentage computation is, in effect, a process of multiplication; it is a process of multiplying the base by the difference between 1 and the rate per cent. Thus $650.00 less 20 per cent is equivalent to $650.00 multiplied by 80 per cent. And $650.00 less the successive discounts of 20 per cent, 10 per cent and 5 per cent is equivalent to $650.00 multiplied by .80, multiplied by .90, multiplied by .95. In multiplying a series of numbers, the order in which they are multiplied does not affect the result. So that our problem would produce exactly the same result if it were restated as $650.00 multiplied by .90, multiplied by .80, multiplied by .95.

PROBLEMS

Since the sequence in which two or more successive discounts are deducted does not affect the result, in what order would you deduct the discounts in the following problems so as to facilitate computation mentally or with a minimum of pencil-and-paper work? Indicate your answers by numbering the per-cent rates in the first five problems, 1 and 2, and in the last five problems, 1, 2 and 3.

1. $100.00 less $33\frac{1}{3}\%$ and 10%.   *Ans.* 2, 1.
2. $80.00 less 5% and $12\frac{1}{2}\%$.   *Ans.* 2, 1.
3. $96.00 less $16\frac{2}{3}\%$ and 20%.   *Ans.* 1, 2.
4. $160.00 less $7\frac{1}{2}\%$ and $37\frac{1}{2}\%$.   *Ans.* 2, 1.
5. $72.00 less $33\frac{1}{3}\%$ and $62\frac{1}{2}\%$.   *Ans.* 1, 2.
6. $40.00 less 25%, $12\frac{1}{2}\%$ and $33\frac{1}{3}\%$.   *Ans.* 1, 3, 2.
7. $135.00 less 20%, $66\frac{2}{3}\%$ and 10%.   *Ans.* 2, 1, 3.
8. $840.00 less $16\frac{2}{3}\%$, 5% and 10%.   *Ans.* 1, 3, 2.
9. $120.00 less $2\frac{1}{2}\%$, $33\frac{1}{3}\%$ and 5%.   *Ans.* 2, 1, 3.
10. $600.00 less 5%, 25% and 10%.   *Ans.* 2, 3, 1.

38. How to Find the Equivalent and the Net Result of Deducting a Series of Successive Discounts. In Art. 33 we saw that when dealing with discounts the process of computing net amounts can be speeded up if, instead of subtracting the amount of the discount, we multiplied by the difference between 100 per cent and the per cent of the discount rate. Thus to find the net amount of $300.00 less 20 per cent, we could obtain the answer very quickly by computing 80 per cent of $300.00 (80 per cent being the difference between 100 per cent and 20 per cent).

This process of multiplying by the difference between 100 per cent and the per cent of the discount rate can be used with excellent effect to compute the net amount of a sum subject to two or more successive discounts. Let us say, for example, that the sum of $200.00 is subject to the successive discounts of 25 per cent and 10 per cent. If we did not know that the equivalent of these two successive discounts is $32\frac{1}{2}$ per cent, we would have to compute first $200.00 less 25 per cent, and then $150.00 (the net amount obtained in the first computation) less 10 per cent, which gives us $135.00. Observe how simple the computation becomes when we calculate $200.00 less the single discount of $32\frac{1}{2}$ per cent; we see immediately that the answer equals $67\frac{1}{2}$ per cent (the difference between 100 per cent and $32\frac{1}{2}$ per cent) of $200.00, or $135.00.

Another example of the speed and simplicity of multiplying by a single equivalent to find the net amount of a sum subject to successive discounts is the series of 40, 10 and 5 per cent rates, which equals 51.3 per cent.

It should be noted, however, that computing by single equivalent values is not always as time-saving. Deducting the successive discounts of 20, 10 and 5 per cent, for example, is equivalent to multiplying by 68.4 per cent, or .684 (which is the difference between 100 per cent and 31.6 per cent—31.6 per cent being the discount rate equivalent of the aforementioned successive per-cent rates). To multiply a sum like $283.19 by .684 would require three separate partial products and about as much pencil-and-paper work as the separate computation of the three discount rates.

However, an understanding of how to find the equivalent of a series of successive discounts or their net result is very important. A businessman, for instance, may be offered a line of merchandise by a manufacturer at a discount of, say, 35 per cent from the list prices; another manufacturer offers the identical merchandise at the same list prices, but at the successive discount rates of 30 per cent and $7\frac{1}{2}$ per cent. He will obviously want to know the equivalent discount of 30 per cent and $7\frac{1}{2}$ per cent and which manufacturer's net prices are lower.

The equivalent value or net result of a series of successive discounts is determined in this manner: Using 1 as the base, we find that 1 (100 per cent) less 30 per cent, for example, equals 70 per cent, or .7; and .7 less 5 per cent (that is, 5 per cent of .7) equals .665, which is the net result.

Knowing the net result we need but to subtract this figure from 100 to obtain the equivalent discount rate. Thus 100 per cent minus $66\frac{1}{2}$ per cent equals $33\frac{1}{2}$ per cent, and this figure is the equivalent of the successive rates of 30 per cent and 5 per cent.

To deduct 30 per cent and 5 per cent, therefore, we have two choices: (1) to deduct the equivalent rate of $33\frac{1}{2}$ per cent; (2) to multiply by $66\frac{1}{2}$ per cent, or .665. And as was pointed out in the opening paragraphs of this article, the latter method is preferred in most instances.

This method of finding the equivalent or net result applies to any series of successive discounts. Thus if a sum were subject to the three successive discounts of 40 per cent, 10 per cent and 5 per cent, we should determine the equivalent net amount as follows:

$$
\begin{aligned}
1.0 \text{ less } 40\% &= .6 \\
.6 \text{ less } 10\% &= .54 \\
.54 \text{ less } 5\% &= .513
\end{aligned}
$$

So that to compute the net amount of a sum subject to the successive discounts of 40, 10 and 5 per cent, we multiply by .513.

The reader is cautioned not to confuse the equivalent

discount rate with the *net result* of a series of successive discounts. The net result of deducting 40, 10 and 5 per cent from 1, as shown in the foregoing illustration, is .513. The equivalent discount rate, however, is the difference between 1 and .513—that is, .487. In other words, deducting 48.7 per cent produces the same result as deducting, successively, 40 per cent, 10 per cent, and 5 per cent. But, again—as has been pointed out—a shorter way of finding the net amount of a sum subject to the discount rate of 48.7 per cent is to multiply by .513.

Problems

Calculate to the nearest tenth of 1%: (a) the number by which to multiply to obtain the net amount of a sum subject to each of the following series of successive discounts; (b) the equivalent discount rate of each series.

1. 20%, 10% and 5%.   *Ans.* (a) .684; (b) 31.6%.
2. 25%, 5% and $2\frac{1}{2}$%.   *Ans.* (a) .695; (b) 30.5%.
3. 10%, 5% and $2\frac{1}{2}$%.   *Ans.* (a) .834; (b) 16.6%.
4. $12\frac{1}{2}$%, 5% and 5%.   *Ans.* (a) .790; (b) 21%.
5. 30%, 10% and 5%.   *Ans.* (a) .599; (b) 40.1%.

Using the "net result" figures obtained in the computation of the foregoing problems, calculate the amounts due on the following invoices:

6. $132.00 less 20%, 5% and 10%.   *Ans.* $90.29.
7. $21.40 less 25%, 5% and $2\frac{1}{2}$%.   *Ans.* $14.87.
8. $95.62 less 5%, $2\frac{1}{2}$% and 10%.   *Ans.* $79.75.
9. $250.00 less 5%, $12\frac{1}{2}$% and 5%.   *Ans.* $197.50.
10. $480.00 less 30%, 5% and 10%.   *Ans.* $287.52.

39. How to Find the Rate Per Cent. One of the most useful bits of knowledge in business mathematics is knowing how to determine the relationship between two values on a percentage basis.

A firm may want to know, for instance, by how many

per cent its July sales exceeded the June sales. Or it may have effected economies in its production processes in the fiscal year just ended, and wants to know the relationship on a percentage basis between the production cost per $100.00 worth of merchandise manufactured in the year just ended and the cost of producing an equal amount of finished merchandise in the previous year. There is virtually no end to the number of uses to which a knowledge of how to find the rate per cent may be put.

Let us take some practical examples and observe how, by the process of simple reasoning, the desired information is obtained quickly and easily.

Example 1: A firm's sales for the month of July amounted to $2400.00. Its sales for the previous month were $2000.00. By what rate per cent did the July sales exceed the June sales?

Solution: The July sales exceeded the June sales by $400.00. The problem, therefore, is: What fraction having 100 as the denominator is equivalent to $\frac{400}{2000}$? Stated in the form of an equation

$$\frac{400}{2000} = \frac{x}{100}$$

x being the unknown number, or the rate per cent.

In order that this equation may be clearly understood, let us digress for a few moments and study a simple rule which will probably never be forgotten if it is concentrated on for a little while: *In any fractional equation, the product of the means equals the product of the extremes.*

Let us take the equation $\frac{2}{4} = \frac{3}{6}$. The means are 4 and

3; their product is 12. The extremes are 2 and 6; their product, too, is 12. It is clear, then, that whenever one fraction equals another fraction, the product of the means *must* equal the product of the extremes.

Coming back to the unfinished part of the solution to our problem, $\frac{400}{2000} = \frac{x}{100}$, we have an equation here in which one of the numerators is an unknown quantity. We know, however, that the product of the means equals the product of the extremes. So that $2000x$ equals 40,000. Now, if $2000x$ equals 40,000, all we need do to find what *one* x equals is divide 40,000 by 2000. The answer, of course, is 20. The answer to our problem, then, is that the sales for July exceed the sales for June by 20 per cent.

Example 2: Linseed oil is one of the ingredients of a certain synthetic product. If in the manufacturing process one pound of this oil is used to make 18 pounds of the finished product, what per cent of the weight of the finished product does the weight of the linseed oil constitute?

Solution: The linseed oil content is one eighteenth of the weight of the finished product. Since we want to show this in the form of a percentage, let us write an equation:

$$\frac{1}{18} = \frac{x}{100}$$

Since the product of the means equals the product of the extremes, we know that $18x$ equals 100. One x, therefore, equals 100 divided by 18, or 5.55. The linseed oil content, therefore, is 5.55% of the weight of the finished product.

Example 3: An employee's weekly salary of $52.00 is increased by $8.00. (a) What rate per cent of $52.00 does the increase constitute? (b) What rate per cent of $60.00 does the increase constitute?

Solution: (a) $\dfrac{8}{52} = \dfrac{x}{100}$

$$52x = 800$$

$$x = \frac{800}{52} = 15.4\%$$

(b) $\dfrac{8}{60} = \dfrac{x}{100}$

$$60x = 800$$

$$x = \frac{800}{60} = 13.3\%$$

In each of the preceding illustrations it was necessary to divide into 100 or a multiple of 100 to find the value of x. In many instances, however, the rate per cent will be obvious at a glance. Thus $\frac{1}{10}$ is equivalent to 10 per cent; $\frac{1}{25}$ equals 4 per cent; $\frac{45}{360}$ equals $\frac{1}{8}$ or $12\frac{1}{2}$ per cent, and so on. Fractions like these shorten the process of computation. The following illustration will help to make this clear.

Example 4: A product costs $80.00, and sells for $120.00. What rate per cent of the selling price does the gross profit constitute?

Solution: The gross profit is $40.00, or one third of the selling price. The rate per cent, therefore, is $33\frac{1}{3}$.

Problems

1. What is a salesman's rate of commission if he receives a check for $61.34 covering the amount due him on a sale of $368.04?
Ans. $16\frac{2}{3}\%$.

★ 2. Currency paper contains a substantial proportion of linen, which gives it hardness, strength and durability. Approximately 1600 tons of paper are used each year to replace the currency worn out, and of this quantity about 1200 tons consist of linen fiber. What per cent of linen fiber would you say is contained in currency paper? *Ans.* 75%.

★ 3. If a man gains $350.00 on an investment of $2100.00, how much per-cent profit did he make on the principal? *Ans.* 16⅔%.

4. A house costing $35,000 is rented for $2800.00 a year. How much per cent per annum gross profit does the owner realize on his investment? *Ans.* 8%.

5. The total expenses of all the departments in an enterprise is $2935.00. What per cent of this total is represented by the department whose expenses amounted to $117.40? *Ans.* 4%.

★ 6. When the selling price of unfrosted doughnuts is 25 cents per half-dozen, the cost of the ingredients, including the frying compound, is about 9 cents. This makes the gross profit on the ingredients 16 cents. Compute the per-cent rate of the gross profit on the selling price. *Ans.* 64%.

7. A bankrupt settles a debt of $2250.00 with a payment of $1735.00. What per cent of his indebtedness does his settlement represent? Compute the answer to the nearest hundredth of a per cent. *Ans.* 77.11%.

8. Brown and Sweet enter into partnership, Brown investing $3000 and Sweet $5500. How much per cent of the total did Sweet invest? Find the answer to the nearest hundredth of a per cent.
Ans. 64.71%.

9. A concern decides to appropriate a certain amount of money to advertise the products of each of its departments. The amount allotted is to be determined by the per-cent relationship between the department's sales and the company's total sales for the last fiscal year. To what per cent of the appropriation would Department A be entitled if the amount of its sales for the year is $84,000 and the total sales of all the departments combined amounted to $630,000? *Ans.* 13⅓%.

10. A firm employs 3 salesmen. The totals of their sales in one week were, respectively, $840.00, $736.00 and $424.00. Compute the per-cent relationship to the total of the amount of business produced by each salesman. *Ans.* 42, 36.8 and 21.2%, respectively.

40. Easy Ways to Remember How to Find a Number When the Value of a Per Cent or Any Fractional Part of It Is Known. The necessity for finding information of this nature occurs quite frequently in business, and the ability to do it quickly is very serviceable.

To begin with a simple example: If 20 per cent of a number is 6, what is the number? We know that 20 per cent is one fifth. Therefore, we reason, if one fifth equals 6, five fifths will equal five times 6, or 30. Similarly, if $33\frac{1}{3}$ per cent (which is exactly one third) of a number is 4, the number will be three times 4, or 12.

Here is a practical example whose solution will require just a little more effort. A salesman receives a check for $45.00 representing commission earned. If his commission rate is 15 per cent, how much business does the check represent? Let us see. We know that 15 per cent of the total sales is $45.00. Fifteen per cent means 15 hundredths, and if 15 hundredths equal $45.00, it is easy to see that one hundredth equals one fifteenth of $45.00, or $3.00. (If this is not clear, think of the hundredths in this example as units, and it will be seen instantly that if 15 units equal $45.00, one unit will equal one fifteenth of $45.00.) Knowing that one hundredth equals $3.00, we find without the need for further computation that 100 hundredths of the number we have set out to compute equal 100 times $3.00, or $300.00.

The reader has doubtless noticed that whereas in the illustrations in the first paragraph we reduced 20 per cent ($\frac{20}{100}$) to a number with the lowest common denominator, namely, $\frac{1}{5}$, and $33\frac{1}{3}$ per cent likewise to a number with the lowest common denominator, namely, $\frac{1}{3}$, in the solution to the problem in the preceding paragraph we did not trouble to reduce 15 per cent ($\frac{15}{100}$) to $\frac{3}{20}$. The reason will be immediately obvious when it is observed that 15 is divisible into $45.00 exactly three times, and that it requires less effort to divide 15 into $45.00 and multiply the result ($3.00) by 100, in order to find the value of 100 hundredths, than to reduce $\frac{15}{100}$ to $\frac{3}{20}$, divide $45.00 by 3 to find the value of $\frac{1}{20}$, and then—in order to find the value of 20 twentieths—to multiply the result ($15.00) by 20.

Example 1: If 17% of a number is $34.00, what is the number?

Solution: $\frac{17}{100}$ of the number is $34.00.

Therefore $\frac{1}{100}$ (which is $\frac{1}{17}$ of $\frac{17}{100}$) of the number equals $\frac{1}{17}$ of $34.00, or $2.00.

If $\frac{1}{100}$ equals $2.00, 100 hundredths will equal 100 times $2.00, or $200.00.

Our number, therefore, is $200.00.

Example 2: If 24% of a value is $78.24, what is the value?

Solution: $\frac{24}{100}$ is equivalent to $\frac{6}{25}$.

If $\frac{6}{25}$ of a value is $78.24, $\frac{1}{25}$ (which is $\frac{1}{6}$ of $\frac{6}{25}$) of the value equals $\frac{1}{6}$ of $78.24, or $13.04.

If $\frac{1}{25}$ equals $13.04, $\frac{25}{25}$ will equal 25 times $13.04, or $326.00.

100% of the value, therefore, is $326.00.

The same technique can be used for finding the value of a number when a fraction, instead of a per cent, of it is known.

Example 3: Three nineteenths of a number equals \$4.29. Find the number.

Solution: $\frac{3}{19}$ of the number is \$4.29.

Therefore $\frac{1}{19}$ (which is $\frac{1}{3}$ of $\frac{3}{19}$) of the number equals $\frac{1}{3}$ of \$4.29, or \$1.43.

If $\frac{1}{19}$ equals \$1.43, $\frac{19}{19}$ will equal 19 times \$1.43, or \$27.17.

Our number, then, is \$27.17.

Example 4: Four ninths of what number equals 0.64?

Solution: $\frac{4}{9}$ of the number is 0.64.

Therefore $\frac{1}{9}$ (which is $\frac{1}{4}$ of $\frac{4}{9}$) of the number equals $\frac{1}{4}$ of 0.64, or 0.16.

If $\frac{1}{9}$ equals 0.16, $\frac{9}{9}$ will equal 9 times 0.16, or 1.44.

The number, therefore, is 1.44.

Problems

1. It occurs to a businessman away from his office that he might not be carrying sufficient fire insurance on his property. He remembers that the insurance rate is 23 cents per \$100 valuation, and that the amount of the one-year premium just paid is \$52.90, but does not remember the amount for which the property is insured. If you were in a similar dilemma how would you determine the amount of insurance carried on the property?

Ans. Divide \$52.90 by .23, and multiply the quotient by 100.

★ **2.** Sixty cubic feet of water occupy 40% of a tank's capacity. What is the volume of the unoccupied space in the tank?

Ans. 90 cubic feet.

3. A baker finds that 3 ounces of a butter-flavor sample produce the desired effect if used with 225 pounds of shortening. Estimate the amount of shortening that could be flavored to the baker's satisfaction with the contents of a 16-ounce bottle of the product.

Ans. 1200 pounds.

★ **4.** If 7 gallons of an asphalt protective coating will cover 28% of an area to be treated, how many gallons will be needed to cover the entire area?   *Ans.* 25 gallons.

★ **5.** A prospective purchaser of property reads an advertisement inserted by an agent whose custom the reader knows it to be to request a cash payment of 15% of the price asked. The advertisement states that the amount of the cash payment is $1200.00. What is the asked price of the property?   *Ans.* $8000.00.

6. If 648 cubic inches of aluminum liquid weigh 57 pounds, how much would the weight of a cubic foot of this element be? (Hint: 648 cubic inches is equivalent to $37\frac{1}{2}\%$ of a cubic foot.)

Ans. 152 pounds.

★ **7.** The total of the discount column of a Cash Receipts Book shows that in a typical month customers deducted cash discounts to the extent of $127.00. If the concern's cash discount rate is 2% and if each remittor took advantage of the cash discount and made no other deduction of any kind, what would the approximate total be of the sums entered in the Accounts Receivable column in the cash book for the month under discussion? (Hint: The amounts entered in the Accounts Receivable column are the amounts to be credited to the accounts—that is, they include the discounts deducted; in other words, each amount represents the sum of the actual amount remitted plus the amount of discount deducted.)

Ans. $6350.00.

★ **8.** An operator of a fruit and vegetable market finds that for one reason or another $16\frac{2}{3}\%$ of the apples he buys decays and becomes unfit for sale. If in one week he accumulates 3 bushels of decayed apples, approximately how many bushels of this fruit were sold in that time? (Hint: Only the difference between 100% of the quantity purchased and $16\frac{2}{3}\%$ could be sold.)   *Ans.* 15 bushels.

CHAPTER VIII

CHECKING RESULTS IN MULTIPLICATION

It is probably no exaggeration to say that failure to check computations is the cause of nine tenths of the errors in business mathematics.

Just as the expert speller, after spelling the word "embarrass" correctly all his life, may suddenly forget himself and spell this word with only one r, the experienced mathematician may at a particular moment—due to haste, or hunger, or any other reason—compute the product of 7 times 9 as 53 instead of 63. And it not infrequently happens that the same error is repeated in the checking operation, particularly if the interval between the two computations is short-spaced.

It is suggested, therefore, that the reader develop the habit of checking his computations, and of using in the checking operations different methods from the ones used to obtain the answer the first time. Employers are urged to emphasize the importance of this phase of office routine to their billing clerks and other employees who work with figures. Prevention is better than cure, and this aid to accuracy may help to avoid costly errors and embarrassing moments.

41. Even Simple Multiplication Problems Can Be Computed in Several Different Ways. There are many ways of checking a calculation. Even the simplest problem may be computed in half a dozen ways or more. Take, for example, the problem 37 times 24. Observe how, in the following illustration, this can be computed by at least six different methods.

The Conventional Method	Transposing Multiplicand and Multiplier
37	24
× 24	× 37
148	168
74	72
888	888

The Double-and-Halve Method	Multiplying and Dividing the Two Factors, Respectively, By Some Other Value Than 2
74 (37 multiplied by 2)	148 (37 multiplied by 4)
× 12 (24 divided by 2)	× 6 (24 divided by 4)
888	888

The Breakdown Method

$$37 \text{ times } 25 \text{ (3700 divided by 4)} = 925$$
$$- 37 \text{ times } 1 \qquad\qquad\qquad = 37$$
$$37 \text{ times } 24 \qquad\qquad\qquad = 888$$

The Method Discussed in Art. 9

$$37 \text{ times } 20 \qquad\qquad = 740$$
$$37 \text{ times } 4 \ (\tfrac{1}{5} \text{ of } 740) = 148$$
$$37 \text{ times } 24 \qquad\qquad = 888$$

Problems

Without calculating the answers show, by restatements of the factors, three different methods, exclusive of the conventional method, of computing or checking the answer to each of the following problems. For example, the restatements of the factors in the five illustrations, exclusive of the conventional method, given in this article would read: 24 times 37; 74 times 12; 148 times 6; 37 times 25, minus 37; and 37 times 20, plus one fifth of the result.

1. The value of 576 machine parts at $3\frac{1}{2}$ cents each.

    Ans. $2.88 times 7; $1.44 times 14; $5.76 times $2\frac{1}{2}$, plus $5.76.

2. The cost value of 400 bushels of oats at $58\frac{1}{2}$ cents per bushel.

    Ans. 4 times $58.50; 200 times $1.17; 400 times $57\frac{1}{2}$ cents, plus $4.00.

3. The area in square inches of a sheet of plywood panel measuring 49 inches by 62 inches.

    Ans. 50 times 62, minus 62; 98 times 31; 49 times 2, plus 30 times the result.

4. The cost of 48 clocks at $3.20 each.

    Ans. 50 times $3.20, minus 2 times $3.20; 24 times $6.40; 4 times the product of 12 times $3.20.

5. The total weight of 27 barrels of cement, each weighing 376 pounds.

    Ans. 30 times 376, minus one tenth of the result; 9 times the product of 3 times 376; 400 times 27, minus $\frac{6}{100}$ of the result.

6. The area in square feet of a loft 120 feet long by 39 feet wide.

    Ans. 12 times 390; 6 times 780; 100 times 39, plus one fifth of the result; 120 times 40, minus 120.

7. The total number of ironing-board covers that can be produced in 40 hours by a girl whose rate of speed is 98 covers per hour.

    Ans. 4 times 980; 8 times 490; 100 times 40, minus 2 times 40.

8. The value of 2 gross of buckles costing 73 cents a dozen.

    Ans. 24 times 75 cents, minus 24 times 2 cents; 12 times $1.46; 6 times $2.92.

9. The amount of pay due an employee for $7\frac{1}{2}$ hours at $1.16 per hour.

> *Ans.* 10 times $1.16, minus one fourth of the result; 15 times $0.58; 30 times $0.29.

10. The weight of 84 cubic inches of iron. (One cubic inch of iron weighs .26 pound.)

> *Ans.* 84 times .25, plus .84; 12 times the product of 7 times .26; 4 times .26, plus 20 times the result.

11. The total number of cocoa beans roasted in a revolving drum in 8 hours at the rate of 720 every 40 minutes.

> *Ans.* 12 times 720; 6 times 1440; 4 times the product of 3 times 720; 700 times 12, plus 20 times 12.

12. The tax due on property assessed at $126,000 at the rate of $2.70 on each $100.

> *Ans.* $1260 times 2.7; 9 times the product of 1260 times .3; $1260 times 3, minus one tenth of the result.

13. The cost of 120 shares of stock at $38\frac{1}{2}$—that is, at $38.50 each.

> *Ans.* 120 at $37.50, plus $120.00; 100 times $38.50, plus one fifth of the result; 12 times $385.00.

14. The value of 2750 pounds of cotton seed oil at $17\frac{1}{2}$ cents a pound.

> *Ans.* 5500 times $0.0875; 275 times $1.75; $1\frac{3}{4}$ times $275.00.

15. The amount due on the purchase of 34 dresses at $13.50 each.

> *Ans.* $\frac{1}{8}$ of $3400.00, plus $34.00; 17 times $27.00; 15 times $27.00, plus 2 times $27.00.

16. The weight of 28 cubic feet of water. (One cubic foot of water weighs $62\frac{1}{2}$ pounds.)

> *Ans.* 14 times 125; 7 times 250; 50 times 28, plus one quarter of the result.

17. The number of feet in 22 rods. (One rod equals $16\frac{1}{2}$ feet.)

> *Ans.* 11 times 33; $5\frac{1}{2}$ times 66; $8\frac{1}{4}$ times 44.

18. The total amount of dry hay yielded by 96 acres at the rate of $7\frac{3}{4}$ tons per acre.

> *Ans.* 100 times 7.75, minus 4 times 7.75; 31 times 24; 31 times 25, minus 31.

42. Checking Multiplication by Casting Out the Nines.
Here is a useful method for checking multiplication when
one or both factors contain three or more digits. (It may
also be used, with a slight modification, for checking addition, subtraction and division, as we shall see later—the
process is substantially the same in all four operations.)
It is simple and interesting, and is not practiced as commonly as it might be.

The method entails the addition of the digits of each
factor and the product, the division of each sum by 9, and
the setting down of the remainder, which we will call the
check number. Thus to prove that the product of 786
times 89 equals 69,954, we proceed as follows:

786	7+8+6	= 21.	Casting out the 9's leaves 3
× 89	8+9	= 17.	Casting out the 9 leaves 8
69954	6+9+9+5+4	= 33.	Casting out the 9's leaves 6

This being a problem in multiplication, we multiply the
check number of the multiplicand (check number 3) by
the check number of the multiplier (check number 8),
which gives us 24. The sum of the digits in 24 is 6. We find
that this is the check number for the answer to our problem, and so we may presume our answer (69954) to be
correct.

Note that we only "presume" the answer to be correct.
Checking multiplication by casting out the nines is not
100 per cent proof. If, by a mischance, digits in the answer
had been transposed, or if a nine or a zero had been added
or omitted, the error would not show up in the proof. For
instance, if the answer to the problem illustrated were in-
correctly shown as 96954, 60954 or 699054, the final check
number, after casting out the nines, would still be 6.

A word of caution should be added here. When the sum of the digits in any factor in a multiplication problem adds up to an exact multiple of 9, the check number is shown as 9; in other words, all the nines but one are cast out. Note that this rule applies only to the factors; it does not apply to the product. One illustration will make this clear:

666	6 $+ 6 + 6$	$= 18.$ Casting out one 9 leaves	9
$\times 3$	3	$= 3.$ No 9's to cast out leaves	3
1998	$1 + 9 + 9 + 8 = 27.$ Casting out the 9's leaves		0

PROBLEMS

Prove by casting out the nines that the answers to the following multiplication problems are correct.

1. 136 times 8 equals 1088.
2. 432 times 17 equals 7344.
3. 613 times 38 equals 23294.
4. 274 times 126 equals 34524.
5. 246 times 324 equals 79704.

CHAPTER IX

SIMPLE INTEREST

The computation of interest is a needlessly distressing and time-consuming experience for a surprisingly large number of businessmen and office workers.

Here, as in the many other types of problems discussed in the preceding chapters, a knowledge of decimals, aliquot parts and the breakdown method of multiplication comes to the rescue. A study of the articles and tables in this chapter should enable the reader to compute interest problems quickly and accurately, regardless of the interest rate or number of days.

43. The Difference Between Ordinary and Exact Interest. *Ordinary* interest is computed on the basis of 360 days in the year. This is the universally accepted method, used particularly when short periods or small sums are involved. *Exact* interest is computed on the basis of 365 days in the year. This is the method used by the Federal Government. It is used by banks and by state and city governments when large sums are involved.

It is interesting to observe that the difference between ordinary and exact interest on $1000 at 1 per cent for 360 days is less than 14 cents.

44. The Cancellation Method of Computing Interest. The conventional method of finding interest is the cancellation method, with the rate and period shown as common fractions. Thus in computing ordinary interest, 38 days would be shown as $\frac{38}{360}$; in computing exact interest, the same period would be indicated by the fraction $\frac{38}{365}$. The rate of 5 per cent would be shown as $\frac{5}{100}$, $3\frac{1}{2}$ per cent as $\frac{7}{200}$, and so on. (The principle of interest computation is, of course, the same, regardless of the method used. A simple formula is: Principal times period times rate.)

Since most readers are probably more or less familiar with cancellation procedure, it is considered unnecessary to accompany the solutions in the following illustrations by explanations. Readers who are not thoroughly conversant with this phase of mathematics are advised to study Art. 107, "Cancellation and How It Simplifies the Process of Multiplying Fractions," in the last chapter, before proceeding further.

Example 1: Find ordinary interest on \$320.00 for the period July 1 to September 1 at 4 per cent.

Solution:
$$\frac{\overset{}{32\cancel{0}} \times \overset{2}{\cancel{60}} \times \cancel{4}}{\underset{\underset{3}{6}}{\cancel{360}} \times \underset{5}{\cancel{100}}} = \frac{32}{15} = \$2.13$$

Example 2: Find exact interest on \$146,000.00 for the period July 8 to September 11 at $3\frac{1}{2}$ per cent.

Solution: Note that the exact number of days in the interest period is 65.

$$\frac{\overset{10}{\underset{}{\cancel{146000}}} \times \overset{13}{\cancel{65}} \times 7}{\underset{\underset{73}{}}{\cancel{365}} \times \cancel{200}} = \frac{910}{1} = \$910.00$$

It is interesting to note that if, in Example 2, ordinary, rather than exact, interest was to be computed, the amount would be $922.64 instead of $910.00.

45. Simplification of the Cancellation Method. Under the cancellation method, as discussed in the preceding article, the last figure in the denominator of the fraction representing the interest period (360) is a zero, and the last two figures of the denominator of the fraction representing the per cent rate are also zeros. It is obvious, therefore, that time would be saved by canceling the three zeros into the principal mentally, before the problem in fractional form is written down. The cancellation is effected by simply pointing off the decimal in the principal three places to the left, that is, one place for each zero.

Thus in Example 1 in the preceding article, in which we were to find the ordinary interest on $320.00 for the period July 1 to September 1 at 4 per cent, the solution would be simplified by writing the fractional form as follows:

$$\frac{.32 \times 60 \times 4}{36}$$

Notice that under the simplified method only one simple paper cancellation is necessary (12 into 60, and 12 into 36), whereas the solution by the conventional method required at least four paper cancellations.

PROBLEMS

Without working them to a finish, show how you would reduce the following problems to fractional form after having canceled the zeros in the denominator into the principal mentally.

1. Find the ordinary interest on $746.00 at 3% for 24 days.

$$Ans. \ \frac{.746 \times 3 \times 24}{36}.$$

2. Find the ordinary interest on an 80-day note of $1364.00 bearing interest at $3\frac{1}{2}\%$.

$$Ans. \quad \frac{13.64 \times 7 \times 8}{72}.$$

3. What will the ordinary interest amount to on a 45-day note of $2300.00 bearing interest at $3\frac{1}{4}\%$?

$$Ans. \quad \frac{2.3 \times 13 \times 45}{144}.$$

4. At the ordinary interest rate of 4% what would it cost to borrow $850.00 for 75 days?

$$Ans. \quad \frac{.85 \times 4 \times 75}{36}.$$

5. What would it cost to borrow $1125.00 at the ordinary interest rate of $4\frac{1}{2}\%$ for 95 days?

$$Ans. \quad \frac{1.125 \times 9 \times 95}{72}.$$

46. The 60-Day, 6 Per Cent Method of Computing Ordinary Interest, and How It Lends Itself to a Basically Valuable Short-Cut. Readers who enjoy working with figures will probably find the study of this article a stimulating experience. Let us take a simple problem and learn why many *ordinary* interest computations can be made speedily and accurately by simply pointing off the decimal in the principal two or three places, as the case may be.

Problem: Find ordinary interest on $378.00 for 60 days at 6 per cent. Setting down the problem for solution by the cancellation method, we have

$$\frac{378 \times 60 \times 6}{360 \times 100}$$

Observe the interesting picture presented by the two fractions—the one representing the interest period, the other the interest rate. Notice that the product of the numerators (60 and 6) equals 360, which is also one of the denominators and may, therefore, be canceled into it. This leaves us with the fraction $\frac{378}{100}$, and we know immediately that our answer is $3.78.

We, therefore, arrive at the following conclusions:

1. To find ordinary interest for 60 days at 6 per cent, it is but necessary to point off the decimal in the principal two places to the left.

2. To find ordinary interest for 6 days at 6 per cent, it is but necessary to point off the decimal in the principal *three* places to the left.

PROBLEMS

Compute mentally, to the nearest cent, the ordinary interest due on the following amounts loaned at 6% for 60 days.

★ 1.	$145.00	*Ans.*	$1.45.
★ 2.	$237.40	*Ans.*	$2.37.
★ 3.	$897.60	*Ans.*	$8.98.
★ 4.	$364.10	*Ans.*	$3.64.
★ 5.	$920.50	*Ans.*	$9.21.
★ 6.	$756.20	*Ans.*	$7.56.
★ 7.	$193.67	*Ans.*	$1.94.
★ 8.	$324.62	*Ans.*	$3.25.
★ 9.	$613.56	*Ans.*	$6.14.
★ 10.	$1162.38	*Ans.*	$11.62.

47. A Quick Way of Computing Ordinary Interest for Any Number of Days When the Rate Is 6 Per Cent. Here we will make another experiment with the breakdown method of multiplication. Readers will find the study easy to follow, and no attempt should be made to memorize the relations shown.

By way of diversion, the following illustrations will be accompanied by little comment. Bear in mind, please, the conclusion arrived at in the preceding article: To find ordinary interest for 60 days at 6 per cent, we need but to point off the decimal in the principal two places to the left.

Example 1: Find the ordinary interest on $194.00 for 80 days at 6%.

Solution: Interest for 60 days   = $1.94
         Interest for 20 days ($\frac{1}{3}$ of $1.94) =   .65
         ───
         Interest for 80 days   = $2.59

Example 2: Find the ordinary interest on $325.00 for 36 days at 6%.

Solution: Interest for 30 days ($\frac{1}{2}$ of $3.25) = $1.625
         Interest for 6 days ($\frac{1}{5}$ of $1.625) =   .325
         ───
         Interest for 36 days   = $1.95

Example 3: Find the ordinary interest on $821.50 for 7 days at 6%.

Solution: Interest for 6 days ($\frac{1}{10}$ of $8.21) = $.821
         Interest for 1 day ($\frac{1}{6}$ of $.821)   =   .137
         ───
         Interest for 7 days   = $.96

Example 4: Find the ordinary interest on $218.00 for 7 months at 6%.

Solution: Interest for 2 months   = $2.18
         Interest for 4 months (twice $2.18)   =   4.36
         Interest for 1 month ($\frac{1}{2}$ of $2.18) =   1.09
         ───
         Interest for 7 months   = $7.63

Example 5: Find the ordinary interest on $381.00 for 1 year 9 months and 15 days at 6%.

Solution: Note that the period may be restated as 21 months and 15 days.

Interest for 20 months
(10 times $3.81) = $38.10
Interest for 1 month ($\frac{1}{2}$ of $3.81) = 1.905
Interest for 15 days ($\frac{1}{2}$ of $1.905) = .952
―――――――――――――――――――――――――――――――
Interest for 21 months and 15 days = $40.96

Example 6: Find the ordinary interest on $243.00 for 85 days at 6%.

Solution: Interest for 60 days = $2.43
Interest for 20 days ($\frac{1}{3}$ of $2.43) = .81
Interest for 5 days ($\frac{1}{4}$ of .81) = .20
―――――――――――――――――――――――――――――――
Interest for 85 days = $3.44

There is no definite rule for breaking down the number of days. In the solution to the last example, for instance, we might just as well have added the interest for 30 days to the interest for 60 days, deducting from the total one sixth of the interest for 30 days.

PROBLEMS

Compute to the nearest cent the ordinary interest due on the following loans at 6%.

★ 1. $165.00 for 120 days.   *Ans.* $3.30.
  2. $843.00 for 150 days.   *Ans.* $21.08.

★ 3. $326.00 for 180 days.   *Ans.* $9.78.
★ 4. $619.60 for 20 days.   *Ans.* $2.07.
  5. $437.54 for 40 days.   *Ans.* $2.92.
  6. $1233.40 for 100 days.   *Ans.* $20.56.
  7. $1476.64 for 50 days.   *Ans.* $12.31.
  8. $1348.00 for 84 days.   *Ans.* $18.87.
  9. $1520.00 for 77 days.   *Ans.* $19.51.
 10. $1054.00 for 68 days.   *Ans.* $11.95.

48. How to Compute Ordinary Interest Quickly When the Rate Is Other Than 6 Per Cent. Here is another interesting study in aliquot parts. In the preceding article we learned how to compute interest when the rate is 6 per cent. With this information at our finger tips it is a comparatively simple matter to find the interest at 5 per cent, $4\frac{1}{2}$ per cent, or any other rate.

The following illustrations will help to fix this process in mind:

Example 1: Find the ordinary interest on $528.00 for 48 days at $5\frac{1}{2}\%$.

Solution: Interest for 60 days at 6%   = $5.28

Interest for 60 days at $5\frac{1}{2}\%$
($\frac{11}{12}$ of 5.28)   = $4.84
— Interest for 12 days at $5\frac{1}{2}\%$
($\frac{1}{5}$ of 4.84)   =   .97

Interest for 48 days at $5\frac{1}{2}\%$ = $3.87

Example 2: Find the ordinary interest on $342.00 for 110 days at $6\frac{1}{2}\%$.

Solution: Interest for 120 days at 6%
            (twice $3.42)   = $6.84
          — Interest for 10 days at 6%
            ($\frac{1}{12}$ of $6.84)   =   .57

          _____

            Interest for 110 days at 6%   = $6.27
            Interest for 110 days at $\frac{1}{2}$%
            ($\frac{1}{12}$ of $6.27)   =   .52

          _____

            Interest for 110 days at $6\frac{1}{2}$% = $6.79

PROBLEMS

Find by the breakdown method, as illustrated in the text, the ordinary interest in the following problems.

1. $508.00 for 54 days at 5%.   *Ans.* $3.81.
2. $276.40 for 80 days at 2%.   *Ans.* $1.23.
3. $1475.00 for 93 days at 3%.   *Ans.* $11.43.
4. $2394.80 for 110 days at $4\frac{1}{2}$%.   *Ans.* $32.93.
5. $1676.25 for 124 days at $2\frac{1}{2}$%.   *Ans.* $14.43.
6. $322.42 for 115 days at 4%.   *Ans.* $4.12.
7. $6781.90 for 140 days at $1\frac{1}{2}$%.   *Ans.* $39.56.
8. $793.34 for 45 days at 7%.   *Ans.* $6.94.
9. $426.57 for 44 days at $3\frac{1}{2}$%.   *Ans.* $1.82.
10. $2043.93 for 82 days at $5\frac{1}{2}$%.   *Ans.* $25.60.

49. Calculations by the 60-Day, 6 Per Cent Method Can Be Easily Proved. Because of its flexibility, the breakdown method of multiplication is an ideal means of proving answers to ordinary interest problems. Note, in the following illustration, the different ways in which this method may be used to compute the ordinary interest on $1798.00 for 140 days at 6 per cent.

Method A: Interest for 120 days
                (twice $17.98)   = $35.96
             Interest for 20 days ($\frac{1}{6}$ of $35.96) =   5.99
             _____
             Interest for 140 days   = $41.95

Method B: Interest for 60 days   = $17.98
             Interest for 15 days
                ($\frac{1}{4}$ of $17.98)   =   4.495
             Interest for 75 days
                ($17.98 plus $4.495)   =   22.475
             _____
             Interest for 150 days   = $44.95
          — Interest for 10 days ($\frac{1}{6}$ of $17.98) =   3.00
             _____
             Interest for 140 days   = $41.95

Problems

Compute the ordinary interest in each of the following problems by two different breakdowns, as shown in the test. Assume an interest rate of 6% in each instance.

1. $1430.00 for 40 days.		*Ans.* $9.53.
★ **2.** $2826.30 for 90 days.		*Ans.* $42.39.
3. $3748.60 for 25 days.		*Ans.* $15.62.
4. $1685.20 for 24 days.		*Ans.* $6.74.
5. $854.70 for 150 days.		*Ans.* $21.37.
6. $1232.40 for 160 days.		*Ans.* $32.86.
7. $763.80 for 135 days.		*Ans.* $17.19.
8. $3046.24 for 85 days.		*Ans.* $43.16.
★ **9.** $4010.00 for 12 days.		*Ans.* $8.02.
10. $6200.00 for 18 days.		*Ans.* $18.60.

50. The Meaning of Compound Interest. For the reader who is not sure of himself on this subject the meaning of compound interest will become clear if he thinks of his savings—a thought, it is hoped, that will inspire a pleasant feeling. If he happens to be a depositor in two banks, and if for a period, say, of two years has confined his deposits to one of them, he will find, upon returning to the other bank, that despite his not having made a single deposit there in that time, the interest credited to his account for each period exceeds the amount of interest credited for the preceding period.

The reason is simply this: When interest is allowed to accumulate, the principal increases—it increases at the end of each interest period by the amount of interest earned for that period. Interest, therefore, is earned not only on the money actually deposited, but also on the interest earned by that money. This, in effect, is what compound interest really is—*interest earned on interest.*

51. The Difference Between Simple Interest and Compound Interest. Compound interest is calculated in the same manner as simple interest—that is, it is found by multiplying the principal by the period by the interest rate. There is one difference however: Simple interest usually concerns itself with but one period, and this period is more often than not for less than a year or, when notes are involved, for 30, 60, 90 or 120 days. And if, in a simple interest transaction, more than one period is involved, the principal at the beginning of each period is the same. Compound interest, on the other hand, involves two or more periods, with an increased principal at the beginning of each succeeding period.

This difference might be best illustrated by considering two loans for identical amounts, periods and interest rates, the interest in one instance to be simple interest, and in the other instance compound interest.

Simple Interest Illustration. Let us suppose that Miller makes a loan to Smith of $2000.00 for two years at the interest rate of 4 per cent per annum, the interest to be paid quarterly. Under this arrangement Smith, at the end of each 3-month period, is to pay to Miller 1 per cent (4 per cent per annum is equivalent to 1 per cent per 3-month period) of $2000.00, or $20.00. The amount of the interest will not increase with each succeeding period, for since the interest is paid as it becomes due, the principal at the beginning of each succeeding period is the same as it was at the beginning of the first period. Each interest computation is exactly the same as the preceding one. So it is easy to see that if the interest per quarterly period is $20.00, the total amount of interest paid in two years will be 8 times $20.00, or $160.00.

Compound Interest Illustration. Let us now suppose that Stone makes a loan to Frost of $2000.00 for two years, the interest at 4 per cent per annum to be computed quarterly as in the simple interest illustration, but *added to the principal.* That is to say, the principal plus all of the accumulated interest is to be paid in one sum upon the maturity date of the note. At the end of the two years, the effect of this arrangement would be as illustrated.

Principal at beginning of period........	$2000.00
Interest for 3 months—1% of $2000.00	20.00
Principal at end of *first* period........	2020.00
Interest for 3 months—1% of $2020.00	20.20

Principal at end of *second* period	2040.20
Interest for 3 months—1% of $2040.20	20.40
Principal at end of *third* period	2060.60
Interest for 3 months—1% of $2060.60	20.61
Principal at end of *fourth* period	2081.21
Interest for 3 months—1% of $2081.21	20.81
Principal at end of *fifth* period	2102.02
Interest for 3 months—1% of $2102.02	21.02
Principal at end of *sixth* period	2123.04
Interest for 3 months—1% of $2123.04	21.23
Principal at end of *seventh* period	2144.27
Interest for 3 months—1% of $2144.27	21.44
Principal at end of *eighth* period	$2165.71

Note that at the end of the loan period Frost owes Stone $2165.71, which includes a total interest charge of $165.71, or $5.71 more than Smith owed to Miller. This, of course, is explained by the fact that Smith had paid his interest by the *simple interest* method—that is, as the interest became due, whereas the interest on the loan to Frost was *compounded*—that is, it was allowed to accumulate, so that Frost was, in effect, paying interest on interest.

The illustration showing the constantly increasing amount of the interest, when it is added to the principal, is given here to provide a clear picture of the effect of such an arrangement. Generally, compound interest is computed on calculating machines or is determined from tables.

52. A Simple Way to Find the Number of Days in Any Interest Period. A quick way to find the number of days in an interest period is to list the number of days in each month separately, and total them. The number of days in the interest period May 4 to September 17 would, therefore, be found as follows:

$$
\begin{array}{ll}
\text{May} & = 27 \text{ days} \\
\text{June} & = 30 \text{ days} \\
\text{July} & = 31 \text{ days} \\
\text{August} & = 31 \text{ days} \\
\text{September} & = 17 \text{ days} \\
\hline
& 136 \text{ days}
\end{array}
$$

PROBLEMS

Show how you would compute by the month-by-month method the number of days in the following interest periods.

1. March 6 to May 19.   *Ans.* 25 + 30 + 19 = 74.
2. April 22 to June 5.   *Ans.* 8 + 31 + 5 = 44.
3. May 27 to July 20.   *Ans.* 4 + 30 + 20 = 54.
4. May 16 to August 31.   *Ans.* 15 + 30 + 31 + 31 = 107.
5. June 20 to September 15. *Ans.* 10 + 31 + 31 + 15 = 87.
6. August 6 to November 10. *Ans.* 25 + 30 + 31 + 10 = 96.
7. April 6 to July 9.   *Ans.* 94 days.
8. September 22 to December 20.   *Ans.* 89 days.
9. August 11 to November 3.   *Ans.* 84 days.
10. March 8 to September 14.   *Ans.* 190 days.

53. Bank Discount and How It Is Calculated. Bank discount is not really a discount; it is the interest charged by banks when money is advanced on a note.

Joseph Walpole, for example, is the holder of a note given him by Albert Ballon. The note is dated July 1 and is a promise to pay $4200.00 one hundred and twenty days "after date," with interest at 3 per cent. On July 11 Walpole, in need of cash, decides to have the note discounted by his bank. He accordingly endorses it over to the bank, which, after calculating the discount—that is, the interest—chargeable on the note, credits Walpole with the net proceeds.

Assuming that the bank's discount rate at the time is 4 per cent, here is how the net proceeds to be credited to Walpole is determined: First the bank computes the amount to be collected from Ballon on the date that the note falls due:

Principal......................	$4200.00
Interest at 3% for 120 days.....	42.00
Maturity value of note.........	$4242.00

Now the bank computes the amount to be charged to Walpole for advancing him $4242.00 for 110 days—110 days being the difference between 120 days (the period of the note) and 10 days (the period that has gone by since the note was issued); $4242.00 for 110 days at 4 per cent equals $51.85.

Maturity value of note.................	$4242.00
Less bank discount.....................	51.85
Amount credited by bank to Walpole.....	$4190.15

The bank, on the other hand, holds the note until the date of maturity, when it will try to collect from Ballon $4242.00.

It should be remembered that the money advanced by the bank to Walpole really constitutes a loan and will be charged to Walpole's account if Ballon does not pay the note on its due date. It is just as though the bank had cashed for Walpole a check drawn by Ballon in his favor; if the check was not honored upon presentation at the bank on which it was drawn, the amount would automatically be charged to Walpole's account by his bank.

Some interesting facts should be noted in connection with this transaction. The amount advanced by the bank was calculated not on the face value of the note nor on the amount advanced, but on the *maturity* value of the note. Also, the bank discount (really the interest charge) was *deducted at the time the money was advanced*. In other words, in having the note discounted, Walpole not only lost the equivalent of 1 per cent on the maturity value of the note (1 per cent because the bank charged him 4 per cent and the note called for an interest payment of 3 per cent), but he also lost the use of $51.85, the bank charge, for 110 days; so that he actually paid slightly more than the 4 per cent charged by the bank. This difference between simple interest and bank discount is discussed further in the article that follows.

Example: A 90-day note is issued on April 2 for $4500.00 with interest at 2% per annum. The note was discounted on April 12 at 3%. Calculate the net proceeds.

Solution: Principal...................... $4500.00

Plus interest at 2% for 90 days (2%
for 1 year would be $90.00; 2%
for 90 days = $\frac{1}{4}$ of $90.00) 22.50

Maturity value of note........... $4522.50
Less bank discount at 3% for 80
days * (90 days minus the period
that elapsed from April 2 to April
12)........................... 30.16

Net proceeds................... $4492.34

PROBLEMS

Calculate the net proceeds for each of the following notes.

Date of Note	Date Discounted	Term	Face Value	Interest Rate	Discount Rate
1. Mar. 11	Mar. 26	60 days	$3000	3%	4%
				Ans. $2999.92.	
2. May 8	May 28	90 days	$8000	$2\frac{1}{2}$%	3%
				Ans. $8003.04.	
3. June 21	July 21	120 days	$2400	3%	$3\frac{1}{2}$%
				Ans. $2402.79.	
4. July 1	July 16	30 days	$4200	2%	3%
				Ans. $4201.74.	
5. Sept. 14	Sept. 24	60 days	$3460	0	3%
				Ans. $3445.58.	
6. Oct. 21	Nov. 10	120 days	$12900	1%	$3\frac{1}{2}$%
				Ans. $12,817.17.	

* Note how simple this computation becomes by the 60-day 6 per
cent method:

$4522.50 for 60 days at 6% = $45.23
$4522.50 for 20 days at 6% ($\frac{1}{3}$ of $45.23) = 15.08

$4522.50 for 80 days at 6% = $60.31

$4522.50 for 80 days at 3% ($\frac{1}{2}$ of $60.31) = $30.16

54. A Simple Explanation of the Difference Between Simple Interest and Bank Discount. It was pointed out in the preceding article that when Walpole discounted his note he paid actually more than the 4 per cent charged him as "bank discount." Let us see why.

In having the note discounted Walpole, in effect, borrowed a sum of money—he borrowed $4190.15 for 110 days, for which privilege he paid the bank $51.85. Now if he had otherwise secured a loan of $4190.15 at the simple interest rate of 4 per cent or, let us say, if he owed someone $4190.15 and had given the creditor a note for this amount, payable in 110 days, with 4 per cent simple interest, Walpole would have had to pay *less* than $51.85. In other words, at the end of 110 days he would owe, in addition to the principal, $\frac{4}{100}$ of $\frac{110}{360}$ of $4190.15 which,

reduced to fractional form, equals $\dfrac{4190.15 \times 4 \times 110}{100 \times 360}$

or $51.21, which amount is $0.64 less than was charged him as "bank discount."

PROBLEMS

Using the figures obtained in working the problems in Art. 53, compute the amount of interest which the note-holder in each instance would have to pay if, instead of discounting the note, he borrowed for the unexpired period of the note a sum of money equal to the net proceeds, at a rate of interest equal to the discount rate charged by the bank.

> *Ans.* (1) $15.00; (2) $46.68; (3) $21.02; (4) $5.25; (5) $14.36; (6) $124.61.

55. How to Determine the Present Value of a Sum of Money Due at a Future Date at Simple Interest. Suppose Henry Branred invested $100.00 at 4 per cent per annum. Assuming that the interest is paid annually, his investment would be worth, at the end of one year, $104.00. Let us now take the transaction in reverse. Suppose Branred had $104.00 coming to him a year hence, and he wanted to know the present value of this sum, assuming the prevailing rate of interest to be 4 per cent. Obviously, the present value of this debt is $100.00.

Let us now do a little reasoning together. Henry Branred's investment of $100.00 at the rate of 4 per cent would be worth, as we have seen, $104.00 at the end of one year. It is clear, then, that his investment at the beginning of the year is equal to $\frac{100}{104}$ of its value at the end of the year. From this we can conclude that *any* principal at 4 per cent per annum is equivalent at the beginning of a one-year period to $\frac{100}{104}$ of what it will amount to at the end of the one-year period. Similarly, any principal at 3 per cent per annum is equivalent at the beginning of a one-year period to $\frac{100}{103}$ of what it will amount to at the end of the one-year period. And so on. The denominator of the ratio, in other words, is the sum of 100 plus the interest rate.

Example 1: What is the present value of an investment that will be worth $468.00 a year hence? Assume the interest rate to be 4% payable annually.

Solution: The present value of the investment equals $\frac{100}{104}$ of the future value.

$\frac{1}{104}$ of $468.00	= $ 4.50
$\frac{100}{104}$ of $468.00 (100 times $4.50)	= $450.00

Proof: 4% of $450.00   = $ 18.00
$18.00 plus $450.00   = $468.00

Example 2: Find the present worth of an investment whose value six months hence will be $252.50. Assume the interest rate to be 2% per annum, payable semiannually.

Solution: An annual interest rate of 2% payable semiannually is equivalent to an interest rate of 1% for six months. So that the present value of this investment equals $\frac{100}{101}$ of the future value.

$\frac{1}{101}$ of $252.50   = $ 2.50
$\frac{100}{101}$ of $252.50 (100 times $2.50) = $250.00

Proof: 1% of $250.00   = $ 2.50
$2.50 plus $250.00   = $252.50

Example 3: A manufacturer sells a bill of goods amounting to $3800.00 on net terms of 90 days. A few weeks after the shipment is billed he finds himself in need of cash. If money is worth 3%, how much should the manufacturer be willing to accept in full payment 60 days before payment is due?

Solution: The problem resolves itself into the question: What is the present worth of $3800.00 due two months hence at 3% per annum?

Two months at 3% per annum is equivalent to one year at $\frac{1}{2}$ of 1%. The present value of $3800.00 due two months hence is therefore $\frac{100}{100\frac{1}{2}}$ or $\frac{200}{201}$ of $3800.00.

$$\frac{200}{201} \text{ of } \$3800 = \frac{200 \times 3800}{201}$$

$$= \frac{\$760,000}{201} \text{ or } \$3781.09.$$

A word of explanation might be added here. In Examples 1 and 2 we computed $\frac{100}{104}$ and $\frac{100}{101}$, respectively, by first dividing by the denominator, and multiplying by the numerator *afterward*. The computations were made in that order principally to emphasize the convenience of this method of procedure; it is obviously easier to divide $468.00 by 104 and then multiply the result by 100 than to multiply $468.00 by 100 and divide by 104 afterward, because $468.00 divided by 104 gives us exactly $4.50. More often than not, however, the process of division is not complete with the determination of the cent digits, and it may be a good plan for the reader to make it a rule to calculate the product of the numerators first, and divide the result by the denominator—as we did in Example 3.

PROBLEMS

Find the present worth of the following sums, at the prevailing rates of interest indicated.

1. A sum worth $2200 one year hence—$3\frac{1}{2}\%$.   *Ans.* $2125.60.
2. A sum worth $3460 six months hence—$3\%$.   *Ans.* $3408.86.
3. A sum worth $8200 nine months hence—$4\%$.

Ans. $7961.16.

4. A sum worth $12,000 three months hence—2%.

Ans. $11,940.30.

5. A sum worth $9600 eight months hence—$3\%$.

Ans. $9411.76.

6. A sum worth $5000 four months hence—$1\frac{1}{2}\%$.

Ans. $4975.12.

CHAPTER X

AVOIDING ERRORS IN ADDITION

The reader may have always taken it for granted that the process of addition is very simple, and there is no doubt that for a great many people this process of computation never presents any difficulty. It is, nonetheless, a fact that errors occur in addition just as frequently as in the other mathematical operations. Moreover, anyone is likely to make an error in addition. Only recently a certified public accountant, who enjoys an enviable practice, said to the author, "I hate to add figures, because I often catch myself making mistakes at it."

The reader will do well to acquaint himself with the various methods of addition discussed in this chapter. He is advised to pay particular attention to the methods described in Arts. 58 and 60; they are interesting as well as important. And a little diversion may even be found in studying the article "Checking Addition by Casting Out the Nines."

56. The Most Practical Method of Reading Combinations of Figures. Many of us fall into the habit of injecting "and" when adding figures. There is really no need for this, and the practice is time-wasting and tends to confuse. Instead of saying, "6 and 9 are 15, and 4 are 19, and 6 are 25," it is better to say (silently, of course), "15, 19, 25," and so on.

Incidentally, it would be well to adopt the habit of leaving out the "and" when reading figures. Instead of reading 798 as "seven hundred and ninety-eight," just read, "seven hundred ninety-eight." Similarly, 1654 should be read "sixteen hundred fifty-four."

57. Mental Addition Without Carrying.

What makes mental addition so difficult for some individuals is the "carrying" part of it. The need for carrying is eliminated when, instead of adding from right to left, we add from left to right.

In adding 3163 and 234, for instance, mentally, it is better to add, first 200, then 30, and lastly 4. The process would, therefore, consist of three simple steps which produce the two partial totals 3363 and 3393, and the final total 3397. Similarly, to add 7847 and 342 mentally, the process would comprise the two partial sums 8147 (7847 plus 300) and 8187 (8147 plus 40), and the final total 8189 (8187 plus 2).

When adding mentally numbers ending in 7, 8 or 9, it is sometimes more convenient to increase the value of the last digit to 10, complete the process of addition, then subtract from the answer the value by which the original number has been increased. Thus in adding 84 and 99, say "84 plus 100 equals 184, minus 1 equals 183." In adding 136 and 68, say "136 plus 70 equals 206, minus 2 equals 204."

The technique will be found most useful when adding numbers the sum of whose digits is 10 or more, as in the examples given. This procedure is not necessary, however, when adding numbers the sum of whose digits is less than 10; for example, in adding 241 to 358, there would be no point in changing 358 to 360.

EXERCISES

Add the following pairs of numbers mentally, then check your answers by adding them by the conventional method.

⋆ 1.	572 and 216.	*Ans.* 788.
⋆ 2.	613 and 324.	*Ans.* 937.
⋆ 3.	735 and 152.	*Ans.* 887.
⋆ 4.	944 and 361.	*Ans.* 1305.
⋆ 5.	245 and 57.	*Ans.* 302.
⋆ 6.	354 and 38.	*Ans.* 392.
⋆ 7.	$8.23 and $4.29.	*Ans.* $12.52.
⋆ 8.	$12.66 and $5.48.	*Ans.* $18.14.
⋆ 9.	$14.75 and $3.42.	*Ans.* $18.17.
⋆ 10.	$16.36 and $15.63.	*Ans.* $31.99.

58. Speeding Addition by Combining Figures. It is always a good plan when adding a column of figures, to combine digits that follow each other and add up to 10 because 10 is added so easily. Thus when 7 is followed by 3, or 3 by 7, instead of adding each digit separately, their *sum* (10) is added. This, of course, applies to any combination—1 and 9, 2 and 8, 4 and 6, and so on.

EXERCISES

Add by the technique discussed in the text the following groups of numbers:

1. 23	2. 13	3. 149	4. 64
47	28	31	128
44	42	74	32
56	53	186	53
12	17	29	324
38	36	140	16

Ans. (1) 220; (2) 189; (3) 609; (4) 617.

59. Adding Two or Three Columns of Figures at One Time. Here is an interesting short-cut that is often overlooked. Note, in the following problem, that the sum of the figures in the tens and units columns is less than 100, and that the digits in the hundreds columns are easy to add. Rather than add each column separately, it is easier to take in at a glance the digits in the hundreds column and say "1400," then run your eye up the tens and units columns saying, "1427, 1449, 1458."

$$309$$
$$422$$
$$408$$
$$319$$

Another illustration will suffice to make this clear:

$$224$$
$$132$$
$$108$$
$$321$$
$$402$$

Say "1100, 1123, 1131, 1163, 1187." No need for carrying, and no need for pencil and paper.

EXERCISES

Add mentally by the technique discussed the numbers in the following groups:

★ 1.	★ 2.	★ 3.	★ 4.
211	125	843	931
324	432	124	129
403	513	308	723
630	707	422	612

Ans. (1) 1568; (2) 1777; (3) 1697; (4) 2395.

60. Addition by Grouping. When the columns of figures are very long—that is, when they consist of about twenty numbers or more—a very practical way to add them is to separate the numbers into groups, drawing a line under every five or six numbers, and total each group separately. The sum of the sub-totals supplies the answer. An illustration follows:

$$
\begin{array}{rr}
142 & \\
84 & \\
256 & \\
138 & \\
\underline{29} & 649 \\
236 & \\
55 & \\
198 & \\
71 & \\
\underline{562} & 1122 \\
784 & \\
32 & \\
109 & \\
128 & \\
\underline{875} & 1928 \\
543 & \\
852 & \\
106 & \\
25 & \\
\underline{481} & \underline{2007} \\
& 5706
\end{array}
$$

The convenience of grouping will be readily appreciated. Instead of adding all twenty numbers in the preceding illustration at one time, only five at a time were added to arrive at a sub-total. And it was necessary to add only four sub-totals to obtain the total. Groups may, of course, be arranged according to one's aptitude for figures—some may find it more convenient to add but four numbers at a time, others may have no difficulty adding six or seven numbers at one time.

PROBLEMS

Add the following sets of figures by the sub-total method, grouping the numbers in Problems 1 and 2 in 4's, and the numbers in Problems 3 and 4 in 5's. Show in your answers the sub-totals as well as the totals.

1. $ 21.41	2. $ 91.20	3. $217.45	4. $139.37
12.83	12.44	82.30	4.13
4.75	137.26	6.17	9.26
18.90	93.12	19.23	11.41
2.06	4.88	4.11	19.19
134.14	17.25	7.14	126.04
25.23	131.60	18.28	32.07
41.17	18.32	.32	4.93
9.18	24.67	12.44	2.16
12.05	130.13	190.26	15.82
7.23	19.24	11.17	72.14
135.64	6.16	4.60	13.06
		29.32	28.18
		15.25	142.02
		23.45	8.23

Ans.
  1. Sub-totals: 57.89, 202.60, 164.10. Total: $424.59.
  2. Sub-totals: 334.02, 172.05, 180.20. Total: $686.27.
  3. Sub-totals: 329.26, 228.44, 83.79. Total: $641.49.
  4. Sub-totals: 183.36, 181.02, 263.63. Total: $628.01.

61. Addition by the Two-Line Method. Many who are
not unaccustomed to working with figures are sometimes
exasperated by the variety of answers obtained when
adding long columns of figures or a series of numbers
which run into six or more figures. Physical interruptions
and thought interruptions are common causes of errors in
addition.

A conventional method of addition—one which makes
it possible to go over a column once more without having
to start all over again—might best be described as the
"two-line" method. By this method each column is added
separately, the unit figure of the total being put down
directly under the figures totaled, while the tens figure is
put down on the line below, one space to the left. The
addition of the two lines of figures supplies the answer.
Note the explanation which accompanies the following
illustration in which four rows of figures are added by
this method.

$$
\begin{array}{r}
3426724 \\
6213816 \\
4167482 \\
2389156 \\
\hline
5075068 \\
1112211 \\
\hline
16197178
\end{array}
$$

The sum of the digits in the unit column is 18, so we
put down the 8 in the unit column of the first partial total,
and 1 on the line below, one space to the left. The sum of
the digits in the tens column is 16, so we put down the 6

in the tens column of the first partial total, and 1 on the line below, one space to the left. And so on. Adding the two partial totals, we arrive at the answer, 16,197,178.

PROBLEMS

Add the following sums by the two-line method.

1. $ 473.56	2. $2612.15	3. $7109.23	4. $2581.17
6235.18	923.81	218.14	1024.83
1920.71	1617.57	3106.27	2151.72
4364.16	2328.18	1934.85	3042.93
		2075.63	4672.57

Ans. (1) $12993.61; (2) $7481.71; (3) $14444.12; (4) $13473.22.

62. Addition by the "Angular" Method. Another helpful device might be aptly described as the "angular" method. Here, as in the two-line method described in Art. 61, the sum of each column of figures is written down as a separate total, but in a different form, the various totals forming an "angle" with the answer. Thus, in the example illustrated, the sum of the units is 22, the sum of the tens 21, and the sum of the hundreds 14.

428	22
743	21
285	14
176	——
——	1632

Note the angle that these sums form with the total. In setting them down care should, of course, be taken to write each sum in the correct place: the last figure in the sum of the tens should be in the tens column, the last figure in the sum of the hundreds in the hundreds column, and so on.

Problems

Add the following sums by the "angular" method, and check your answers by the two-line method.

1. $1.89	2. $52.60	3. $102.46	4. $244.27
3.42	84.73	273.91	183.46
5.86	91.26	91.82	701.50
8.27	15.92	146.73	236.41
		51.20	238.56

Ans. (1) $19.44; (2) $244.51; (3) $666.12; (4) $1604.20.

63. Checking Addition by Adding in Reverse Order. As in the other mathematical processes, it is a good plan always to prove the answer to a problem in addition by adding the figures a second time. The second time, however, the figures should be added in reverse order. Thus, if the total is obtained the first time by starting at the top, it should be obtained in the proving operation by starting at the bottom.

The reason for this is that often when a series of numbers is added in a hurry a wrong total may be applied to a combination of certain digits, and if the addition is done again in exactly the same way the same mistake is likely to be repeated.

In proving totals obtained by the "angular" method, discussed in Art. 62, the same principle may be applied, but with a slight modification: the columns are added from left to right instead of from right to left; and the figures are added in the opposite direction, that is, starting from the top instead of from the bottom, and vice versa.

Taking the example illustrated in Art. 62, our scratch pad would show the two processes (the original computation and the proving operation) as follows:

Problem in Addition	First Process	Second Process
428	22	14
743	21	21
285	14	22
176	——	——
——	1632	1632

PROBLEMS

Add the sums in the following groups in any way you wish, then check your answers by the "angular" method—first from right to left, then from left to right, as illustrated in the text.

1. $25.47	2. $17.63	3. $46.35	4. $55.23
18.72	4.22	14.89	91.28
34.66	27.60	29.62	76.45
19.25	9.24	57.18	83.20
		15.90	4.06

Ans. (1) $98.10; (2) $58.69; (3) $163.94; (4) $310.22.

64. Checking Addition by Casting Out the Nines. This method, the principle of which is the same in all four mathematical operations, entails nothing more than the addition of the digits of each number including the answer, dividing each total by 9, and setting down the remainder.

Thus to prove the sum of 4562, 3895 and 4263 we proceed as follows:

4562   4 + 5 + 6 + 2 = 17. Casting out the 9 leaves   8

3895   3 + 8 + 9 + 5 = 25. Casting out the 9's leaves 7

4263   4 + 2 + 6 + 3 = 15. Casting out the 9 leaves   6

————

12720   1 + 2 + 7 + 2 = 12. Casting out the 9 leaves   3

Having set down the "remainders" for the four numbers (8, 7, 6 and 3), we proceed to check them, and this too is done by casting out the nines. The sum of 8, 7 and 6 is 21, and casting out the nines leaves 3. Since 3 is the check number ("remainder") for the answer to our problem, we may presume the answer (12720) to be correct. But as explained in Art. 42, "Checking Multiplication by Casting Out the Nines," this method of calculation by casting out the nines is not infallible.

PROBLEMS

Prove by casting out the nines that the answers to the following problems in addition are correct.

1. 374 plus 296 plus 570 equals 1240.
2. 912 plus 485 plus 366 plus 281 equals 2044.
3. 2468 plus 1767 plus 45 plus 197 equals 4477.
4. 95 plus 2076 plus 853 plus 124 equals 3148.
5. 184 plus 236 plus 8745 plus 14 plus 296 equals 9475.

CHAPTER XI

AVOIDING ERRORS IN SUBTRACTION

Subtraction is a comparatively simple operation, for problems in subtraction involve but three values: the number from which we are to subtract, the number to be subtracted, and the difference.

However, one is more subject to err in subtraction than in a simple problem in addition; therefore, the former operation calls for more concentrated attention than the latter.

A study of Art. 65 should enable the reader to perform mentally a larger variety of problems in subtraction than seemed possible heretofore. And readers who hitherto have not used it very commonly are urged to familiarize themselves with the method of checking subtraction by addition, discussed in Art. 66.

65. A Simple Method of Mental Subtraction. Suppose you made a purchase amounting to $2.95 and tendered a $10.00 bill in payment. You doubtless would have no difficulty determining mentally just how much change to expect: you would subtract $3.00 from $10.00 and add 5 cents to the difference.

It is really very simple. Yet many individuals find it difficult to subtract 43 cents from 97 cents mentally.

A very practical procedure is to take the number to be subtracted and increase it mentally to the nearest multiple of 10, then to mentally increase the other quantity by the same value. Restated, then, the foregoing problem, 97 cents minus 43 cents, would be $1.04 minus 50 cents, and we should know instantly that the answer is 54 cents.

In subtracting 348 from 624 we should find it more practical to increase the number to be subtracted to the nearest hundred. Thus 348 becomes 400, and 624 becomes 676. And we see at a glance that 400 subtracted from 676 leaves 276.

The solution to the problem 6420 minus 5865 may require just a little more effort to obtain the answer mentally. Here we increase the number to be subtracted to 6000. Since we have added 135 to 5865, we must likewise add 135 to 6420. Our problem has thus been changed to read 6555 minus 6000. And without giving it another thought we know that the answer is 555.

The principle of this method is, of course, based on the fact that it is easier to add than to subtract.

PROBLEMS

The answers to these problems should be computed mentally.

★ **1.** What is the difference between the capacities of two tanks, one of which holds 365,000 gallons of water, the other 328,000?

Ans. 37,000 gallons.

★ **2.** The distance from New York City to Boston, Massachusetts, via Cape Cod Canal and Long Island Sound is 234 nautical miles. From New York City to Fall River, Massachusetts, via Long Island

Sound, the distance is 159 nautical miles. By how many nautical miles is Boston more distant from New York than Fall River?

Ans. 75 nautical miles.

★ **3.** A home was purchased for $29,750 and sold for $33,500. How much profit was made on the sale?   *Ans.* $3750.

★ **4.** If it costs $3.64 to ship a 77-pound package by one transportation system, and $1.36 to ship a package of the same weight by another system, how much more costly is one than the other?

Ans. $2.28.

★ **5.** A cubic foot of Portland cement weighs 183 pounds. A cubic foot of concrete weighs 144 pounds. What is the difference in weight per cubic foot between the two substances?   *Ans.* 39 pounds.

★ **6.** The automobile touring distance from Nashville, Tennessee, to Atlanta, Georgia, is 258 miles. From Nashville to Columbia, South Carolina, the distance is 479 miles. How much greater is the latter road distance than the former?   *Ans.* 221 miles.

★ **7.** When the flying time from Los Angeles to Buenos Aires was 107 hours and 50 minutes a route was proposed that would reduce the flying time to 28 hours and 15 minutes. How much of a saving in time did the new route constitute?

Ans. 79 hours and 35 minutes.

★ **8.** The horsepower range of a heavy-duty Diesel engine is from $16\frac{1}{2}$ to 55. By how many horsepower does the latter figure exceed the former?   *Ans.* $38\frac{1}{2}$ horsepower.

★ **9.** How much is $5.60 less 15%?   *Ans.* $4.76.

66. Checking Subtraction by Addition. The method of checking subtraction by addition is undoubtedly the simplest of all checking methods. In the subtraction problem that follows, for instance, all we need do to check the answer is add it mentally to 2964 (the subtrahend), and if the sum equals 4573 (the minuend) we may be sure that 1609 is the correct answer.

$$
\begin{array}{r}
4573 \\
-\ 2964 \\
\hline
1609
\end{array}
$$

Problems

Check your answers to the following subtraction problems by addition.

1. A firm's net profit in 1958 was $183,423. Its net profit in 1957 was $142,893. How much more did the firm earn in 1958 than in the previous year? *Ans.* $40,530.

2. The land areas of North Carolina and South Carolina are 49,142 and 30,594 square miles, respectively. By how many square miles is the area of North Carolina greater than the area of South Carolina? *Ans.* 18,548 square miles.

3. A tank filled with milk weighs 7456 pounds. If the tank when empty weighs 2463 pounds, how many pounds of milk does it contain? *Ans.* 4993 pounds.

4. A highway system of 33,129 miles is made up of 4,837 miles of primary road and the remainder of secondary road. Estimate the total number of miles represented by the secondary roadway.

Ans. 28,292 miles.

5. A survey revealed that of the 2,581,059 dwelling units in New York City as of July, 1957, only 383,961 were built since July, 1940. According to this survey, how many dwelling units in New York City would you say were more than 17 years old in July, 1957? *Ans.* 2,197,098.

★ 6. A yard of No. 5, 36-inch, Wide Duck fabric weighs 22.91 ounces. A yard of No. 6, 40-inch, Wide Duck fabric weighs 23.64 ounces. By what fraction of an ounce is the latter fabric heavier than the former? *Ans.* .73 ounces.

7. The water distance in winter from New York City to Bombay, India, via the Suez Canal, is 8,174 nautical miles, while the distance to Calcutta, India, in the same season and via the same route, is 9,816 nautical miles. How much farther from New York City is Calcutta than Bombay? *Ans.* 1,642 nautical miles.

★ 8. One hundred feet of $2\frac{1}{2}$-inch-diameter 3-strand Manila rope weigh 167 pounds. The same length of the same rope in $2\frac{5}{8}$-inch diameter weighs 191 pounds. How much heavier per 100 feet is the $2\frac{5}{8}$-inch rope than the $2\frac{1}{2}$-inch? *Ans.* 24 pounds.

9. The dimensions of two wall openings are, respectively, 13 feet by 17 feet and 15 feet by 19 feet. What is the difference in square feet between the areas of the two openings?

Ans. 64 square feet. (*Arts.* 1, 11)

★ **10.** A cubic centimeter of nickel weighs 8.8 grams. The same volume of solid tin weighs 7.184 grams. How much heavier per cubic centimeter is nickel than solid tin?   *Ans.* 1.616 grams.

67. Checking Subtraction by Casting Out the Nines.

The use of this method of checking subtraction is essentially the same as in checking multiplication and addition (see Arts. 42 and 64). The only difference is that the check numbers ("remainders"), instead of being multiplied or added, are subtracted.

Thus to prove that 5368 minus 3982 equals 1386, we proceed as follows:

5368 $5 + 3 + 6 + 8 = 22$. Casting out the 9's leaves 4
-3982 $3 + 9 + 8 + 2 = 22$. Casting out the 9's leaves 4
——— −

1386 $1 + 3 + 8 + 6 = 18$. Casting out the 9's leaves 0

Since the "remainder" in the answer, after casting out the nines, is 0, and the difference between the "remainder" in the minuend and the "remainder" in the subtrahend is also zero, we may presume our answer (1386) to be correct.

The following illustration is of special interest for the reason that the "remainder" in the minuend (4734) in this problem is 0. When this is the case, we insert as the check number not 0, but 9.

4734 $4 + 7 + 3 + 4 = 18$. Casting out one 9 leaves 9
-2562 $2 + 5 + 6 + 2 = 15$. Casting out the 9 leaves 6
——— −

2172 $2 + 1 + 7 + 2 = 12$. Casting out the 9 leaves 3

In like manner, in the event that the subtrahend is greater than the minuend, we add 9 to the minuend and then make our subtraction. The remainder should then be equal to the check number.

As explained in the aforementioned Arts. 42 and 64, this method of calculation is not infallible. It is described here mainly for the interest it may have for many who are mathematically inclined. It is not recommended as a substitute for the simpler and surer method of checking subtraction by addition, as discussed in the preceding article.

PROBLEMS

Compute the answers to the following subtraction problems, and check them by casting out the nines.

1. Subtract $64,235.40 from $127,486.28.   *Ans.* $63,250.88.

2. In the fall a farmer put 3960 bushels of corn into his cribs. When he sold the corn in the spring he found that it had shrunk to 3482 bushels. Estimate the amount of the shrinkage.

Ans. 478 bushels.

3. One thousand board feet of Southern Cypress weighs 2670 pounds. An equal number of board feet of American Elm weighs 2920 pounds. How much heavier is 1000 board feet of the latter wood than the former?   *Ans.* 250 pounds.

4. In 1957, the average hourly wage earned by workers in the electrical machinery industry was $3.716. The average in the men's clothing industry for the same period was $2.139. What is the difference between the two figures?   *Ans.* $1.577.

5. The weight of a finished 6-inch-thick wall of hollow clay tile is 3190 pounds per 100 square feet. The weight of a finished 10-inch-thick wall of the same material is 4580 pounds per 100 square feet. How much heavier per 100 square feet is the 10-inch-thick wall than the 6-inch-thick wall?   *Ans.* 1390 pounds.

6. A manufacturer wishing to expand his facilities considers renting a loft of 6380 square feet. His present loft measures 103 feet by 58 feet. How much additional floor space would he have if he moved from the one loft to the other? *Ans.* 406 square feet. (*Art.* 3)

7. Cream containing 28% of butter fat has a weight of 8.37 pounds a gallon. Cream containing 40% of butter fat weighs 8.28

pounds a gallon. What would be the difference in weight between 36 gallons of cream of the higher fat content and 32 gallons of cream of the lower fat content?   *Ans.* 30.24 pounds. (*Arts.* 4, 5)

8. A grower of flaxseed obtained an average of $6\frac{1}{2}$ bushels per acre from his 250 acres of land. A more fortunate grower secured 11 bushels per acre from his 420 acres. By how much did the total production of one grower exceed that of the other?

Ans. 2995 bushels. (*Art.* 1-f)

9. The highest altitude in the state of Oregon is Mount Hood, reputed to be 11,245 feet high. The highest altitude in the state of Washington is Mount Rainier, whose height is 14,408 feet. How much higher is Mount Rainier than Mount Hood?   *Ans.* 3163 feet.

10. Compute the difference in weight between 16 carcasses having an average weight of 603 pounds and 18 carcasses whose average weight is 618 pounds.   *Ans.* 1476 pounds. (*Arts.* 15, 18)

CHAPTER XII

DIVISION CAN BE AS SIMPLE AS MULTIPLICATION

No other mathematical operation is disliked so much by so many as division. Yet the truth is that in a great many instances division can be as simple as multiplication.

It is hoped that most readers will find this chapter of special interest and significance. The articles contained herein will point—perhaps more than any other chapter in this book—to the fact that many difficult-looking problems can be solved with fascinating ease and speed, and quite often without recourse to pencil and paper.

68. How to Divide Quickly and Easily by 5, 15, $7\frac{1}{2}$, $12\frac{1}{2}$, $37\frac{1}{2}$, $62\frac{1}{2}$, $112\frac{1}{2}$. The reader's interest in the study of this article may be considerably enhanced if he will first review Art. 1, which deals with the subject of multiplying by some of these numbers. The text that follows is in a way a continuation of that article, and for this reason is accompanied by little explanatory detail.

68a. To divide by 5, multiply by 2 and divide by 10.

Example: Divide 175 by 5.

Solution: 175 times 2 = 350 which, divided by 10, equals 35.

68b.   To divide by 15, multiply by 2 and divide by 30.

Example: Divide 135 by 15.

Solution: 135 times 2 = 270 which, divided by 30, equals 9.

68c.   To divide by $7\frac{1}{2}$, multiply by 4 and divide by 30.

Example: Divide 390 by $7\frac{1}{2}$.

Solution: 390 times 4 = 1560 which, divided by 30, equals 52.

68d.   To divide by $12\frac{1}{2}$, multiply by 8 and divide by 100.

Example: Divide 175 by $12\frac{1}{2}$.

Solution: 175 times 8 = 1400 which, divided by 100, equals 14.

68e.   To divide by $112\frac{1}{2}$, multiply by 8 and divide by 900.

Example: Divide $1912\frac{1}{2}$ by $112\frac{1}{2}$.

Solution: $1912\frac{1}{2}$ times 8 = 15300 which, divided by 900, equals 17.

68f.   To divide by $37\frac{1}{2}$, multiply by 8 and divide by 300.

Example: Divide 675 by $37\frac{1}{2}$.

Solution: 675 times 8 = 5400 which, divided by 300, equals 18.

68g.   To divide by $62\frac{1}{2}$, multiply by 8 and divide by 500.

Example: Divide $812\frac{1}{2}$ by $62\frac{1}{2}$.

Solution: $812\frac{1}{2}$ times 8 = 6500 which, divided by 500, equals 13.

The reader will do well to familiarize himself with the reason why the divisor in each of the foregoing illustrations was converted to a multiple of 10 or 100, and with the method by which the divisors were changed to multiples of 100.

The reason will be readily apparent. Changing the divisor to a multiple of 10 or 100 simplifies the problem. It is easier to multiply by 2 and divide by 10 than to divide by 5; to multiply by 2 and divide by 30 than to divide by 15; to multiply by 4 and divide by 30 than to divide by $7\frac{1}{2}$. And with regard to the last four illustrations (68d, e, f and g), it is obviously easier to multiply by a single digit and divide the result by another single digit than to divide by a number which comprises two digits and a fraction. We need not be unduly concerned with the fact that the digit in the new divisor is followed by one or two zeros, for dividing by 10 or 100 requires nothing more than moving the decimal point to the left one or two places, as the case may be.

In Chapters VI and VII ("Aliquot Parts" and "Percentages and Discounts"), the method of converting numbers to multiples of 100 was explained in detail. We know, for instance, that since $12\frac{1}{2}$ is one eighth of 100 ($\frac{100}{8}$), multiplying a number by 8 and dividing the result by 100 produces precisely the same result as dividing the number by $12\frac{1}{2}$.

It may be well, for the benefit of those who have found some difficulty with division, to introduce here an important principle concerning this operation. When we multiply by a fraction we multiply by the numerator and divide by the denominator; thus 60 multiplied by $\frac{3}{5}$ is equivalent to 180 divided by 5, which equals 36. To *divide* by a fraction the process is reversed: we multiply by the denominator and divide by the numerator; thus 60 divided by $\frac{3}{5}$ becomes 60 multiplied by $\frac{5}{3}$, which equals 300 divided by 3, or 100.

The method of converting $37\frac{1}{2}$ and $62\frac{1}{2}$ into multiples of 100 is based on exactly the same principle as converting $12\frac{1}{2}$ into a multiple of 100. The number $37\frac{1}{2}$ is equivalent to $\frac{3}{8}$ of 100, or $\frac{300}{8}$; therefore, when we divide by $37\frac{1}{2}$ all we need do is multiply by 8 and divide by 300. Similarly, $62\frac{1}{2}$ is equivalent to $\frac{5}{8}$ of 100, or $\frac{500}{8}$, and therefore to divide by $62\frac{1}{2}$ we multiply by 8 and divide by 500.

The number $112\frac{1}{2}$, however, is not an aliquot part of 1000, but a quick glance reveals that it is $\frac{1}{8}$ of 900 ($\frac{900}{8}$), so that division by $112\frac{1}{2}$ may be effected by multiplying by 8 and dividing by 900.

A rereading of this article may be found well worth while. It will help the reader to appreciate the practicability of extending the application of this short-cut method of division to such numbers as $33\frac{1}{3}$, $16\frac{2}{3}$, $66\frac{2}{3}$, etc.

Problems

★ 1. A practical way of packing mince meat for consumer distribution is to put it up in 5-pound wood pails. Estimate the number of pails of this size that can be filled from 3400 pounds of this product.
Ans. 680.

★ 2. How many 5-ounce packages can be packed from 2000 pounds of dehydrated eggs?   *Ans.* 6400.

★ 3. What quantity of stone will be crushed in 12 minutes by a stone-crushing machine having a capacity of 275 tons per hour? (Hint: 12 minutes equals one fifth of an hour.)   *Ans.* 55 tons.

4. If it takes 15 squares of shingles to roof a house, how many houses can be roofed with 435 squares of shingles?   *Ans.* 29.

5. A food producer finds it profitable to put up maraschino cherries in brandy syrup in 15-ounce jars. If he can produce the finished product in batches of 1125 pounds per week, how many dozen jars would he use weekly in packing his product?
Ans. 100 dozen. (*Art.* 15)

★ 6. If a pound of oyster shell (a widely fed source of calcium carbonate for laying-hens) contains sufficient lime for the shells of $7\frac{1}{2}$ dozen eggs, how many pounds of oyster shell would be needed to supply the required quantity of lime for an estimated production of 60 cases of eggs, packed 30 dozen eggs to the case?

Ans. 240 pounds.

7. If the net weight of a container of oysters is $7\frac{1}{2}$ ounces, how many dozen containers can be filled from 450 pounds of this food product? *Ans.* 80 dozen.

★ 8. How long would it take to plow 175 acres of ground at a speed of $12\frac{1}{2}$ acres per day? *Ans.* 14 days.

9. Compute in square feet the area of the bottom of a ditch $12\frac{1}{2}$ feet deep, from which 25 cubic yards of dirt is to be removed. (Hint: Convert 25 cubic yards to cubic feet by multiplying by 27.)

Ans. 54 square feet.

10. A manufacturer uses a wood tank to furnish his daily requirement of $37\frac{1}{2}$ gallons of water. If the tank is filled to its capacity of 3225 gallons, for how long will the daily requirement be satisfied?

Ans. 86 days.

11. If the cost of constructing $37\frac{1}{2}$ miles of road was $874,320, what was the average cost per mile? *Ans.* $23,315.20.

★ 12. If a dealer's gross profit on a 1-pound container of a food specialty is $62\frac{1}{2}$ cents, how many units would he have to sell to make a gross profit of $200.00? *Ans.* 320.

13. If an oil burner, consuming $112\frac{1}{2}$ gallons of oil per hour, is in operation for 10 hours each day, how many days would a supply of 16,000 gallons of oil last? *Ans.* $14\frac{2}{9}$ days.

14. The price of a $112\frac{1}{2}$-acre farm offered for sale is $24,075. How much does that average per acre? *Ans.* $214.00.

69. A Short Way of Dividing by Numbers Which Can Be Factored, Such as 24, 32, 56, 64, 121. In Art. 4 we learned how to *multiply* by numbers which can be factored; namely, to break up the multiplier into factors and multiply separately by each factor. We learned, for instance, that 24 might be broken up into the factors 8 and 3 (the product of 8 multiplied by 3 being 24); or into the factors 6 and 4, or 12 and 2.

In dealing with factors in division the method is the same as with multiplication, except that we divide instead of multiply.

Example 1: Divide 4488 by 24.

Solution: 4488 divided by 4 = 1122
           1122 divided by 6 =   187

Example 2: Divide 5824 by 64.

Solution: 5824 divided by 8 = 728
           728 divided by 8 =   91

The foregoing illustrations will suffice to convince the reader of the time-saving advantage of dividing by factors whenever it is possible to do so. A word of caution, however, should be noted. Whereas, in multiplying by factors, it makes little difference by which factor we multiply first, in *division* it may be simpler to divide by one factor first than by the other.

Let us consider the problem of dividing 378 by 56. The most practical factors of 56 are 7 and 8. But it is obvious (see Table I, Art. 72) that if 378 is divided by 8 there will be a fraction in the quotient ($47\frac{1}{4}$). However, if we divide first by 7, the quotient (54) is a whole number. And it goes without saying that it is easier to divide 54 by 8 than $47\frac{1}{4}$ by 7.

A good practice to adopt when one factor of the divisor is an odd number and the other factor an even number is to divide by the odd number first if the unit digit of the dividend or the numerator in the fraction is an odd number, and to divide by the even factor first if the unit digit of the dividend or the numerator in the fraction is an even number; unless, of course, a quick glance reveals that the reverse procedure would be better, or that the order of division is immaterial.

Example 3: A tank 6 feet deep and 6 feet in diameter holds 1269 gallons of water. If 12 gallons are taken from the tank twice each day, how many days will the supply last?

> *Solution:* Twelve gallons taken twice a day is equivalent to 24 gallons a day. And since a quick glance reveals that 1269 is exactly divisible by 3, we will use the factors 3 and 8, and divide by 3 first.
>
> 1269 divided by 3 = 423
> 423 divided by 8 = $52\frac{7}{8}$
>
> > *Ans.* $52\frac{7}{8}$ days.

The use of this method may, of course, be extended to such numbers as 14 (factors 2 and 7), 16 (factors 4 and 4, or 8 and 2), and 18 (factors 2 and 9, or 6 and 3), etc.

Problems

1. Motion picture film scrap, used in the artificial leather and textile coating industries, is available in standard solutions containing 24 ounces of dry film to a gallon of solvent mixture. If a minimum quantity of 20 pounds of this film is required, how many gallons of the mixture should be purchased? *Ans.* 14 gallons.

2. A news report states that an Arabian-American oil refinery is "producing 170,000 barrels, or 24,000 tons a day." According to these figures how many barrels are required to hold a ton of oil?
Ans. $7\frac{1}{12}$ barrels.

3. If it takes 32 gallons of sap obtained from the sugar maple tree to make one gallon of syrup, how many gallons of syrup can be obtained from 544 gallons of sap? *Ans.* 17 gallons.

4. If 100 square feet of welded wire reinforcement weighs 56 pounds, how many square feet of this product will be represented by a total weight of 2744 pounds?   *Ans.* 4900 square feet.

5. If a worker, performing all the essential operations required in the making of modern calf leather, turns out about 64 square feet a day, how many days may he be expected to take to produce 1150 square feet? Compute the answer to the nearest whole day.

Ans. 18 days.

6. The area of a loft is 7502 square feet. The length is 121 feet. What is the width?   *Ans.* 62 feet.

7. The automobile touring mileage from Cincinnati, Ohio, to Detroit, Michigan, is 254 miles. At the rate of 18 miles per gallon, how many gallons of gasoline would be consumed on a one-way trip between these points? Give your answer to the nearest gallon.

Ans. 14 gallons.

8. A plane takes off the ground in a run of 1782 feet in 27 seconds. How many feet per second does that average?

Ans. 66 feet.

9. An electro-automatic Chinese typewriter prints 5400 characters with 36 keys. How many characters does that average per key?   *Ans.* 150 characters.

10. If a foot of $\frac{5}{8}$-inch-diameter wire rope weighs .63 pound, how many feet might be expected to be contained in $19\frac{1}{2}$ pounds of this rope? Compute the answer to the nearest whole foot.

Ans. 31 feet.

11. It takes three girls 12 hours (that is, 36 hours in all) to assemble 81 mechanical units. If each girl is paid at the rate of $1.32 an hour, how much is the labor cost per unit? Compute the answer to the nearest cent.   *Ans.* 59 cents.

70. How to Divide Mentally, Without Pencil and Paper, by a Power of 2, as 4, 8, 16, etc. If the reader has not already done so, it is suggested that he acquaint himself with the subject of Art. 18, wherein is discussed the method of multiplying mentally by powers of 2. The procedure in dividing mentally by a power of 2 is the same, except that the process is reversed. Thus to divide 72 by

4 mentally, we say to ourselves, "72 divided by 4 equals 36 divided by 2, equals 18."

If the divisor were 8 instead of 4, we should continue the process of division one more step, and the answer would be 9. Note that in division, the suggested monologue is a little different from that recommended for multiplication. In *multiplying* by a power of 2 by this method, we start with "times 2," continue with "times 4," and so on, regardless of the magnitude of the multiplier, until we reach the original number by which we were to multiply. In division, however, we start with the divisor itself, and go down instead of up. Thus to divide 72 by 8 (to use a simple illustration) we say, "72 divided by 8 equals 36 divided by 4, equals 18 divided by 2, equals 9." If 72 were to have been divided by 16 instead of by 8, we would start off in this manner, "72 divided by 16 equals 36 divided by 8, and so on."

Naturally, when pencil and paper are available, it is unnecessary to divide, let us say, 768 by 8 by this continued halving process. The method, as the article heading indicates, is recommended only when it is necessary to divide mentally, without the use of pencil and paper. In these circumstances the advantages of this method cannot be overemphasized.

Here, for instance, is an illustration of a typical experience which recently came to the author's attention. A manufacturer, beset with business worries and unable to fall asleep, tried to solve a little problem which presented itself to him after he had retired for the night. The room was dark, pencil and paper were out of reach, and the worried gentleman was not inclined to put on a light. The problem was this: he contemplated producing 6000 ounces of a new product and wanted to know the equivalent weight in pounds. There being 16 ounces to the pound, it was necessary to divide 6000 by 16. But to compute this mentally was for this gentleman, whom we will call Mr. X, quite a task. Mr. X, of course, did not need to solve his problem by the conventional method—he could have obtained the desired figure quickly and easily by mentally breaking down the divisor, first to 8, then to 4, and finally to 2, as follows: 6000 divided by 16 equals 3000 divided by 8, equals 1500 divided by 4, equals 750 divided by 2, equals 375 pounds.

PROBLEMS

The following problems should be worked in their entirety without pencil and paper. Only the answers are to be written down.

★ 1. A food company puts up vinegar in quart bottles and has ready for delivery a shipment of 372 filled bottles. How many gallons of vinegar were required to make up this order?   *Ans.* 93 gallons.

★ 2. A brewer has on hand 624 pounds of hops. If he uses this product in the proportion of 0.8 pound per barrel of lager beer, for how many barrels of this beer will his stock of hops suffice? (Hint: Dividing 624 by 0.8 is equivalent to dividing 6240 by 8.)

Ans. 780 barrels.

★ 3. Tobacco can be packed mechanically in 8-ounce tins at the rate of 80 a minute. How long would it take at this rate of speed to pack 2320 pounds of tobacco? (Hint: Dividing 4640 by 80 is equivalent to dividing 464 by 8.)   *Ans.* 58 minutes.

★ 4. Metal lath is available in sheets 24 inches by 96 inches. If it were necessary to cut sample pieces of 16 square inches, how many pieces of this size could be obtained from one sheet? (Hint: No need to compute the area of the sheet and divide the result by 16; simply divide 96 by 16, then multiply the result by 24.)   *Ans.* 144 pieces.

★ 5. A perfume manufacturer receives, C.O.D. for $15.20, a package containing 32 ounces of an essential oil that he ordered. What is his cost per ounce?   *Ans.* $47\frac{1}{2}$ cents.

★ 6. A food products company offers a 5-gallon can (640 fluid ounces) of a butter flavor for $108.80. How much is that per ounce?

(Hint: 640 ounces for $108.80 is equivalent to 64 ounces for $10.88.)

Ans. 17 cents.

★ 7. Estimate the number of cords in 1408 cubic feet of wood. (One cord of wood equals 128 cubic feet.) *Ans.* 11 cords.

71. How to Divide Quickly by 14, 16, 18, 20, 22, 24. If the reader has had occasion to refer to the last chapter in this book—the chapter dealing with decimals and fractions—he may have paused to contemplate the article on the subject of cancellation. A moment's reflection will reveal the interesting fact that just as cancellation is a process of division, division is a process of cancellation.

Now we turn to a relatively simple technique—a technique which simplifies problems in division by first reducing dividend and divisor by half. Thus to divide 56 by 14 we need but to restate the problem to read 28 divided by 7 to see instantly that the answer is 4. Similarly, the division of 128 by 16 can be accomplished mentally and effortlessly by changing the problem to 64 divided by 8. In fact, the labor of dividing by any even number can be reduced to a greater or lesser degree by first dividing dividend and divisor by 2.

Example 1: Divide 3114 by 18.

Solution: 1557 ($\frac{1}{2}$ of 3114) divided by 9 ($\frac{1}{2}$ of 18) = 173

Example 2: Divide 5256 by 24.

Solution: 2628 ($\frac{1}{2}$ of 5256) divided by 12 ($\frac{1}{2}$ of 24) = 219

The ease of dividing any number by 2 mentally makes this an especially valuable technique. Taking the foregoing illustration, for instance, compare the speed with which the answer was obtained by this method with the process of division by the conventional method:

$$\begin{array}{r} 219 \\ \hline 24)\overline{5256} \\ 48 \\ \hline \\ 45 \\ 24 \\ \hline \\ 216 \end{array}$$

Observe that by the conventional method it was necessary to write down no fewer than 18 figures, whereas by the technique under consideration we needed to write down no more than the seven figures in 2628 and 219, to say nothing of the expenditure of effort and energy and the greater possibility of error connected with the solution of the problem by the conventional method.

The eagle-eyed reader may have noticed that the divisor 24, discussed here, was also under consideration in Art. 69. But this should be no cause for confusion. While the result of dividing by 24 in different ways is the same, one method may be more practical in a particular instance than another. Thus to divide 4488 by 24 (the illustration given in Art. 69) it is obviously better to break up the divisor into the factors 4 and 6, for one quick glance shows that 4488 can be divided by 4 in a flash. On the other hand, in the problem 5256 divided by 24 (the illustration given in this article), the divisibility of 5256 by 4 is not effected quite so speedily. It is all a matter of choice. The net result is the important thing, and familiarity with the different techniques of accomplishing the same result will help establish a confidence in the reader that should enable him to perform these and other problems in division with incredible ease.

The divisor 20 is, of course, the simplest of all of the numbers mentioned in this article heading. For to divide by 20 it is only necessary to take one half of one tenth of the dividend. Thus 2460 divided by 20 is equivalent to 246 divided by 2, which equals 123; and 187 divided by 20 is equivalent to 18.7 divided by 2, which gives us 9.35.

Example 3: The expected result of the careful cultivation of sorghum is a yield of 14 bushels per acre. If this is accomplished, how many acres should produce a total of 1500 bushels of sorghum?

Solution: 750 ($\frac{1}{2}$ of 1500) divided by 7 ($\frac{1}{2}$ of 14) = $107\frac{1}{7}$.

Ans. $107\frac{1}{7}$ acres.

Problems

1. A roll of 12-inch-wide asphalt-saturated mesh fabric (a material used in the building industry as a reinforcing agent) weighs approximately 14 pounds. If the net weight of a shipment of this material is 252 pounds, how many rolls might the shipment be presumed to contain? *Ans.* 18 rolls.

2. Compressed nitrogen (a gas supplied for the protection of material susceptible to oxidation) is available in cylinders containing 244 cubic feet each. If 14 cubic feet of this gas are used every five business days, in how many business days will the contents of one cylinder be consumed? Estimate your answer to the nearest whole day. *Ans.* 87 days.

3. If a cow gives 16 pounds of milk a day, how many cows of this average production capacity would be needed to supply a daily requirement of 272 pounds of milk? *Ans.* 17 cows.

4. How long would it take to obtain 432 feet of finished white prints from a reproduction machine synchronized to print and develop 16 feet of these prints per minute? *Ans.* 27 minutes.

5. The approximate acreage used for growing strawberries in the United States is 180,000 acres, and the crop value is about $35,000,000. What would you say is the value of the average production per acre? (Hint: By canceling the zeros, the problem resolves itself into dividing $3500 by 18.)   *Ans.* 194\frac{4}{9}$.

★ 6. Twenty years after its purchase the value of a house exceeded the sum of its original cost and total maintenance by approximately $28,000. How much was the average gain per year?

Ans. $1400.

7. How many bottles can be filled with 200 tablets each from the production of a tablet machine operated for 4 hours at a speed of 350 tablets a minute.   *Ans.* 420 bottles. (*Art.* 16)

★ 8. A regulation of the United States Department of Agriculture states that on ships carrying livestock there shall be one attendant to each 22 head. On this basis how many attendants should be found on a ship carrying 198 head of livestock?

Ans. 9 attendants.

9. If the profit on a yard of fabric is 24 cents, how many yards would have to be sold to produce a total profit of $75.00?

Ans. 312$\frac{1}{2}$ yards.

★ 10. A variety of felt slippers is made in a 60-inch-wide felt weighing 24 ounces per yard. If the net weight of a shipment of this material is 840 pounds, how many yards may it be expected to contain? (Hint: Instead of multiplying by 16 and dividing by 24, multiply by 2 and divide by 3.)   *Ans.* 560 yards.

72. How to Divide Quickly by Multiples of 11, Like 33, 44, 55, 66, etc. The procedure in dividing by these numbers is fundamentally the same as that discussed in the preceding article. The only difference is that instead of dividing dividend and divisor by 2, we divide by 3, if the divisor is 33; by 4, if the divisor is 44; and so on.

Example 1: Divide 429 by 33.

Solution: 143 ($\frac{1}{3}$ of 429) divided by 11 ($\frac{1}{3}$ of 33) = 13

Example 2: Divide 1276 by 44.

Solution: 319 ($\frac{1}{4}$ of 1276) divided by 11 ($\frac{1}{4}$ of 44) = 29

TABLE I

How to Determine Whether a Number Is
Exactly Divisible by 3, 6, 9, 4, 8, 11.

A Number Is Exactly Divisible by	If
3	the sum of its digits is divisible by 3. Thus 4605 is divisible by 3 because 15, the sum of its digits, is divisible by 3.
6	it is an even number and the sum of its digits is divisible by 3.
9	the sum of its digits is divisible by 9.
4	its last two figures are zeros, or if the last two figures are divisible by 4. Thus 924 is divisible by 4 because 24 is divisible by 4.
8	the last three figures are divisible by 8. Thus 7144 is divisible by 8 because 144 is divisible by 8.
11	the difference between the sum of the figures in the even places and the sum of the figures in the odd places is 0 or 11. Thus 53031 may be recognized as a number divisible by 11 because 1 plus 0 plus 5 equals 6, and 3 plus 3 equals 6, and 6 minus 6 equals 0. The number 162679 is divisible by 11 because 9 plus 6 plus 6 equals 21; 7 plus 2 plus 1 equals 10; and 21 minus 10 equals 11.

This technique is used to the best advantage when the dividend is exactly divisible by the respective multiple of 11—namely, by 3, 4, etc.—because it is so much easier to divide a whole number by 11 than a number containing a fraction, as for example $106\frac{2}{3}$. The question now arises, how can one know quickly whether a number is exactly divisible by 3 or 4, etc.? This question is answered by Table I, which explains that a number is divisible by 3 if the sum of its digits is divisible by 3; that a number is divisible by 4, if its last two figures are zeros, or if the last two figures are divisible by 4; and so on.

Example 3: Divide $16,146.57 by 33.

Solution: The sum of the digits 1, 6, 1, 4, 6, 5 and 7 is 30. And 30 is exactly divisible by 3. So the problem resolves itself into dividing $5,382.19 (which is one third of $16,146.57) by 11 (which is one third of 33).
$5,382.19 divided by 11 = $489.29

Example 4: Divide $8,671.08 by 44.

Solution: The last two figures (.08) are exactly divisible by 4. So we proceed as follows:
$2,167.77 ($\frac{1}{4}$ of $8,671.08) divided by 11 ($\frac{1}{4}$ of 44)   = $197.07

It is obvious that a number is exactly divisible by 5 if the last figure is 5 or a zero. So let us continue with an illustration in which the divisor is 66.

Example 5: Divide 29832 by 66.

Solution: Table I tells us that a number is divisible by 6 if it is an even number and the sum of its digits is divisible by 3. We find that the sum of the digits 2, 9, 8, 3 and 2 is divisible by 3. So we may be sure, as we were in the preceding illustrations, that when we come to divide by 11, the dividend will be a whole number.
4972 ($\frac{1}{6}$ of 29832) divided by 11 ($\frac{1}{6}$ of 66) = 452

Although the technique operates beautifully when the original dividend is exactly divisible by the original divisor, that is, when the final result is a whole number, it is just as practical to use when the result in the final answer contains a fraction, as will be seen in the following illustration:

Example 6: Divide 19216 by 88.

> *Solution:* The last three figures (216) are divisible by 8, so we know that the entire number is divisible by 8. Note, also, that in this instance we took the last three digits as a *whole number*, not the *sum* of the digits as when dividing by 3, 6 or 9.
>
> 2402 ($\frac{1}{8}$ of 19216) divided by 11
> ($\frac{1}{8}$ of 88) $= 218\frac{4}{11}$

Example 7: Glass asbestos in the 36-inch width is available in rolls of approximately 33 square feet. If 4176 square feet are required, and if the product can be purchased only in whole rolls, how many rolls will be needed?

Solution: 1392 ($\frac{1}{3}$ of 4176) divided by 11 ($\frac{1}{3}$ of 33)
$= 126\frac{6}{11}$ *Ans.* 127 rolls.

PROBLEMS

1. A contractor wishes to estimate the number of boxes of panes, 12 by 18 inches, required in the construction of a building. The panes, of which 1404 will be needed, are packed 33 to a box. How many boxes of the glass will be used on the job? Estimate your answer to the nearest whole box.   *Ans.* 43 boxes.

2. At a speed of 3300 bobbins per hour, how long would it take a machine to clean 39,000 bobbins. Compute the answer to the nearest tenth of an hour. (Hint: Dividing 39,000 by 3300 is equivalent to dividing 390 by 33.)

Ans. 11.8 hours, or 11 hours and 48 minutes.

★ **3.** If 44 feet of $\frac{1}{4}$-inch-diameter sash cord weigh approximately one pound, what should be the approximate net weight of a package containing 572 feet of this cord?   *Ans.* 13 pounds.

4. A store's total receipts for the day were $598.40. If this represented 440 sales, what was the average amount per sale?

Ans. $1.36.

★ **5.** A rigidly mounted tool cuts yellow brass $\frac{5}{32}$ of an inch deep at 550 feet per minute. Estimate the time required to cut 15,400 feet of this metal to the aforementioned depth.   *Ans.* 28 minutes.

6. If it takes .55 hours to punch three holes in 1000 sheets of a heavy weight paper $8\frac{1}{2}$ by 11 inches, how many sheets could be punched in 8 hours? Compute your answer to the nearest half a thousand sheets. (Hint: Dividing 8 by .55 is equivalent to dividing 800 by 55.)   *Ans.* 14,500 sheets.

7. The cost of the labor and material to paint a building exterior was $384.00. If the painted surface comprised an area of 6600 square feet, what was the cost per square foot? Compute your answer to the nearest cent.   *Ans.* 6 cents per square foot.

8. A square foot of asbestos mill board, $\frac{3}{32}$ inch thick, weighs 6.6 ounces. Compute the approximate number of square feet in a stack of this board weighing $239\frac{1}{4}$ pounds.   *Ans.* 580 square feet.

9. A printer finds that it takes 7.7 hours to trim the pages of one thousand 880-page books. If his plant operates on an $8\frac{3}{4}$-hour-day basis, how many books could be completed in five days?

Ans. 5682 books.

10. If a turret lathe cuts annealed tool steel at a speed of 77 feet per minute, how long would it take to cut 6300 feet of this material? Compute the answer to the nearest minute.

Ans. 82 minutes, or 1 hour 22 minutes.

11. A pharmaceutical manufacturer finds that he can market a quality product by using 88 ounces of a special ingredient to every one gross bottles. If he purchased 125 pounds of the ingredient, for approximately how many gross bottles will the material suffice? Estimate the total to the nearest gross.   *Ans.* 23 gross.

12. If the net weight of 120 tin plate sheets, 14 by $19\frac{1}{4}$ inches, is 88 pounds, how many sheets would be represented by an inventory of 1496 pounds of this material?   *Ans.* 2040 sheets.

13. Of $2\frac{1}{4}$-inch plain washers there are approximately 121 to the pound. If a counting scale indicates an inventory of approximately 4050 of these parts, how many pounds should this inventory weigh? State the answer to the nearest half pound.   *Ans.* $33\frac{1}{2}$ pounds.

14. If a foot of $2\frac{3}{4}$-inch-diameter hoisting rope weighs approximately 12.1 pounds, how many feet of this material would be contained in a net weight of 1331 pounds?   *Ans.* 110 feet.

73. Division by the Short Continental Method. This method of division is another valuable little short-cut seldom taken advantage of in the business world. By this method the partial products are subtracted mentally, and only the remainders are written down.

Example: Find the cost per unit of 37 like radios, the total cost of which is $793.65.

Conventional Method	*Short Continental Method*
21.45	21.45
37)793.65	37)793.65
74	53
——	166
53	185
37	
——	
166	
148	
——	
185	
185	

The step-by-step procedure in performing this problem by the short Continental method is as follows: The divisor is contained in 79 twice, so we write 2 in the quotient just as we would if the problem were worked by the conventional method. Now 37 times 2 equals 74, so we deduct 74 *mentally* from 79; the remainder is 5, so we write 5 under the 9.

Now 3 is brought down from the dividend, making the next number to be divided, 53. Thirty-seven goes into 53 once, so 1 is written into the quotient; and subtracting 37 from 53 mentally, only the difference, 16, is written down.

The next figure to be brought down from the dividend is 6, making the number now to be divided, 166. Thirty-seven into 166 goes 4 times with 18 left over, so 4 is written down as the next figure in the quotient, and 18 is shown as the remainder.

Now the 5 is brought down, making the last number to be divided, 185. Thirty-seven goes into 185 exactly five times, so 5 is inserted as the next and last figure in the quotient. The insertion of the decimal point completes the answer, which is $21.45.

Note that not only does the short Continental method of division reduce the amount of pencil-and-paper work, but the process of computation is speeded up too.

While this method may be applied regardless of the number of figures in the divisor, it is used to the best advantage when the divisor contains fewer than four figures, and when there is a zero or low digit in the divisor. Let us take some examples of problems which contain the latter type of divisor, using the reduced equivalents of the dividends and divisors as they appear in the solutions, and observe the rapidity and ease with which the answers are obtained by this time-saving method of mental subtraction.

Example 1: Divide 8715 by 105.

Solution:

$$\begin{array}{r} 83 \\ 105\overline{)8715} \\ \hline 315 \end{array}$$

Ans. 83.

There was really no need to write down 840 (the product of 8 times 105), for it is so easy to subtract 840 from 871 mentally.

Example 2: Divide 75 by 26, and state the answer to the nearest hundredth of a unit.

Solution:

$$\begin{array}{r} 2.884 \\ 26\overline{)75} \\ \hline 230 \\ \hline 220 \\ \hline 120 \end{array}$$

Ans. 2.88.

Here, too, there was no necessity for writing down the product of twice 26, for 52, the product, can be subtracted from 75 without any effort at all. Similarly, the product of 8 times 26 (which, by the breakdown method, is computed by adding the product of 8 times 25 to 8 times 1) can be subtracted from 230 with less effort than it takes

to write down 208. And the same applies to the rest of
the problem.

Example 3: Divide 51181 by 403.

Solution:

$$\begin{array}{r} 127 \\ \hline 403)\overline{51181} \\ \hline 1088 \\ \hline 2821 \end{array}$$

Ans. 127.

The relative ease with which 403 can be subtracted
from 511 and 806 from 1088 should make it an unforgiv-
able offense for the reader to solve a problem of this nature
by the conventional method after reading this article.

Example 4: Divide \$200.00 by 301, and state your
answer to the nearest cent.

Solution:

$$\begin{array}{r} .664 \\ \hline 301)\overline{200} \\ \hline 1940 \\ \hline 1340 \end{array}$$

Ans. 66 cents.

Notice how the presence of a zero in the divisor makes
this method so easy. Six times 301 equals 1806; 1800 subtracted from 2000 equals 200, and 6 subtracted from 200
equals 194.

Example 5: Divide 2000 by 51, and state the answer to the nearest whole unit.

Solution:

$$\begin{array}{r} 39.2 \\ \hline 51)\overline{2000} \\ \hline 470 \\ \hline 110 \end{array}$$

Ans. 39.

Here, as in the preceding illustration, the presence of a 1 in the divisor makes the method very practical. Note, also, that even when the divisor is multiplied by a high digit like 9, the task of subtracting the product mentally is very simple.

PROBLEMS

1. If a glassblower can turn out 23 dozen units in a day, in how many days will he be able to produce 300 dozen units? Compute the answer to the nearest whole day.   *Ans.* 13 days.

2. If a cubic foot of loose coal weighs 31 pounds, how many cubic feet would be occupied by 4123 pounds of this coal?

Ans. 133 cubic feet.

3. Lumber is measured in terms of board feet. For example, a board 1 foot long, 1 foot wide, and 1 inch thick is said to contain one board foot of lumber; and a board 26 feet long, 3 inches wide, and 2 inches thick contains 13 board feet of lumber. How many boards of the latter dimensions should be supplied to equal a total of 4056 board feet?   *Ans.* 312 boards.

4. If a bolt of lace contains 105 yards, how many whole bolts can be made up with 25,000 yards of this material? (Hint: Dividing 25,000 by 105 is equivalent to dividing 5000 by 21.)

Ans. 238 bolts.

5. A salesman's commissions for the year total $5902.00. How much does that average per week?   *Ans.* $113.50.

6. Estimate the number of 34-ounce containers of boned turkey that can be filled from a total of 435 pounds of this product. (Hint: Remember to convert the pounds to ounces before dividing by 34.)   *Ans.* 204 containers.

7. If three million barrels of oil are obtained from 17,000 wells, what is the average number of barrels obtained from each well?
          Ans. 176 barrels.

8. How many 19-ounce tins of tomatoes can be filled from a net quantity of 2300 pounds of tomatoes?   *Ans.* 1936 tins.

9. It is sometimes necessary in radio practice to convert meters to kilocycles. To obtain the approximate equivalent, 300,000 is divided by the number of meters. Find the approximate equivalent in kilocycles of 114 meters, computing the answer to the nearest whole unit. (Hint: Notice that both numbers are divisible by 6.)
          Ans. 2631 kilocycles.

10. How many 117-pound bales of a spice can be packed from 14,000 pounds of this food product?   *Ans.* 119 bales.

74. Checking Division by Multiplication. The surest way of proving the answer to any problem in division is to multiply the quotient by the divisor—the result should equal the dividend.

Let us say that in dividing $176.48 by 8 we obtained the answer $22.06. To prove its correctness we need but to multiply $22.06 by 8. The result is $176.48, which is the figure we started with, and we may therefore be reasonably sure that $22.06 is the correct answer. We could double-check the answer, if we wanted to, using the "double-and-halve" method and multiplying $44.12 (twice $22.06) by 4 (half of 8).

Let us try a simple example mentally: Find the cost of 20 units priced at $2.40 a hundred, and prove the answer. Twenty is one fifth of 100, so we need but to divide $2.40

by 5, which gives us 48 cents. To prove the answer, 48 cents is multiplied by 5, which equals $2.40, and we know that our answer is correct.

Problems

Check your answers to the following problems by multiplication.

1. Estimate the number of cubic feet that would be occupied by $1812\frac{1}{2}$ pounds of water. (One cubic foot of water weighs $62\frac{1}{2}$ pounds.) *Ans.* 29 cubic feet. (*Art.* 68)

2. If a strip of the material used in the better grades of textile belting weighs $37\frac{1}{2}$ ounces, how many strips will comprise a stack of this material weighing 511 pounds? Calculate the total to the nearest whole unit. *Ans.* 218 strips. (*Art.* 68)

3. A reproduction machine can turn out letters at the rate of 5600 an hour. Without taking into consideration the time that the machine is not running, how much time would be consumed in reproducing the following quantities of letters: 23,000, 18,500, 14,000, 16,000, 20,000? Compute the answer to the nearest hour.
Ans. 17 hours. (*Art.* 69)

4. If there are approximately 6720 whole cloves to one pound, how many would there be to one ounce? *Ans.* 420. (*Art.* 69)

5. If the weight of a box of drawing instruments is 33 ounces, how many boxes would comprise a total weight of $148\frac{1}{2}$ pounds?
Ans. 72 boxes. (*Art.* 72)

6. How many hogsheads are there in 2331 gallons? One hogshead equals 63 gallons. *Ans.* 37 hogsheads.

7. If a machine bores automobile cylinder blocks at the rate of 107 an hour, how long would it take to have 6000 blocks bored? Compute the total to the nearest hour. *Ans.* 56 hours. (*Art.* 73)

8. A rug measuring 12 feet by 17 feet costs $1098.00. How much does that average per square foot? *Ans.* $5.38. (*Art.* 73)

75. Checking Division by Casting Out the Nines. The principle of casting out the nines in checking division is

the same as in checking addition, subtraction and multiplication. In division, however, the proof consists in multiplying the check number of the quotient by the check number of the divisor; the check number of the product should equal the check number of the dividend.

Thus to prove that 3741 divided by 43 equals 87, we proceed as follows:

(Dividend) 3741 $3 + 7 + 4 + 1 = 15$.   Casting out the 9 leaves 6

(Divisor)   43 $4 + 3$ $= 7$.   There is no 9 to cast out, so we write down   7

(Quotient)   87 $8 + 7$ $= 15$.   Casting out the 9 leaves 6

Multiplying the check number of the quotient (check number 6) by the check number of the divisor (check number 7) gives us 42; and the sum of the digits in 42 is 6. This agrees with the check number of the dividend, and so we may presume our answer to be correct.

In the foregoing illustration the quotient happens to be a whole number. However, in division there is often a remainder; for example, 3483 divided by 13 equals 267 and 12 left over, 12 being the remainder. In that event we simply add the sum of the digits in the remainder to the product of the check numbers of quotient and divisor, and proceed in the usual manner. Thus to prove the answer to the aforestated problem, we proceed in the following manner. (Note that when the sum of the digits in the dividend or divisor is an exact multiple of 9, we show 9 as the check number.)

(Dividend) 3483 $3 + 4 + 8 + 3 = 18.$ Casting out
                                            one 9 leaves 9

(Divisor)   13 $1 + 3$ $= 4.$ There is no 9
                                            to cast out,
                                            so we write
                                            down   4

(Quotient)   267 $2 + 6 + 7$ $= 15.$ Casting out
                                            the 9 leaves 6

(Left over)   12 $1 + 2$ $= 3.$ See explana-
                                            tion above

Multiplying the check number of the whole number in
the quotient (check number 6) by the check number of
the divisor (check number 4) gives us 24; the sum of the
digits in the remainder (the quantity left over in the
operation of division) is 3 which, added to 24, equals 27;
and the sum of the digits in 27 is 9. This agrees with the
check number of the dividend, and we may presume our
answer, 267 with 12 left over, to be correct.

Here, as with the other operations—addition, subtraction and multiplication—the reader is reminded that
this method of proving division is not always error-proof.

Problems

Prove your answers to these problems by the method of casting
out the nines.

★ 1. A man's "take-home" pay for 5 days is $48.65. How much
does that average per day?   Ans. $9.73. (Art. 68)

2. A cotton batting and felt combination—a product used in
the upholstery industry—is put up in rolls averaging about 15
pounds to the roll. How many rolls can be made up from 4320
pounds of this material?   Ans. 288 rolls. (Art. 68)

3. How many bushels are contained in 1500 quarts? (One bushel
equals 32 quarts.) Give your answer to the nearest whole unit.

                                   Ans. 47 bushels. (Art. 69)

4. If it cost $22.56 to dig a trench 36 feet long, 3 feet wide and 6 feet deep, what was the average cost per cubic yard? (Hint: Instead of computing the product of 36 times 3 times 6, and dividing the result by 27 to obtain the total number of cubic yards, cancel 9 into the length, and 3 into the width or depth, and consider the product of the reduced dimensions as cubic yards.)

Ans. 94 cents per cubic yard. (*Art.* 69)

5. A combination of asphalt emulsion and asbestos fiber for troweling on insulation surfaces has a covering capacity of 9 square feet per gallon. How many gallons would be necessary to cover an area of 585 square feet of insulation surface? *Ans.* 65 gallons.

6. If a loft 72 feet long has an area of 2232 square feet, what is its width? *Ans.* 31 feet. (*Art.* 71)

7. If olive oil weighs .033 pounds per cubic inch, how many full gallons can be obtained from 132 pounds of this food product? One gallon equals 231 cubic inches. *Ans.* 17 full gallons. (*Art.* 72)

8. If a sheet of asbestos ebony 42 by 96 inches weighs 257.6 pounds, how much would one square foot of this material weigh? (Hint: Instead of multiplying 42 by 96 and dividing the result by 144 to obtain the number of square feet, cancel 12 into 42 and 96, and consider the product of the reduced dimensions as square feet.)

Ans. 9.2 pounds per square foot. (*Art.* 73)

9. If a gas engine consumes one gallon of lubricating oil for 19,000 horsepower hours, how many gallons would it consume in producing 361,000 horsepower hours? *Ans.* 19 gallons. (*Art.* 73)

CHAPTER XIII

THE "DOUBLE-AND-DOUBLE" METHOD
OF DIVISION

There is an interesting similarity between the technique introduced in this chapter and the method discussed in Chapter III (The "Double-and-Halve" Method of Multiplication). These are sister chapters in the real sense of the term. The principle of the method in Chapter III is based on the fact that when two factors in a multiplication problem are multiplied and divided, respectively, by the same value, the product is not affected. In this chapter we will discuss a process based on the fact that when both the dividend and the divisor in any problem are multiplied or divided by the same value the quotient is not affected.

The four articles in the present chapter are among the most important in this book, and the reader is advised to give them his special attention. They should help deepen his insight into the remarkable speed and accuracy with which many problems in division can be worked mentally or with surprisingly little use of pencil and paper.

76. How to Divide Mentally and Quickly by $1\frac{1}{2}$, $2\frac{1}{2}$, $3\frac{1}{2}$, $4\frac{1}{2}$, $5\frac{1}{2}$ and $7\frac{1}{2}$. To divide by any of these numbers, simply double the dividend and double the divisor, and proceed with the problem. Thus to divide 36 by $1\frac{1}{2}$ we would change the dividend to 72 and the divisor to 3, which revision would enable us to see at once that the answer is 24. Similarly, $37\frac{1}{2}$ divided by $2\frac{1}{2}$ is equivalent to 75 divided by 5, and, without having to write down a single figure, we see that the answer is 15.

Problems in which the divisor is $3\frac{1}{2}$, $4\frac{1}{2}$ or $5\frac{1}{2}$ would be revised in exactly the same way. Thus to divide 28 by $3\frac{1}{2}$ we would divide 56 by 7; and the division of 315 by $4\frac{1}{2}$ is equivalent to the division of 630 by 9. By keeping this principle in mind, the answer to the problem of dividing $247\frac{1}{2}$ by $5\frac{1}{2}$ is immediately apparent; $247\frac{1}{2}$ divided by $5\frac{1}{2}$ is equivalent to 495 divided by 11, and without going a step farther we know, from our experience with the multiplier 11 (Art. 1-f), that 495 is the product of 45 times 11. So that our answer to this problem is 45.

Here, as in any other problem in division, it should be remembered that if we double the dividend we must also double the divisor, and vice versa, in order that the quotient may not be affected. In this connection it might be well to review Art. 13, which deals with the subject of multiplying by some of the numbers discussed here, and to observe the difference between the procedure in multiplying and the procedure in dividing. In multiplying by $2\frac{1}{2}$, if we double the multiplier we must *halve* the multiplicand, or vice versa—that is, if we double the multiplicand we must halve the multiplier. In dividing by $2\frac{1}{2}$, if we double the divisor we must also *double* the dividend, or vice versa.

The term "double-and-double" method of division—as the term "double-and-halve" method of multiplication (Chapter III)—was chosen for its descriptive value. And here—as with the double-and-halve method of multiplication—the value by which the two numbers are increased need not be limited to 2. To divide by $2\frac{1}{2}$, for instance, it is often more convenient to multiply the dividend and divisor by 4 rather than by 2. In revising figures for quick mental computation it is easier, for example, to restate the problem $42\frac{1}{2}$ divided by $2\frac{1}{2}$ as 170 divided by 10, rather than as 85 divided by 5. Similarly, to divide by $7\frac{1}{2}$ it is very convenient to multiply dividend and divisor by 4; thus the problem 420 divided by $7\frac{1}{2}$ becomes solvable mentally simply by changing it to read 1680 divided by 30; or, to simplify the problem still further, 420 can be divided by 30, and the quotient (that is, 14) multiplied by 4.

The divisor $7\frac{1}{2}$, incidentally, was previously discussed in Art. 68. Mention of the technique is repeated here to underscore the ease with which it is possible to divide by this number mentally.

Example: A paint product reputed to protect building exteriors against the ravages of weather and having a covering capacity of 100 square feet per gallon is sold in units of $7\frac{1}{2}$ gallons. Compute mentally the number of units of this material needed to treat an area of 21.000 square feet.

Solution: At 100 square feet per gallon, 210 gallons would be needed to treat 21,000 square feet. 210 gallons divided by $7\frac{1}{2}$ gallons is equivalent to 840 divided by 30, or 84 divided by 3.

And it is seen at a glance that the answer is 28 units.

Oftentimes it is easier to work problems of this type by performing the processes of multiplication and division in the following order rather than in the order discussed so far:

1. Increase the divisor.
2. Divide the dividend by the increased divisor.
3. Multiply the quotient.

For example, suppose we wished to divide 273 by $1\frac{1}{2}$. Multiplying the divisor by 2 changes it to 3. We see at a glance that 3 goes into 273 exactly 91 times; so instead of multiplying 273 by 2 and dividing the result by 3, we divide 273 by 3 and multiply the quotient by 2. The following illustration will give a clear picture of the advantage of the second method over the first.

Method A

$$2 \text{ times } 273 \qquad = 546$$
$$2 \text{ times } 1\frac{1}{2} \qquad = \quad 3$$
$$546 \text{ divided by } 3 = 182$$

Method B

$$2 \text{ times } 1\frac{1}{2} \qquad\qquad\qquad = \quad 3$$
$$273 \text{ divided by } 3 \text{ (mentally)} \quad = \quad 91$$
$$91 \text{ multiplied by } 2 \text{ (mentally)} = 182$$

Another good example would be 459 divided by $4\frac{1}{2}$ which, by Method B, is solvable mentally quick as a flash. Multiplying $4\frac{1}{2}$ by 2 gives us 9; 459 divided by 9 equals 51; and 51 multiplied by 2 equals 102.

Problems

★ 1. A liquid preparation for making concrete water-resistant is used in the proportion of $1\frac{1}{2}$ gallons per cubic yard of 1:2:4 concrete. What quantity of 1:2:4 concrete would be indicated by a consumption of $25\frac{1}{2}$ gallons of this product? *Ans.* 17 cubic yards.

★ 2. Glass wool, a fibrous material made from glass slag and used for insulation, weighs $1\frac{1}{2}$ pounds per cubic foot. Compute the number of cubic feet represented by 63 pounds of glass wool.

Ans. 42 cubic feet.

★ 3. If a tractor consumes an average of $2\frac{1}{2}$ quarts of oil per day, how many days would a 60-gallon drum of oil last? *Ans.* 96 days.

★ 4. Ascorbic acid, used by apple juice packers, is put up in $2\frac{1}{2}$ kilo drums. How many drums of this size can be filled from a quantity of 460 kilos? *Ans.* 184 drums.

★ 5. If one bushel of flaxseed yields $2\frac{1}{2}$ gallons of oil, how many bushels would be necessary to obtain 420 gallons?

Ans. 168 bushels.

★ 6. The daily average of pedestrians over 12 years of age passing a store between the hours of 11 A.M. and 2:30 P.M. is 2450. How many pedestrians does that average per hour? *Ans.* 700.

★ 7. How many $3\frac{1}{2}$-yard lengths can be cut from a 40-yard bolt of cloth? *Ans.* $11\frac{3}{7}$ lengths.

★ 8. How many times would it be necessary to fill a 14-quart bucket to empty a tank containing 28 gallons of water? (One gallon equals 4 quarts.) *Ans.* 8 times.

★ 9. A formula for a decorative coating calls for the use of $4\frac{1}{2}$ pounds of a pigment known as titanium barium, per gallon. Estimate the number of pounds of this pigment that should be used to produce 180 gallons of the coating. *Ans.* 40 pounds.

★ 10. If $4\frac{1}{2}$ acres of land produce $85\frac{1}{2}$ bushels of wheat, what is the average production per acre? *Ans.* 19 bushels.

★ 11. A government regulation requires that an adult-size, cork life-preserver shall contain a minimum of $5\frac{1}{2}$ pounds of cork. On this basis how many life-preservers can be made with 1870 pounds of cork? *Ans.* 340.

★ 12. If a polo ball weighs $5\frac{1}{2}$ ounces, how many polo balls would be contained in a shipment whose net weight was 1320 pounds?

Ans. 240 polo balls.

★ 13. In the tanning industry a series of vats are used so that the tanning liquid comes from the bottom of one vat and overflows into the top of the next. If the cubic capacity of each of these vats is 264 cubic feet and the height of one is $5\frac{1}{2}$ feet, what is the area of the base? *Ans.* 48 square feet.

★ 14. A manufacturer contemplates the installation of a tank to hold 800 gallons of a liquid. How many cubic feet of space would a tank of this capacity occupy? (One cubic foot equals $7\frac{1}{2}$ gallons.) *Ans.* $106\frac{2}{3}$ cubic feet.

★ 15. The result of an experiment shows that $7\frac{1}{2}$ ounces of a special ingredient used along with other materials will produce 135 ounces of a desired product. How many ounces of the finished product would contain one ounce of the special ingredient? *Ans.* 18 ounces.

77. How to Speed Up Division by Any Number Containing the Fraction $\frac{1}{2}$, e.g., $8\frac{1}{2}$, $15\frac{1}{2}$, $21\frac{1}{2}$. The process of dividing by any number containing the fraction $\frac{1}{2}$ is exactly the same as that of dividing mentally by any of the numbers discussed in the preceding article. The only difference is that the computation may have to be completed on paper.

Example 1: Divide 204 by $8\frac{1}{2}$.

Solution: Changing the problem to 408 divided by 17, and completing the computation by the short Continental method (Art. 73), we proceed as follows:

$$\frac{24}{17)\overline{408}}$$

$$68$$

Ans. 24.

Example 2: Divide 6696 by $15\frac{1}{2}$.

Solution: Revising the problem to read 13392 divided by 31, the answer is obtained as follows:

$$\frac{432}{31)13392}$$

$$\overline{99}$$

$$\overline{62}$$

Ans. 432.

Example 3: Divide \$313.90 by $21\frac{1}{2}$.

Solution: This problem is equivalent to \$627.80 divided by 43.

$$\frac{14.60}{43)627.80}$$

$$\overline{197}$$

$$258$$

Ans. \$14.60.

Problems

1. One of the uses of wood skewers is for the application of insulation layers. If 1000 skewers, $5\frac{1}{2}$ inches by $\frac{1}{4}$ inch, weigh $6\frac{1}{2}$ pounds, how many pins of this size would comprise a total weight of 221 pounds?　　　　　　　　　*Ans.* 34,000 pins.

2. If $9\frac{1}{2}$ ounces of flour are used to bake a loaf of bread, how many loaves can be baked with 1900 pounds of flour?

Ans. 3200 loaves.

★ **3.** Without considering the brokerage fees, etc., connected with the purchase, estimate the number of shares quoted at $11\frac{1}{2}$—that is, at $11.50—that can be purchased for $460.00.   *Ans.* 40 shares.

4. If a dumping truck has a payload capacity of $13\frac{1}{2}$ cubic yards, how many loads would be necessary to clear 324 cubic yards?
          Ans. 24 loads.

5. How many $15\frac{1}{2}$-ounce tins of smoked shad can be packed from 600 pounds of this food product? Estimate the total to the nearest unit.   *Ans.* 619 tins.

6. How many $31\frac{1}{2}$-gallon barrels would be necessary to dispose of 756 gallons of liquid?   *Ans.* 24 barrels.

78. How to Divide Quickly by Numbers Containing Fractions Other Than $\frac{1}{2}$, e.g., $2\frac{1}{3}$, $28\frac{3}{4}$, $45\frac{5}{9}$. The process of "doubling" dividend and divisor is never more useful than when dealing with divisors which contain fractions. And here, as in Arts. 76 and 77, we will observe that while for the purpose of explanation the technique is referred to as "doubling," actually it makes no difference whether the dividend and divisor in any problem are multiplied by 2, 3, 4, 5 or any other number, for when the dividend and the divisor are multiplied by the same value the quotient is not affected.

Example 1: Divide 133 by $2\frac{1}{3}$.

Solution: As in the preceding two articles, our objective is to eliminate the fraction from the divisor, so let us multiply both numbers by 3 (3 being the denominator of the fraction).

133 multiplied by 3 = 399
$2\frac{1}{3}$ multiplied by 3 =   7
399 divided by 7   = 57

Example 2: Divide 1961 by $13\frac{1}{4}$.

Solution: Here the denominator in the fraction is 4, so
let us multiply both numbers by 4. This
changes the problem to 7844 divided by 53,
which is readily computed by the short
Continental method:

$$\frac{148}{53)7844}$$

$$\overline{254}$$

$$\overline{424}$$

                                        Ans. 148.

Example 3: Divide 9940 by $28\frac{2}{5}$.

Solution: Note that the numerator in the fraction here
is 2, so in converting the divisor to a whole
number we must remember to add 2 to the
product of 28 times 5.

9940 multiplied by 5 = 49700
$28\frac{2}{5}$ multiplied by 5 =   142

$$\frac{350}{142)49700}$$

$$\overline{710}$$

                                        Ans. 350.

Example 4: Divide 230 by $28\frac{3}{4}$.

Solution:

      230 multiplied by 4 = 920
      $28\frac{3}{4}$ multiplied by 4 = 115
      920 divided by 115 =   8

Example 5: Divide 410 by $45\frac{5}{9}$.

Solution: Multiplying each number by 9, our problem
is 3690 divided by 410, and the briefest
glance tells us that the answer is 9.

Example 6: Divide $711\frac{3}{4}$ by $31\frac{1}{3}$, and give the answer
to the nearest whole unit.

Solution: To convert the divisor in this problem to a
whole number we must multiply it by 3.
This changes our problem to $2135\frac{1}{4}$ (or
2135.25) divided by 94.

$$\frac{22.7}{94)2135.25}$$

$$255$$

$$672$$

Ans. 23.

Let us pause here to see if we understand the reason
for the procedure in the foregoing illustration. In each of
the other examples, the dividend was automatically
changed to a whole number along with the divisor. How-

ever, the essential consideration in this technique is to eliminate the fraction from the divisor. In solving the problem in Example 6 we might easily have multiplied both numbers by 12, thus eliminating the fraction from the dividend as well as from the divisor, but this would have resulted in a divisor having three digits, and it is certainly easier to divide 2135.25 by the two-digit number 94 than 8541 by the three-digit number 376.

The ease of dividing by numbers containing decimal fractions which are aliquot numbers is surprisingly overlooked by many. To divide by numbers which contain such decimal fractions as .125 and .625, for example, there is no need to burden oneself with the task of dividing by each of the three digits in these fractions—for .125 is an aliquot part of 1 (it is $\frac{1}{8}$); so that a divisor like 5.125 can be conveniently considered as $5\frac{1}{8}$. Similarly, since .625 is equivalent to $\frac{5}{8}$, the divisor 7.625 can be readily changed to $7\frac{5}{8}$.

As often as not the reader will find that the elimination of decimal fractions from a divisor not only shortens the process of computation, but may completely eliminate the need for further calculation.

Example 7: Divide \$20.50 by 5.125.

Solution: 5.125 is the same as $5\frac{1}{8}$, and \$20.50 divided by $5\frac{1}{8}$ is equivalent to \$164.00 divided by 41. Without the need for further computation, it is seen that the answer is \$4.00.

Having discussed decimal fractions which are aliquot parts, we will now consider mixed numbers that are aliquot parts, and note the interesting results of converting these numbers.

Let us begin with the number $1\frac{1}{4}$. To divide by $1\frac{1}{4}$ should one multiply dividend and divisor by 4? Multiplied by 4, the number $1\frac{1}{4}$ becomes 5, and as we learned in another place in this book, division by 5 can be simplified by multiplying dividend and divisor by 2. But, instead of multiplying first by 4 and then by 2, we can just as easily multiply by 8 in one operation (8 being the product of 4 times 2). Thus 45 divided by $1\frac{1}{4}$ becomes 360 (which is 8 times 45) divided by 10 (which is 8 times $1\frac{1}{4}$), and quick as a flash we see that the answer is 36.

To divide by $1\frac{2}{3}$ we would proceed in the same manner. Instead of multiplying $1\frac{2}{3}$ by 3, which would give us 5, we multiply by 6, which equals 10. In this way, division by $1\frac{2}{3}$ is made as easy as ABC. Thus the problem $80.85 divided by $1\frac{2}{3}$ becomes $485.10 divided by 10, and in a split second we know that the answer is $48.51.

Note the method of procedure in the following illustration where the mixed-number divisor, when multiplied by the figure in the denominator, is a commonly known aliquot part of 100.

Example 8: Divide $396.00 by $8\frac{1}{3}$.

Solution: If we multiplied these numbers by 3, the divisor would be 25. However, since it is so much easier to divide by 100 than by 25, let us multiply the numbers by 4 times 3, since 25 is contained in 100 four times.

12 times $396.00   = $4752.00
12 times $8\frac{1}{3}$ = 100
$4752.00 divided by 100 = $47.52

Here we can use with excellent effect the technique mentioned at the end of Art. 76—namely, that it is sometimes easier to multiply the quotient rather than the dividend. Thus in working the problem 560 divided by $2\frac{1}{3}$, we see at a glance that 7 (the product of 3 times $2\frac{1}{3}$) goes exactly 80 times into 560; so instead of multiplying 560 by 3 and dividing the result by 7, we divide 560 by 7 and multiply the quotient by 3. Similarly, in dividing 34 by $4\frac{1}{4}$, instead of dividing 136 (the product of 4 times 34) by 17 (the product of 4 times $4\frac{1}{4}$), we would divide 34 by 17 and multiply the quotient (2) by 4.

EXERCISES

Perform the following problems in division by the procedure indicated.

	Multiply the dividend by	And divide the result by	
★ 1. Divide 960 by $3\frac{1}{3}$.	3	10	*Ans.* 288.
2. Divide $787\frac{1}{2}$ by $3\frac{3}{4}$.	8	30	*Ans.* 210.
3. Divide 6225 by $6\frac{1}{4}$.	16	100	*Ans.* 996.
4. Divide 6775 by $8\frac{1}{3}$.	12	100	*Ans.* 813.
5. Divide 1716 by $9\frac{1}{11}$.	11	100	*Ans.* 188.76.
6. Divide \$517.00 by $11\frac{1}{5}$.	9	100	*Ans.* \$46.53.
7. Divide \$1295.00 by $14\frac{2}{7}$.	7	100	*Ans.* \$90.65.
8. Divide \$1842.00 by $16\frac{2}{3}$.	6	100	*Ans.* \$110.52.
9. Divide \$7437.50 by $31\frac{1}{4}$.	16	500	*Ans.* \$238.00.
10. Divide \$936.00 by $33\frac{1}{3}$.	3	100	*Ans.* \$28.08.

PROBLEMS

1. It is reported that in a single year no less than 42,000 bushels of sea-stars (a class of starfish very destructive to mussels and oysters) have been removed from the oyster beds of Connecticut. If approximately one cubic foot is equivalent to $1\frac{1}{4}$ bushels, how many cubic feet of space would be occupied by the aforementioned quantity of sea-stars, assuming that it were possible to pack them all together? *Ans.* 33,600 cubic feet.

★ **2.** A good yield of fiber flax is about $2\frac{1}{4}$ tons of air-dried straw per acre. On this basis how many acres would be required to produce 270 tons of this product? *Ans.* 120 acres.

★ **3.** A tailor's inventory shows that he has three bolts of cloth suitable for men's suits, totaling 91 yards. If the average suit length is $3\frac{1}{4}$ yards, how many suits could be made from the three bolts?
Ans. 28 suits.

★ **4.** How many $3\frac{1}{4}$-inch strips can be cut from a sheet of zinc 39 inches wide? *Ans.* 12 strips.

5. Toluol, a product used in the manufacture of lacquers, weighs approximately $7\frac{1}{4}$ pounds per gallon. Compute the equivalent in gallons of 406 pounds of this product. *Ans.* 56 gallons.

6. What should the net weight be of 133 yards of four-leaf twill fabric, if $1\frac{3}{4}$ yards of this material weighs one pound?
Ans. 76 pounds.

★ **7.** If a one-foot bar of steel weighs $2\frac{3}{4}$ pounds, how many feet would be contained in 374 pounds of this steel? *Ans.* 136 feet.

★ **8.** If a truck averages $4\frac{3}{4}$ cubic yards of dirt to the load, how many trips must it make to haul 190 cubic yards of dirt?
Ans. 40 trips.

9. A job lot of $5\frac{3}{4}$ gross metal parts is offered at $20.70 for the lot. How much does this average per gross parts? *Ans.* $3.60.

10. In lumbermen's boots there is usually a heavy felt sole, stitched just above the leather sole. This felt material is made in sheets weighing $7\frac{3}{4}$ pounds and measuring 40 by 60 inches by $\frac{5}{16}$-inch. How many square feet of this material would be contained in a total weight of 1860 pounds? *Ans.* 4000 square feet.

11. If a roll of 16-inch building paper contains 666 square feet, what is the length of the roll? (Hint: 16 inches equals $1\frac{1}{3}$ feet.)
Ans. $499\frac{1}{2}$ feet.

12. How many ivory billiard balls, each weighing $4\frac{2}{3}$ ounces, may be expected to be found in a total net weight of 42 pounds?
Ans. 144.

13. Insulating wool blankets, approximately 23 inches wide and 2 inches thick, are packed in lengths of $44\frac{1}{3}$ feet to the carton. If a total of 665 feet of this material is required, how many cartons should be purchased? *Ans.* 15 cartons.

14. A manufacturer purchased bolts of cloth whose total yardage was 1323 yards. He planned to make aprons requiring $1\frac{1}{8}$ yards of this material per apron. If no material is wasted in production, how many aprons should he be able to make? *Ans.* 1176 aprons.

15. How many bricks $2\frac{1}{8}$ inches thick would make 8 stacks, each 5 feet 8 inches high? *Ans.* 256 bricks.

79. Speeding Up Division by Whole Numbers Like 35, 75, 125, 135, 165, 175, 250, 350, 750, 850, 1450, etc.

Having in mind the thought that it is easier to divide by a single digit than by a two-digit number, and by a two-digit than by a three-digit number, let us look into the interesting possibilities of speeding by the double-and-double method the solution of problems in which the divisor is a whole number.

The number 35 contains two digits. By doubling it, however, a single-digit number is obtained. So that the answer to a problem like 420 divided by 35 becomes obvious at a glance: 840 divided by 70 is equivalent to 84 divided by 7, which equals 12.

When 75 is doubled we still have a two-digit number— namely, 150. But when 75 is multiplied by 4 a single-digit number is obtained. Thus the problem 1200 divided by 75 can be quickly worked mentally when the numbers are changed to 4800 and 300, respectively, for all we need do is divide 48 by 3, which equals 16.

Example 1: Divide 510 by 15.

Solution: Twice 510 = 1020
Twice 15 = 30
1020 divided by 30 equals 102 divided by 3.
102 divided by 3 equals 34.

The same principle, without any variation, can be applied to numbers ending in 5. Thus three-digit numbers, e.g., 135 and 165, when multiplied by 2, become two-digit numbers—namely, 270 and 330. And it is obviously easier to divide by 270 than by 135, and by 330 than by 165. If a number ends with 50, it does not make one bit of difference; thus the divisor 850 can be as conveniently changed to 1700 as 85 to 170.

Example 2: A plot of land 25 by 100 feet is offered for sale at a price of $80,000. How much does this average per square foot?

Solution: The area of the plot is 2500 square feet. Canceling the two ciphers in 2500 and the last two ciphers in 80,000, we have the equivalent of 25 square feet costing $800. Since 25 is one fourth of 100, let us multiply both numbers by 4; 100 square feet (4 times 25) equals $3200 (4 times 800). And we see at once that the cost is $32 per square foot.

Problems

1. If the net weight of a case of frozen eggs is 35 pounds, how many cases can be filled from 2695 pounds of this food product?

Ans. 77 cases.

2. The covering capacity of a waterproof cement for applying cork covering and lagging is 35 square feet per gallon. Estimate the number of gallons that would be required to cover 5740 square feet.

Ans. 164 gallons.

⋆ **3.** An electrically operated mimeograph can produce 125 letters a minute. At this rate of speed how long would it take to produce 45,000 copies of a letter? Assume that the machine runs smoothly from start to finish, and without any loss of time.

Ans. 6 hours. (*Art.* 2-c)

⋆ **4.** How many cubic feet of space would be occupied by 7125 pounds of a medium quality brickwork having a weight of 125 pounds per cubic foot?   *Ans.* 57. (*Art.* 2-c)

5. How many bars of electrolytic copper, each weighing 135 pounds, would be contained in 2835 pounds of this material?

Ans. 21 bars.

6. To seed his wheat field of 175 acres, a farmer used 306 bushels of seed. How much seed did this average per acre? Compute the answer to the nearest quarter of a bushel.   *Ans.* $1\frac{3}{4}$ bushels.

7. It costs a manufacturer $416.25 to assemble 185 units. How much is that per unit?   *Ans.* $2.25.

⋆ **8.** A trailer body, loading frozen products at around 0° F., requires 250 pounds of dry ice for each day that the load is to be in transit. At this rate of consumption, for how many days will 4250 pounds of dry ice suffice?   *Ans.* 17 days.

⋆ **9.** A pound of green lake printing ink will cover approximately 250,000 square inches on Enamel No. 1 stock. If the estimated number of square inches to be printed in this color on the mentioned stock is 23,687,000, how many pounds of ink will be used on the job? Compute the answer to the nearest pound.   *Ans.* 95 pounds.

⋆ **10.** How many 350-pound barrels of sugar can be filled from seven short tons of this food product? (Hint: A short ton equals 2000 pounds.)   *Ans.* 40 barrels.

⋆ **11.** At the rate of 350 acres per hour, how long would it take to dust 8400 acres by airplane?   *Ans.* 24 hours.

12. One pound of commercially pure aluminum, .001 inch thick, can cover an area of 10,250 square inches. What quantity of this material would be needed to cover an area of 2 million square inches? Compute the answer to the nearest pound.

Ans. 195 pounds.

CHAPTER XIV

AVERAGES AND PROPORTIONS

If the reader finds it pleasurable as well as useful to know how to cut time and ensure accuracy in mathematical computations, another delightful adventure is in store for him here. One of the techniques in the opening article is a particularly interesting study which, apart from the subject discussed, might happily expand the reader's mathematical horizon.

80. A Simple Way to Find the Average Due Date of Several Bills. For any of a number of reasons a businessman may wish to pay at one time several bills which fall due on different dates. He may be unable to pay the first bill on its due date, or he may have a special reason for wanting to pay all the bills from a certain creditor—including some bills that are not yet due—in one lump sum.

Let us suppose that on February 24 a man decides to pay at one time on the average due date a creditor's two bills—one for $340.00 due on March 9, and another for $460.00 due on March 20. On what date could he cancel his indebtedness with a payment of $800.00, the sum of the two amounts?

A good method of procedure is based on the fact that

the interest earned, let us say, on $100 in 8 days is equivalent to the interest earned on $200 in 4 days, or on $400 in 2 days, or on $800 in 1 day. The method is as follows: Start with the last day of the month preceding the earliest due date. Take each bill separately and calculate the amount of the principal which, for one day, would earn as much interest as the amount of the bill would earn for the number of days indicated by the due date. The total of the principal amounts divided by the total amount of the bills equals the average due date. Taking the aforementioned two bills, here are the actual figures:

$340 due March 9.	$340 for 9 days =	$ 3,060 for 1 day
460 due March 20.	$460 for 20 days =	9,200 for 1 day
$800		$12,260 for 1 day

This computation indicates that if the debtor had paid the sum of $800 on the last day of February, instead of paying the two bills, each on its due date, the amount of interest of which he would have deprived himself would be equal to the interest on $12,260 for 1 day. So what we do is this: We divide $12,260 by $800, which gives us 15, and it is on the 15th day of March that the entire debt may be canceled by a payment of $800.

The same method would be applied to an account consisting of any number of bills, as will be seen in the following demonstration.

Example: Find the average due date of three bills: one for $100 due April 11, one for $150 due April 20, and one for $150 due April 26.

Solution:

$100 due April 11.	$100 for 11 days =	$1100 for 1 day
150 due April 20.	150 for 20 days =	3000 for 1 day
150 due April 26.	150 for 26 days =	3900 for 1 day

$400 $8000 for 1 day

$8000 divided by $400 equals 20. So that the entire account may be canceled by a payment of $400 on April 20.

Problems

Find the average due date of each of the following accounts.

1. $100.00 due February 6, $250.00 due February 22, and $150.00 due February 26.   *Ans.* February 20.

2. $375.00 due March 4, $125.00 due March 8, and $204.00 due March 25.   *Ans.* March 11.

3. $75.00 due May 3, $250.00 due May 8, $250.00 due May 9, $125.00 due May 10, and $425.00 due May 13.   *Ans.* May 10.

4. $212.50 due July 11, $347.00 due July 14, and $106.25 due July 20.   *Ans.* July 14.

5. $312.31 due September 10, $219.43 due September 20, and $624.62 due September 25.   *Ans.* September 20.

81. Three Good Ways of Dividing Profits Among Partners.

There are three commonly accepted ways of dividing profits among partners.

1. *In the ratio of capital.* This method is the simplest of all. If Smith, for example, has $10,000 invested, and his partner Brown $5000, Smith (whose investment constitutes two thirds of the total capital) receives two thirds of the profit, and Brown (whose investment represents one third of the total capital) receives one third of the profit.

2. *In an agreed-upon ratio after interest has been credited to each partner's capital account.* In some partnerships

there is an agreement by which the partners share alike,
even though the individual investments are unequal.
There may be any number of reasons for such an arrangement. The partner with the smaller investment may, for
instance, have special abilities or be more active in the
business. In such circumstances it is sometimes also agreed
that before the profits are divided, interest at a specified
rate be credited to each partner's capital account. Let us
say that the gentlemen mentioned under the first arrangement agreed to divide profits equally, and that interest at
the rate of 4 per cent be credited to their respective capital
accounts before the profit is divided. Assuming that the
profit amounted to $35,000, the amounts received by each
would be as follows:

Smith would receive 4 per cent interest on his $10,000
   investment, or $400.

Brown would receive 4 per cent interest on his $5000
   investment, or $200.

The profit of $35,000 has been reduced by these interest
   credits to $34,400, and since the profit is to be divided
   equally, each partner will receive half of $34,400, or
   $17,200.

Smith will therefore be credited with $400 plus $17,200,
   or $17,600.

And Brown will be credited with $200 plus $17,200, or
   $17,400.

It should be remembered that when the agreement provides that interest be credited to each partner's capital
account, the interest is credited regardless of whether there
is a profit or a loss, and regardless of whether the profit
does or does not exceed the total of the interest credits. If,

for instance, the profit, before the interest is credited, amounted to only $500, the net loss, too, would be shared equally. In that event the amounts credited to the individual partners would be as follows:

Smith would be credited with $400 interest, less
    $50 (half of the loss),* or $350.
Brown would be credited with $200 interest less
    $50 (half of the loss),* or $150.

If, instead of a profit of $500, the business sustained a loss of $900, the interest would still be credited to the partners' capital accounts, and then the total loss would be shared equally. By total loss is meant, of course, the net loss after interest has been credited. Since the interest credits amount to $600, the total loss would be $1500 ($9.00 plus $600). Here is how the partners' capital accounts would be affected:

Smith would be credited with $400 interest, and debited
    with $750 (half of the loss of $1500), resulting in a
    net debit to his account of $350.
Brown would be credited with $200 interest, and
    debited with $750 (half of the loss of $1500), result-
    ing in a net debit to his account of $550.

3. In the ratio of average capital. An agreement of this nature might be in effect when the partners are in the habit of making withdrawals or additions to their capital during the business year. Let us suppose that Smith and Brown, instead of leaving their respective investments

---

* A profit of $500 becomes a loss of $100 after a total of $600 in interest has been credited to the partners' capital accounts.

untouched during the entire year, made withdrawals and additions as follows:

Smith			*Brown*	
Jan. 1		$10,000	Jan. 1	$5,000
Mar. 1 Withdrew		1,000	Apr. 1 Added	1,500
Aug. 1 Added		2,500	July 1 Withdrew	500
Nov. 1 Withdrew		2,000		

The logic of a profit-sharing arrangement based on average capital will be appreciated when it is observed that while Smith withdrew during the year $500 more than he added, Brown added $1000 more than he withdrew; and further, that the additions and withdrawals were made on widely varying dates.

The procedure here is somewhat similar to that followed in the preceding article, where we learned how to find the average due date of several bills. Our object here will be to determine how many months each partner's capital remains unchanged, then to compute the equivalent amount for one month. Taking each partner's capital account separately, here is how the equivalents are computed:

Smith's Investment

Capital for 2 months (Jan. 1 to Mar. 1),	$10,000 =	$ 20,000 for 1 month
Capital for 5 months (Mar. 1 to Aug. 1),	9,000 =	45,000 for 1 month
Capital for 3 months (Aug. 1 to Nov. 1),	11,500 =	34,500 for 1 month
Capital for 2 months (Nov. 1 to Dec. 31),	9,500 =	19,000 for 1 month
12 months		$118,500 for 1 month

Brown's Investment

Capital for 3 months
    (Jan. 1 to Apr. 1), $5,000 = $15,000 for 1 month
Capital for 3 months
    (Apr. 1 to July 1),   6,500 = 19,500 for 1 month
Capital for 6 months
    (July 1 to Dec. 31),   6,000 = 36,000 for 1 month

    12 months $70,500 for 1 month

We have, in effect, reduced the individual capital accounts of Smith and Brown to a common basis. Smith's investment for the year is the equivalent of $118,500 for one month, and Brown's investment for the year is the equivalent of $70,500 for one month.

Since the sum of these equivalent investments is $189,000, it is clear that Smith's investment constitutes $\frac{118,500}{189,000}$ (or $\frac{1185}{1890}$) of the total amount invested in the business by both partners, and that Brown's investment constitutes $\frac{70,500}{189,000}$ (or $\frac{705}{1890}$) of the total.

If the profit for the year amounted to $11,340, it would therefore be shared as follows:

Smith would receive $\frac{1185}{1890}$ of $11,340, or $7110.
Brown would receive $\frac{705}{1890}$ of $11,340, or $4230.

Let us now take a slightly more difficult example—a partnership between Kent and Stern, whose respective capital accounts for the year show the following additions and withdrawals:

	Kent		*Stern*	
Jan. 1	$7,000	Jan. 1		$4,000
June 16 Added	1,000	Apr. 10 Withdrew	1,000
Aug. 23 Withdrew	2,000	Oct. 14 Added	1,000

Since in this instance the changes were made *during* the month rather than on the first day of the month, it will be necessary to take the averages for one day. And since the round number 360 is used so conveniently in interest computations to represent the number of days in a year, let us use this number here too.

Kent's Investment

Capital for 166 days (Jan. 1 to June 16),	$7,000 =	$1,162,000 for 1 day
Capital for 67 days (June 16 to Aug. 23),	8,000 =	536,000 for 1 day
Capital for 127 days (Aug. 23 to Dec. 31),	6,000 =	762,000 for 1 day
360 days		$2,460,000 for 1 day

Stern's Investment

Capital for 100 days (Jan. 1 to Apr. 10),	$4,000 =	$ 400,000 for 1 day
Capital for 184 days (Apr. 10 to Oct. 14),	3,000 =	552,000 for 1 day
Capital for 76 days (Oct. 14 to Dec. 31),	4,000 =	304,000 for 1 day
360 days		$1,256,000 for 1 day

The sum of the equivalent investments of Kent and Stern for one day is the sum of $2,460,000 and $1,256,000, or \$3,716,000. So that Kent's share of the profit will be $\frac{2,460,000}{3,716,000}$ or $\frac{2460}{3716}$, and Stern's share will be $\frac{1,256,000}{3,716,000}$ or $\frac{1256}{3716}$.

If the profit for the year was \$13,006, it would be shared as follows:

Kent would receive $\frac{2460}{3716}$ of \$13,006, or \$8610.
Stern would receive $\frac{1256}{3716}$ of \$13,006, or \$4396.

When Profits Are to Be Shared Among More Than Two Partners. The method of dividing profits when there are more than two partners is substantially the same as when only two partners are involved. Thus under the first method—by which profits are shared in the ratio of capital—if along with Smith who had \$10,000 invested, and Brown who had \$5000 invested, there was a third partner Kane, who invested \$5000, the ratios would be as follows:

Smith's investment of \$5000 would constitute $\frac{5000}{20000}$, or one fourth.
Brown's investment of \$10,000 would constitute $\frac{10000}{20000}$, or one half.
Kane's investment of \$5000 would constitute $\frac{5000}{20000}$, or one fourth.

Note that the denominator represents the sum of the individual investments; and, conversely, that the sum of the numerators equals the amount, or number, in the denominator.

Under the second method—by which partners share

alike after interest has been credited to their accounts—
each partner would be credited or debited (according to
whether there was a profit or a loss) on the basis of the
number of partners. Each of three partners would share a
third; each of four partners a fourth; and so on.

And if, under the third method—that of sharing in the
ratio of average capital—Smith and Brown had a third
partner, Morrison, the procedure would not be altered one
bit. The monthly equivalents would be computed for each
of the three partners, the equivalent investments would
be totaled, and then each partner would share in the ratio
of his monthly equivalent to the total.

Thus, if Morrison's monthly equivalent was $41,000,
the sum of the three equivalents (Smith's $118,500,
Brown's $70,500, and Morrison's $41,000) would be
$230,000. Each would therefore share as follows:

Smith would receive $\dfrac{118,500}{230,000}$ of the total profit.

Brown would receive $\dfrac{70,500}{230,000}$ of the total profit.

Morrison would receive $\dfrac{41,000}{230,000}$ of the total profit.

PROBLEMS

1. Three partners agree to share profits in the ratio of capital.
Wilson's capital is $6000, Lewis invested $4000, and Field $5000. If
the total profit is $12,000, how much will each receive as his share
of the profit?   *Ans.* Wilson $4800, Lewis $3200, Field $4000.

2. What would each partner's share be in Problem 1 if all
shared equally and each was credited with 3% interest on his in-

vestment before the profit was divided? The word "share" is used
here to mean profit plus interest.

Ans. Wilson $4030, Lewis $3970, Field $4000.

3. Assume that the partners in the foregoing problems made
the following additions and withdrawals from their respective capital
accounts and that the profit was shared in the ratio of average
capital. What would each receive if the total profit was $12,000?
Assume that the capital of each partner was invested on January 1.

Wilson withdrew $500 on July 1.

Lewis added $1000 on May 1, and withdrew $500 on July 1.

Field withdrew $2000 on May 1 and added $1000 on September 1.

Ans. Wilson $4870.59, Lewis $3741.18, Field $3388.23.

82. How to Find Average Cost or Selling Price.

When a
product is made by the mixing of different materials it is
necessary, if the selling price is to be determined, to know
the average cost. A manufacturer of pharmaceuticals, for
instance, may produce a preparation by mixing so many
gallons of one ingredient with so many gallons of another,
and in order to have a definite figure on which to base the
selling price, he must know what the mixture costs him
per gallon, quart or pint. Similarly, a company, contemplating the combination of different wools, may want to
determine the average cost per pound of the mixture. The
procedure is simple: The total cost of the mixture is divided
by the total quantity of the materials used.

Example 1: A mill owner desires to know the average
cost per pound of a mixture formed by the combination
of the following lots of wools:

179 lb. @ $1.12 per lb.   188 lb. @ $1.07 per lb.
346 lb. @   1.04 per lb.   411 lb. @   1.16 per lb.

Estimate the average cost to the nearest cent.

Solution:

179 lb. @ $1.12 per lb. =		$200.48
346 lb. @ 1.04 per lb. =		359.84
188 lb. @ 1.07 per lb. =		201.16
411 lb. @ 1.16 per lb. =		476.76
1124 lb.	=	$1238.24

$1238.24 divided by 1124 equals $1.10, which is the average cost per pound of the mixture.

Exactly the same procedure is followed when it is desired to obtain the average selling price, as demonstrated in the solution to the following problem.

Example 2: A farmer made the following sales of cotton during the gathering season, for which he received the amounts shown:

Number of Bales	Weight in Pounds	Price Per Lb. (*in cents*)	Total
13	14,320	31.25	$4,475.00
16	15,168	31.55	4,785.50
12	11,026	31.60	3,484.22
24	23,872	30.95	7,388.38

Compute to the nearest hundredth of a cent the average price per pound received by the farmer.

Solution: The total number of pounds of cotton sold is 64,386, and the total amount received is $20,133.10.

$20,133.10 divided by 64,386 equals 31.27 cents.

The farmer received, therefore, an average price of 31.27 cents per pound.

PROBLEMS

1. A company makes a food product by mixing 112 pounds of one mixture costing $26\frac{1}{2}$ cents a pound with 35 pounds of another mixture costing 23 cents a pound. Estimate the average cost per pound of the finished product to the nearest hundredth of a cent. *Ans.* 25.67 cents per pound. (*Art.* 11)

2. A retail nut shop mixes the following nuts: 25 pounds costing 68 cents a pound, 30 pounds costing 87 cents a pound, and 50 pounds costing 99 cents a pound. Compute the average cost per pound to the nearest cent. *Ans.* 88 cents per pound. (*Art.* 73)

3. A druggist prepared a laxative from the following formula, using the quantities specified:

> 1 gallon Cascara — costing $12.75 per gallon
> 2 gallons Rhubarb and Soda costing 4.10 per gallon
> $\frac{3}{4}$ gallon Milk of Magnesia costing 2.85 per gallon
> $1\frac{1}{4}$ gallons Syrup of Licorice costing 6.41 per gallon

Estimate to the nearest quarter of a cent his average cost per pint. (Hint: 8 pints equal one gallon.) *Ans.* $77\frac{3}{4}$ cents per pint.

4. A candy manufacturer decides to offer a mixture which he made from the following:

> 128 lb. of a quality sold for $0.35 per lb.
> 85 lb. of a quality sold for .28 per lb.
> 114 lb. of a quality sold for .24 per lb.
> 23 lb. of a quality sold for .40 per lb.

At how much per pound should he sell the mixture if he is to receive for the entire quantity the same amount that he would have received if he sold the four different qualities separately at the indicated prices? *Ans.* 30 cents per pound. (*Arts.* 2-b, 11, 79)

5. A baker sold the following cookies: 32 pounds at $1.10 a pound, 48 pounds at 90 cents a pound, and 70 pounds at 70 cents a pound. Compute to the nearest cent the average selling price per pound.   *Ans.* 85 cents per pound. (*Arts.* 1-d, 73, 79)

6. The records of a cafeteria showed that the following sales were made in one day:

43 @ $0.10	206 @ $0.40	96 @ $0.70
56 @ .15	240 @ .45	84 @ .75
84 @ .20	320 @ .50	80 @ .80
90 @ .25	310 @ .55	62 @ .85
164 @ .30	262 @ .60	33 @ .90
140 @ .35	130 @ .65	

Estimate to the nearest cent the amount of the average sale for the day.   *Ans.* 50 cents. (*Arts.* 1-b, 1-d, 2-a, 2-b, 11, 69)

83. How to Determine the Exact Quantity Necessary of Each of a Number of Variously Priced Materials to Produce a Mixture at a Specified Cost. Manufacturers frequently find it necessary to determine the exact proportion in which to mix a number of different materials in order to produce a mixture to cost a specified amount. It is usual in such circumstances to mix one or more materials whose cost per unit of measurement is *less* than that of the desired mixture, with one or more materials costing *more*. In some instances, as in Example 1, no particular proportion is specified; in others, as in Example 2, the formulation provides for the consumption of a specified quantity of one of the materials; and in still others, as in Examples 3 and 4, the proportion in which two of the materials are to be mixed is predetermined.

We will study four different types of mixtures. In each case the solution to the problem entails three steps. In the first step we will deal (a) with materials costing *less* per unit of measurement than the desired mixture, when there is no specified proportion, or (b) with the material of which a specified quantity is to be used. In the second step we will deal (a) with materials whose cost per unit of measurement *exceeds* that of the desired mixture, when there is no specified proportion, or (b) with materials which are to be used in a specified proportion, regardless of cost. It will be noted that in one step (it may be the first step and it may be the second) we find what is called the *gain*; and in the other step the *loss*—i.e., a key figure which will enable us, in the third step, to determine how much of each of the materials dealt with in the second step is to be used with the materials dealt with in the first step.

A careful study of the subject matter that follows, including the summary at the end of the article, will make this clear.

WHEN IT IS DESIRED TO DETERMINE THE PROPOR-
TION IN WHICH TO USE THREE MATERIALS—TWO
COSTING "LESS" PER UNIT OF MEASUREMENT
THAN THE DESIRED MIXTURE, AND ONE COSTING
"MORE":

Example 1: A manufacturer of textile products has on hand three lots of wool, of which he wishes to make a mixture at a material cost of $1.18 per pound. The cost per pound of the three lots is $1.03, $1.14 and $1.24, respectively. In what proportion should the materials be used to produce the desired mixture?

Solution:

First step:

$1.18 minus $1.03 = .15; 15 times 1 (1 lb.) = 15
1.18 minus 1.14 = .04; 4 times 1 (1 lb.) = 4
                                              ——
                                    Gain = 19

Second step:

   $1.18 minus $1.24 = minus .06.   Loss = 6

Third step:

   19 (gain) divided by 6 (loss)   = $3\frac{1}{6}$

Conclusion: A mixture costing $1.18 a pound could
               therefore be produced by mixing the
               materials as follows:

1 lb. of the material costing $1.03 per lb. = $1.03

1 lb. of the material costing $1.14 per lb. = 1.14

$3\frac{1}{6}$ lb. of the material costing $1.24 per lb. = 3.93
_____

$5\frac{1}{6}$ lb.   = $6.10

Proof: $6.10 divided by $5\frac{1}{6}$ = $1.18.

WHEN A SPECIFIED QUANTITY OF MATERIAL COST-
ING "MORE" PER UNIT OF MEASUREMENT THAN
THE DESIRED MIXTURE IS TO BE USED WITH
AN UNDETERMINED QUANTITY OF A MATERIAL
COSTING "LESS" THAN THE DESIRED MIXTURE:

Example 2: A manufacturer wishes to use 374 pounds
of material costing $1.16 a pound to produce a mixture
costing $1.12 a pound. To be used in the mixture is a
material of which several hundred pounds are available,
the cost of which is $1.02 a pound. How much of the latter
material will be needed to produce the mixture?

Solution:

First step: $1.12 minus $1.16 = minus .04.
                 Minus 4 times 374 (374 lb.)
                 = minus 1496.   Loss = 1496

Second step: $1.12 minus $1.02 = .10.   Gain =   10

Third step: 1496 (loss) divided by 10 (gain) = $149\frac{6}{10}$

Conclusion: A mixture costing $1.12 a
pound could therefore be
produced by mixing the
materials as follows:

374 lb. of the material
costing $1.16 per lb.   = $433.84

$149\frac{6}{10}$ lb. of the material
costing $1.02 per lb.   =   152.59

_____   _____

$523\frac{6}{10}$ lb.   = $586.43

Proof: $586.43 divided by 523.6 = $1.12.

WHEN A SPECIFIED QUANTITY OF MATERIAL COST-
ING "LESS" PER UNIT OF MEASUREMENT THAN
THE DESIRED MIXTURE IS TO BE USED WITH TWO
MATERIALS COSTING "MORE" THAN THE DESIRED
MIXTURE, AND IN EQUAL PROPORTION:

Example 3: A manufacturer has 120 pounds of material
costing 70 cents a pound, which he plans to use in a mixture, the materials of which are to cost him $1.00 a pound.
Along with the 70-cent material are to be used, in equal
quantities, a material costing $1.15 a pound and a mate-
rial costing $1.05 a pound. How many pounds of each of
the last-mentioned materials will be used in the mixture?

Solution:

First step: $1.00 minus $0.70 = .30; 30 times 120
(120 lb.) = 3600.   Gain = 3600.

Second step: $1.00 minus $1.15 = minus .15;
$1.00 minus $1.05 = minus .05;
Minus 15 plus minus 5 = minus 20.

Total loss = 20
Average loss = 10

Third step: 3600 (gain) divided by 10 (average
loss) = 360. The loss of 360 must now
be equally divided between the two
products—that is, the one costing
$1.15 a pound, and the other costing
$1.05 a pound. In other words, it will
be necessary to use 180 pounds of each
of the two materials.

Conclusion: A mixture costing $1.00 a pound could
therefore be produced by mixing the
materials as follows:

120 lb. of the material costing
$0.70 per lb.   = $ 84.00
180 lb. of the material costing
1.15 per lb.   = 207.00
180 lb. of the material costing
1.05 per lb.   = 189.00

480 lb.   = $480.00

Proof: $480.00 divided by 480 = $1.00.

WHEN A SPECIFIED QUANTITY OF MATERIAL COST-
ING "LESS" PER UNIT OF MEASUREMENT THAN
THE DESIRED MIXTURE IS TO BE USED WITH TWO
MATERIALS COSTING "MORE" THAN THE DESIRED
MIXTURE, AND IN THE PROPORTION OF 3 TO 1:

Example 4: One hundred pounds of a material costing $2.00 a pound are to be used along with 3 parts of a material costing $2.35 a pound to 1 part of a material costing $2.70 a pound, to produce a mixture costing $2.30 a pound. What quantities of the 3-to-1 materials will need to be used?

Solution:

First step: $2.30 minus $2.00 = .30; 30 times 100
               (100 lb.) = 3000.   Gain = 3000

Second step: $2.30 minus $2.70 = minus
              .40; minus 40 times 1
              (1 lb.)   = minus 40
              $2.30 minus $2.35 = minus
              .05; minus 5 times 3
              (3 lb.)   = minus 15

                        ─────────────────
              Total loss =   55
              Average loss = $13\frac{3}{4}$*

Third step: 3000 (gain) divided by $13\frac{3}{4}$ (average
              loss) = 218. Since two of the materials
              are to be used in the proportion of 3
              parts of the $2.35 quality to 1 part of
              the $2.70 quality, we now divide 218
              by 4, which gives us $54\frac{1}{2}$. And it is
              clear that we will need to use $163\frac{1}{2}$ lb.
              of the $2.35 material with $54\frac{1}{2}$ lb. of
              the $2.70 material.

─────────────────
* The "loss" on one pound of the $2.70 material is 40, and the loss on three pounds of the $2.35 material is 15; therefore, the loss on four pounds of both materials used in the specified proportion is 55, or $13\frac{3}{4}$ per pound.

Conclusion: The mixture will therefore be as follows:
100 lb. of the material costing
  $2.00 per lb.   = $200.00
$163\frac{1}{2}$ lb. of the material costing $2.35 per lb.   = 384.22
$54\frac{1}{2}$ lb. of the material costing $2.70 per lb.   = 147.15

_____   _____

318 lb.   = $731.37

Proof: $731.37 divided by 318 = $2.30.

SUMMARY

Example 1: The step-by-step procedure was comparatively simple. Neither of the two conditions common to
the other problems obtained here. That is, no specified
quantity of any material was to be used, and no materials
were to be used in any particular proportion. So under
the first step to the solution, we dealt with the materials
costing *less* per unit of measurement than the desired mixture; and under the second step, with the material costing
more than the desired mixture.

Also, since none of the materials was to be used in a
specified quantity, we used, under the first step, one
pound as the basis of computation.

Example 2: A definite quantity of material was specified.
Since the second step to the solution is used as a guide for
computing under the third step the *unknown* quantities,
it is understandable that the *known* quantities should be
disposed of under the first step.

Example 3: Here, too, a definite quantity of material was to be used in the mixture. So, as in Problem 2, the known quantity was dealt with under the first step, and the unknown quantities under the second step. It is important to observe that under the third step, in dividing the gain by the loss, we arrived at the *total* weight of the two materials dealt with under the second step. Since the two materials were to be used in equal proportion, 360 (the total) was divided by 2.

Example 4: This problem is similar to that in Example 3. A specified quantity of material was to be used, and two other materials were to be mixed in a certain proportion. The only difference is that, instead of being in equal proportion, the two materials in this instance were to be used in the ratio of 3 to 1.

Thus, while in Example 3, where the materials are used in equal proportion, we divided the total loss by 2 to obtain the average loss, here, the ratio being 3 to 1, we divided the total loss by 4 (since 3 plus 1 equals 4) to obtain the average loss.

And, while in Example 3, where the proportion was equal, we divided 360 (the figure obtained under the third step) by 2, here, the ratio being 3 to 1, we divided 218 (the figure obtained under the third step) by 4, apportioning three fourths of 218 to the one material and one fourth to the other.

It is interesting to note that it makes no difference whether the gain is determined in the first step and the loss in the second, or vice versa. It should be remembered, however, that the larger number is always divided by the smaller number; thus, while in Examples 1, 3 and 4, the gain was divided by the loss, in Example 2 the loss was divided by the gain.

It is a fascinating study—this subject of mixtures—and a rereading of this article will make it seem not nearly so difficult as it may appear after the first reading.

Problems

1. It is desired to make a mixture of two materials—one costing $3.40 a pound, the other $3.95 a pound. If the cost of the materials used in the mixture is to be $3.75 a pound, in what proportion should the materials be mixed?

> *Ans.* 1 pound of the $3.40 material to $1\frac{3}{4}$ pounds of the $3.95 material.

2. A mixture is to be made of three materials which cost, respectively, $2.00, $2.40 and $2.85 a pound. If the cost of the finished product is to be $2.60 a pound, in what proportion should the three materials be used?

> *Ans.* One pound of the $2.00 material, one pound of the $2.40 material, and $3\frac{1}{5}$ pounds of the $2.85 material.

3. A manufacturer has 226 pounds of a product costing $1.84 a pound. He wishes to use this entire quantity along with another product to make a mixture costing $2.20 a pound. If the other material costs $2.35 a pound, how many pounds of it should be used?

> *Ans.* 542.4 pounds.

4. If the situation in the preceding problem were reversed, the 226 pounds costing $2.35 a pound and the other material $1.84 a pound, how many pounds of the $1.84 material should be used with the 226 pounds? *Ans.* $94\frac{1}{6}$ pounds.

5. Two materials—one weighing 83 pounds and costing $2.10 a pound, the other weighing 120 pounds and costing $1.30 a pound—are to be used with a third material costing $4.20 a pound, to produce a mixture costing $2.80 a pound. How many pounds of the $4.20 material will be needed to produce the desired mixture?

> *Ans.* 170 pounds.

6. Two materials—one weighing 125 pounds and costing $2.00 a pound, the other weighing 64 pounds and costing $5.00 a pound—

are to be mixed with a third material costing $4.00 a pound, to produce a mixture costing $3.50 a pound. How much of the third material should be used? (Hint: Even though one of the materials to be used in a specified quantity—the one costing $5.00 a pound—exceeds the price of the mixture, it may be included along with the material costing $2.00 a pound under the first step; in other words, the minus quantity representing the $5.00 material will be deducted from the plus quantity representing the $2.00 material, and the difference will represent the gain.) *Ans.* 183 pounds.

7. Three pounds of a material costing $3.00 a pound are to be used with two pounds of a material costing $4.00 a pound, along with a third material costing $8.00 a pound and in a quantity to be determined, to make a mixture costing $6.50 a pound. How many pounds of the third material should be used to produce the desired mixture? *Ans.* $10\frac{1}{3}$ pounds.

8. Two hundred pounds of a material costing $1.80 a pound are to be part of a mixture costing $2.40 a pound. Two other materials are to be used in the following proportion: 5 pounds of a material costing $3.00 a pound for every 3 pounds of a material costing $2.60 a pound. What quantities of the last-mentioned products will be needed?

Ans. $166\frac{2}{3}$ pounds of the $3.00 material and 100 pounds of the $2.60 material.

9. Sixty pounds of a product costing $2.30 a pound are to be used with two other materials to produce a mixture costing $3.00 a pound. How many pounds of each of these other materials will be required if they are to be used in the proportion of 2 to 1 and cost, respectively, $3.60 and $3.90 a pound?

Ans. 40 pounds of the $3.60 material and 20 pounds of the $3.90 material.

10. Eighty pounds of a material costing 90 cents a pound and 40 pounds of a material costing $1.00 a pound are to be mixed with three other materials to form a product costing $1.40 a pound. The other three materials, which are to be mixed in the proportion of 3, 2 and 1, cost, respectively, $1.70, $1.60 and $1.50 a pound. How many pounds of each will be required to produce the desired mixture?

Ans. 120 pounds of the $1.70 material, 80 pounds of the $1.60 material, and 40 pounds of the $1.50 material.

84. **How to Determine Proportionate Values, Dimensions of Reductions and Enlargements, etc.** One of the commonest sources of headaches to many businessmen is the subject of proportion. A merchant, for example, receiving an offer of a piece of property in exchange for his present property, may want to make a comparison on a square-foot basis. A manufacturer who has purchased a casting which weighs 160 pounds may want to know the exact cost of another casting weighing 288 pounds. Or a farmer, finding that 223 pounds of milk produced 7 pounds of butter fat, may want to determine the quantity of milk required to produce, let us say, 44 pounds of butter fat. These are just a few of virtually countless kinds of problems which can be solved easily and quickly by simple proportion.

Proportion means the relation of one to another. And when we speak of the relation which the value of one number has to another, we are referring to the ratio of the two numbers. Thus the relation of 50 to 100 can be expressed by the ratio of 1 to 2 (written 1:2), because 50 is $\frac{1}{2}$ of 100. Similarly, the relation of 25 to 100 can be expressed by the ratio of 1 to 4, or 1:4; the relation of 7 to 21 by the ratio 1 to 3, or 1:3; the relation of 6 to 9 by the ratio 2 to 3, or 2:3.

As will be seen from the foregoing, the ratio of two numbers consists of the fraction which results from the division of one number by the other. Thus the relation of 50 to 100 is represented by the ratio 1:2 because, as has been pointed out, $\frac{50}{100}$ is equivalent to $\frac{1}{2}$. Similarly, the relation of $\frac{25}{100}$ is expressed by the ratio 1:4 because $\frac{25}{100}$ is equivalent to $\frac{1}{4}$. And the relation of 160 to 288 (the weights of the two castings referred to in the first paragraph) can be expressed by the ratio 5:9, since $\frac{5}{9}$ is the fraction obtained from $\frac{160}{288}$ by cancellation.

When we speak of the relation between two equal ratios we speak of them as being in proportion. Thus $\frac{50}{100}$ is in proportion or is equivalent to $\frac{200}{400}$. Reason? 50 divided by 100 equals $\frac{1}{2}$, and 200 divided by 400 equals $\frac{1}{2}$. It is clear, then, that 50:100 equals 200:400, which is read "50 is to 100 as 200 is to 400."

Example 1: A businessman owning 3 lofts of 2500 square feet each is offered a plant of 12,000 square feet in exchange. What is the ratio of the sum of the areas of the three lofts to the area of the plant?

Solution: The sum of the areas of the 3 lofts is 7500 square feet.

The ratio, therefore, is $\dfrac{7500}{12,000}$, which is equivalent to $\frac{5}{8}$.

Ans. 7500:12,000 = 5:8.

In the example just worked, the equivalent ratio was obtained automatically and with very little effort, because it was simply a matter of canceling one number into the other. Frequently, however, one of the values in the equivalent ratio is predetermined, and it is necessary to calculate the fourth value. Thus, to use a simple illustration, if we were to solve the problem: What ratio having 10 as the denominator is equal to the fraction $\frac{2}{4}$, we would write, using x as the unknown quantity, 2:4 = x:10, or $\dfrac{2}{4} = \dfrac{x}{10}$.

Attention is now called to a very interesting rule in connection with ratios and proportion, which reads, "In any fractional equation the product of the means equals the product of the extremes." This has already been discussed in Art. 39 ("How To Find the Rate Per Cent"), to which the reader is urged to refer for further study. It is interesting to observe that "the product of the means equals the product of the extremes" is another way of saying that in any equation (e.g., $\frac{2}{4} = \frac{5}{10}$), the numerator of the first fraction multiplied by the denominator of the second fraction (2 times 10 in the example just cited) equals the product of the denominator of the first fraction multiplied by the numerator of the second fraction (4 times 5 in the same example). So that to solve the problem in the preceding paragraph, we would simply divide 20 (the product of 2 times 10) by $4x$ (4 times x) to find the value of one x which, of course, is 5. In other words, $2:4 = 5:10$, or $\frac{2}{4} = \frac{5}{10}$.

The process of finding proportionate values is similar to that of finding the rate per cent (see Art. 39). The only difference is that instead of finding the new value in relation to 100, it is found in relation to the number indicated. Thus in the case of the manufacturer who wanted to know the cost of a casting weighing 288 pounds, the fourth value would be 288; and in the case of the farmer who wished to determine the number of pounds of milk that would be required to produce 44 pounds of butter fat, the fourth value would be 44.

Example 2: A manufacturer pays $11.25 for a casting weighing 160 pounds. He wishes to purchase another casting weighing 288 pounds. What will the cost be of the larger casting?

Solution: $\dfrac{\$11.25}{160} = \dfrac{x}{288}$

160 times x (the product of the
means) $= 160x$

288 times $11.25 (the product of the
extremes) $= \$3240$

Since the product of the means
equals the product of the extremes,
$160x$ equals $3240.

Therefore, $1x$ equals $3240 divided
by 160. $3240 divided by 160 $= \$20.25$

Ans. $20.25.

Example 3: If 223 pounds of milk produce 7 pounds of
butter fat, how many pounds of milk may be expected to
produce 44 pounds of butter fat?

Solution: $\dfrac{223}{7} = \dfrac{x}{44}$

7 times x (the product of the means) $= 7x$

223 times 44 (the product of the extremes) $= 9812$

$7x$ equals 9812. Therefore $1x$ $= 1401\frac{5}{7}$

Ans. $1401\frac{5}{7}$ pounds.

A type of proportion which is a little different from that
discussed thus far is one in which several parts have
definite relations to each other. A man, for instance, be-
queaths his estate to four sons—Walter, John, Henry and
Bill—stipulating that their portions be in the relation of
1, 2, 3 and 4, respectively. The net amount of his estate,

after all taxes, etc., have been paid, is $20,000. What is
the exact amount received by each son?

It is but necessary to add the relative parts of the
estate, and then to compute the fractional part to which
each son is entitled. The sum of the relative parts is the
sum of 1, 2, 3 and 4, which is 10. The part received by
each son will, therefore, be as follows:

Walter	$\frac{1}{10}$ of $20,000 =	$ 2000
John	$\frac{2}{10}$ of 20,000 =	4000
Henry	$\frac{3}{10}$ of 20,000 =	6000
Bill	$\frac{4}{10}$ of 20,000 =	8000

$$\frac{10}{10} \text{ of } \$20,000 = \$20000$$

Example 4: A product weighing 272 pounds is to be
divided into 4 parts in the proportion of 1, 3, 5 and 8.
Compute the weight of each of the 4 parts.

Solution: The sum of the relative parts is 17. The 4
divisions will, therefore, be as follows:

First part	$\frac{1}{17}$ of 272 pounds =	16 pounds
Second part	$\frac{3}{17}$ of 272 pounds =	48 pounds
Third part	$\frac{5}{17}$ of 272 pounds =	80 pounds
Fourth part	$\frac{8}{17}$ of 272 pounds =	128 pounds

$$\frac{17}{17} \text{ of } 272 \text{ pounds} = 272 \text{ pounds}$$

Estimating Dimensions of Reductions. It is sometimes
necessary to estimate the dimensions to which a picture
or photograph should be reduced for the purpose of order-
ing a photo-engraving or otherwise providing a specified
space in an advertisement or other printed matter. In re-

ducing small surfaces, like pictures, the procedure is very simple. A sheet of paper is cut to the size of the picture, or the space occupied by the picture is ruled off on a sheet of paper. A diagonal line is then drawn from the top left hand corner to the bottom right hand corner. Now the required width is marked off on the top line, from left to right, or the required height is marked off on the vertical line at the left—according to which of the two dimensions is more important. A line is then drawn from the point thus marked (vertically or horizontally, as the case may be) to the opposite border. This will result in an intersection of the diagonal line. A line is now drawn from this point of intersection in the other direction (horizontally to the left, or vertically to the top, as the case may be). A new figure has now been formed representing the desired reduction. A reduction of a picture 3 inches wide by 2 inches high to a width of $2\frac{1}{4}$ inches would, therefore, be indicated by the following markings.

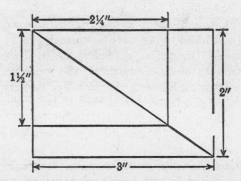

Note that the height of the reduction is $1\frac{1}{2}$ inches. This figure could have been easily determined by the equation $2:3 = x:2\frac{1}{4}$. However, it is not always practical to determine reductions of pictures and photographs mathematically, as dimensions often include cumbersome fractions of an inch. The simplest and quickest way for all practical purposes, and the way which is least subject to error, is to use the diagonal-line method.

The subject of proportion plays a very important part in the business of sign making. An artist, for example, is asked to make up a panel 8 feet high by 16 inches wide. It obviously would be unwise to start off by sketching on a sheet of these dimensions. A more practical way would be to "reduce to scale." The scale is determined by the minimum amount of paper needed to make a miniature which, other requirements being satisfied, would serve as a guide in the preparation of the final design.

One important fact should always be borne in mind in reducing the size of any square-cornered surface: the width must be reduced in exactly the same proportion as the height, and vice versa. Thus if it is desired to reduce the aforementioned 8-foot panel to 8 inches, which is equivalent to reducing it to one twelfth, the width, too, should be reduced to one twelfth—namely, to $1\frac{1}{3}$ inches.

Estimating Dimensions of Enlargements. To estimate the dimensions of an enlargement, the procedure is the reverse of that explained in the preceding paragraphs.

Suppose, for instance, it is desired to know what space would be occupied in an advertisement by an enlargement to a width of $3\frac{1}{4}$ inches of a photograph $1\frac{3}{4}$ inches wide by 1 inch high.

A rectangle, as illustrated, would be drawn, $1\frac{3}{4}$ inches wide by 1 inch high, with an extended top horizontal line, an extended left vertical line, and an extended diagonal line. The line at the top is then marked off at $3\frac{1}{4}$ inches, and a vertical line drawn from that point to intersect the diagonal line. Now a horizontal line is drawn from the intersection of the diagonal line to the left vertical line. Measuring the height of this enlarged line at the left (that is, from the top to the point of intersection made by the bottom horizontal line) we find that it is just about $1\frac{7}{8}$ inches, which approximate figure, for practical purposes, would in all probability be good enough.

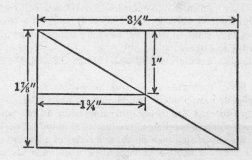

Problems

★ 1. What is the ratio of 12 quarts to 18 gallons?   *Ans.* 1:6.

★ 2. If the scale to a map is $\frac{3}{8}$ of an inch to 25 miles, how many miles would be represented by $1\frac{1}{2}$ inches?   *Ans.* 100 miles.

3. When water freezes it expands 9% of its volume. Compute the number of cubic feet of water needed to make $381\frac{1}{2}$ cubic feet of ice. (Hint: Start with the ratio $381\frac{1}{2}$:109.)   *Ans.* 350 cubic feet.

4. If broken rock occupies 80% more space than solid rock, approximately how many cubic yards of solid rock will, when broken, occupy a space of 432 cubic yards? (Hint: Start with the ratio 100:180.)   *Ans.* Approximately 240 cubic yards.

5. The space occupied by a motor truck completely knocked down is 188 cubic feet, which is 65% of the space occupied by the truck when completely assembled. On this basis how many cubic feet would be occupied by 10 similar motor trucks completely assembled? Compute the answer to the nearest whole cubic foot.

Ans. 2892 cubic feet. (*Arts.* 79, 73)

6. Carbon dioxide is made up of 3 parts of carbon to 8 parts of oxygen by weight. Estimate the relative weights of these elements in $38\frac{1}{2}$ grams of the gas.

Ans. $10\frac{1}{2}$ grams of carbon and 28 grams of oxygen.

7. A feed mixture of 40 pounds bone meal, 40 pounds ground limestone and 20 pounds common salt is a good source of calcium and phosphorus for livestock. How many pounds of bone meal would be required to make 360 pounds of this feed mixture?

Ans. 144 pounds.

8. Five men enter into partnership as follows: A invests $3000, B $2000, C $4000, D $5000, and E $6000. If the profit is to be shared in the ratio of capitals, what will be each partner's share of a profit amounting to $16,820?

Ans. A will receive $2523, B $1682, C $3364, D $4205, and E $5046.

★ **9.** Seven men are put to work assembling instruments. Four are skilled and can produce 4 units each per hour. Each of the other 3 men can produce 3 units per hour. How many hours would it take the 7 men working together to produce 1000 units? *Ans.* 40 hours.

★ **10.** An advertising man planning a series of advertisements for a client orders a photo-engraving to be made of a photograph 6 inches wide by 8 inches deep, the width to be reduced to $4\frac{1}{2}$ inches. Compute mentally the depth of the reduction.   *Ans.* 6 inches.

85. Proportion in Reverse.

A type of proportion problem different from those discussed in the preceding article, and one which can be quickly worked by simple reasoning, is the following: If a certain quantity of work can be done by 7 girls in 30 hours, in how many hours could the same amount of work be done by 10 girls?

It is obvious that we cannot proceed by the method outlined in Art. 84. But the problem is really very simple. Let us see.

It is understandable that 7 girls will do 7 times as much work in 30 hours as one girl. So that 7 girls in 30 hours will do the equivalent of 210 man-hours of work. Using this figure as a basis, and assuming that each girl works independently of the others, it is easy to compute the number of hours in which the same work can be done by virtually any number of girls, simply by dividing the number of girls into 210 hours. Thus 4 girls can do the same work in $\frac{210}{4}$ hours, or $52\frac{1}{2}$ hours; 5 girls, in $\frac{210}{5}$ hours, or 42 hours; 6 girls, in $\frac{210}{6}$ hours, or 35 hours; and 10 girls, in $\frac{210}{10}$ hours, or 21 hours.

Example: A contractor agrees to do a job in 80 working days, and hires 6 men to work on the project five days a week. At the end of the fourth week he finds that the men have done only one sixth of the job. How many additional men will the contractor need to hire in order that the work may be completed in the agreed-upon time?

Solution: Six men in 20 days do one sixth of the job.

Therefore, the remaining five sixths of the job will take 6 men 5 times 20 days, or 100 days.

So that the remaining five sixths of the job represents 600 man-days of work (6 men working 100 days equals 600 man-days).

The question now is, how many men will be needed to do 600 man-days of work in 60 days (60 days being the remainder of the contract period).

And the answer is obtained simply by dividing 600 (the number of man-days) by 60 (the number of days), which gives us 10.

Ten men will be required to complete the work in the remaining 60 days, and it will therefore be necessary for the contractor to hire 4 additional men.

PROBLEMS

★ **1.** If a supply of feed will last 25 days for 40 hens, how long would it last if the number of hens was increased to 50? (Hint: Divide the product of 40 times 25 by 50.)   *Ans.* 20 days.

2. An airplane flying at a speed of 220 miles an hour can cover a specified distance in 5 hours. How long would it take another plane flying at a speed of 185 miles an hour to cover the same distance? Compute the answer to the nearest quarter of an hour.

Ans. 6 hours. (*Art.* 73)

3. A contractor agrees to do a job in 30 days. After 6 days he finds that the 8 men assigned to the work have done one third of the job. How many men can he afford to assign to other work with the assurance that the job will be completed on time by the remaining men?   *Ans.* 4 men can be assigned to other work.

86. The Difference Between "Reduce by" and "Reduce to." These are two of the most misunderstood terms in the English language. Since they are directly connected with the subject of proportion, a word to clarify their meaning will not be amiss.

To reduce *by* one third means to subtract *one third*. To reduce *to* one third means that only one third is to remain; in other words, to subtract *two* thirds. The following examples will serve to illustrate.

6 inches reduced *by* one third means 6 inches minus 2 inches, or 4 inches.

6 inches reduced *to* one third means one third of 6 inches, or 2 inches.

8 inches reduced *to* one fourth means one fourth of 8 inches, or 2 inches.

12 feet reduced *by* one fourth means 12 feet minus 3 feet, or 9 feet.

15 feet reduced *to* one fifth means one fifth of 15 feet, or 3 feet.

24 reduced *by* one sixth means 24 minus 4, or 20.

50 reduced *by* two fifths means 50 minus 20, or 30.

63 reduced *to* four ninths, means four ninths of 63, or 28.

PROBLEMS

★ 1. Reduce 36 by one ninth.   *Ans.* 32.

★ 2. Reduce 45 by one fifth.   *Ans.* 36.

★ 3. Reduce 720 to one sixth.   *Ans.* 120.

★ 4. Reduce 330 to two elevenths.   *Ans.* 60.

★ 5. Reduce 560 by three eighths.   *Ans.* 350.

★ 6. Reduce $24.60 to two thirds.   *Ans.* $16.40.

★ 7. Reduce $96.00 by two thirds.   *Ans.* $32.00.

★ 8. Reduce 4.27 by one seventh.   *Ans.* 3.66.

★ 9. Reduce 88.4 to one fourth.   *Ans.* 22.1.

★ 10. Reduce 1.2 to one tenth.   *Ans.* .12.

★ 11. A catalogue states, "Illustrations $\frac{7}{8}$ actual size." Does this mean that the actual size was reduced *by* $\frac{1}{8}$ or *to* $\frac{1}{8}$?   *Ans.* By $\frac{1}{8}$.

★ 12. If the price of a fabric which formerly sold at $4.00 a yard now sells at $3.50 a yard, by what fraction was the former price reduced?   *Ans.* By $\frac{1}{8}$.

★ 13. A company's imports in one year were valued at $10,000. Its imports the following year amounted to $2000. To what fraction of its imports in the former year were the imports reduced in the year that followed?   *Ans.* To $\frac{1}{5}$.

★ 14. As a result of time lost by striking, a workman's earnings one month were reduced to one third of that in the preceding month, in which he earned $240.00. How much did he earn during the strike month?   *Ans.* $80.00.

★ 15. A company reduced the size of one of its packages to 14 ounces. If this constitutes a reduction by one eighth of the previous size, what was the previous size?   *Ans.* 16 ounces.

★ 16. A peanut harvester reduces by seven eighths the labor required to harvest peanuts. How long would it take with the aid of this machine to do the work which formerly required 56 man-hours of labor?   *Ans.* 7 hours.

CHAPTER XV

PROFIT RATIOS

With a mental conception of the mathematical relation of profit to cost price and profit to selling price, the subject of profit ratios becomes uniquely simple. It will be our objective in this chapter to gain an acquaintance with the method that will provide us with this mental conception.

87. How to Determine Instantly the Ratio of Profit to Selling Price, Given the Ratio of Profit to Cost Price. The matter of determining profit ratios would not seem nearly so difficult if we thought of it as simple addition or subtraction. If we add $1.00 to $2.00, the $1.00 added constitutes one third of the total. Let us now look upon these amounts as cost price and profit, respectively—the $2.00 representing cost, and the $1.00 representing profit. It is clear that the profit of $1.00 is one third of the selling price. In other words, the ratio of profit to selling price is 1 to 3.

This may seem very simple. But could the reader say without hesitation what is the ratio to the selling price of a profit of $\frac{2}{5}$ of the cost price? This, admittedly, calls for a little more concentration. By a very simple method, however, any ratio of this nature can be determined in a matter of seconds.

When we speak of a $\frac{2}{5}$ profit on the cost price we mean, of course, two parts profit for every five parts of cost. Thus if an item costs \$5.00, a $\frac{2}{5}$ profit on the cost would be \$2.00, and the selling price would be \$7.00. Notice the interesting relation between the selling price and the numbers in the fraction representing the profit on the cost. The profit of $\frac{2}{5}$ on the cost price becomes $\frac{2}{7}$ of the selling price because 2 (the numerator in the fraction representing the profit on the cost price) plus 5 (the denominator) equals 7. In the same way, a $\frac{3}{5}$ profit on the cost price equals a profit of $\frac{3}{8}$ of the selling price. And a profit of $\frac{1}{7}$ on the cost price is equivalent to a profit of $\frac{1}{8}$ of the selling price.

The following graphic illustration of what we have just discussed will help toward a thorough understanding of this principle.

Ratio of Profit to Cost Price	Ratio of Profit to Selling Price
$\frac{2}{5}$	$\frac{2}{5 \text{ plus } 2} = \frac{2}{7}$
$\frac{3}{5}$	$\frac{3}{5 \text{ plus } 3} = \frac{3}{8}$
$\frac{1}{7}$	$\frac{1}{7 \text{ plus } 1} = \frac{1}{8}$

No attempt should be made to memorize the ratios, as a clear understanding of the explanation makes this entirely unnecessary.

Problems

Find the ratio of profit to the selling price when the ratio of the profit to the cost price is:

★ 1. $\frac{1}{2}$ (50%)   Ans. $\frac{1}{3}$.
★ 2. $\frac{1}{3}$ Ans. $\frac{1}{4}$.
★ 3. 25% ($\frac{1}{4}$)   Ans. $\frac{1}{5}$.
★ 4. 20%   Ans. $\frac{1}{6}$.
★ 5. $66\frac{2}{3}$% ($\frac{2}{3}$)   Ans. $\frac{2}{5}$.
★ 6. 40%   Ans. $\frac{2}{7}$.
★ 7. 15% ($\frac{15}{100}$)   Ans. $\frac{15}{115}$ or $\frac{3}{23}$.
★ 8. 35%   Ans. $\frac{7}{27}$.

88. How to Determine Instantly the Ratio of Profit to Cost Price, Given the Ratio of Profit to Selling Price. The method of procedure here is exactly the reverse of that in the preceding article. Here, instead of going forward, from cost price to selling price, we move backward, from selling price to cost price. In other words, instead of increasing the second term in the ratio of the profit to the selling price, it is reduced; it is reduced by subtracting the value representing the first term, as will be seen in the following illustration:

Ratio of Profit to Selling Price	*Ratio of Profit to Cost Price*
$\dfrac{2}{7}$	$\dfrac{2}{7 \text{ minus } 2} = \dfrac{2}{5}$
$\dfrac{3}{8}$	$\dfrac{3}{8 \text{ minus } 3} = \dfrac{3}{5}$
$\dfrac{1}{8}$	$\dfrac{1}{8 \text{ minus } 1} = \dfrac{1}{7}$

PROBLEMS

Find the ratio of profit to the cost when the ratio of the profit to the selling price is:

★ 1. $\frac{1}{6}$ *Ans.* $\frac{1}{5}$.

★ 2. $\frac{1}{9}$ *Ans.* $\frac{1}{8}$.

★ 3. $\frac{3}{8}$ *Ans.* $\frac{3}{5}$.

★ 4. 25%   *Ans.* $\frac{1}{3}$ or $33\frac{1}{3}\%$.

★ 5. 35% ($\frac{35}{100}$)   *Ans.* $\frac{35}{65}$ or $\frac{7}{13}$.

★ 6. $\frac{1}{2}$ *Ans.* $\frac{1}{1}$ or 100%.

89. How to Find the Selling Price, Given the Cost Price and the Per Cent of Profit on the Selling Price. When the cost price is \$80.00, and the profit 20 per cent of the selling price, what is the selling price? A brief glance at these figures tells us that the selling price is \$100.00. But why is it \$100.00? Let us see.

We are told that the profit is 20 per cent of the selling price. Now, since the selling price is made up of two things—cost price and profit—it is clear that if the profit is 20 per cent of the selling price, the cost inevitably constitutes the rest of the selling price—namely, 80 per cent, for 100 per cent minus 20 per cent equals 80 per cent.

Knowing the exact amount of the cost, and knowing also that this amount represents 80 per cent of the selling price, we need but to find the relative value of 20 per cent and add it to the cost price, to determine the selling price.

Example 1: The cost price of a product is \$60.00. If it is desired to make a profit of 25% on the selling price, what should the selling price be?

Solution: If the profit is to be 25% of the selling price,
　　　　　the cost price ($60.00) will represent 75%
　　　　　of the selling price.

75% of selling price　　　　　　　　　　= $60.00
25% of selling price ($\frac{25}{75}$, or $\frac{1}{3}$, of $60.00) =　20.00
_____

100% of selling price　　　　　　　　　= $80.00

Ans. Selling price is $80.00.

Example 2: If the cost price is $84.00 and the profit is
to be 30% of the selling price, what should the selling
price be?

Solution: If the profit is to be 30% of the selling price,
　　　　　the cost price ($84.00) will represent 70%
　　　　　of the selling price.

70% of selling price　　　　　　　= $ 84.00
30% of selling price ($\frac{3}{7}$ of $84.00) =　36.00
_____

100% of selling price　　　　　　　= $120.00

Ans. Selling price is $120.00.

Example 3: The profit on an item is to be 32% of the
selling price. If the cost is $140.25, what will the selling
price be?

Solution: If the profit is to be 32% of the selling price,
　　　　　the cost will be 68% of the selling price.

68% of selling price　　　　　　　　　= $140.25
32% of selling price ($\frac{32}{68}$, or $\frac{8}{17}$, of $140.25) =　66.00
_____

100% of selling price　　　　　　　　= $206.25

Ans. Selling price is $206.25.

PROBLEMS

★ **1.** A jobber plans to dispose of miscellaneous products which cost him a total of $280.00. If he is to make a profit of 20% of the selling price, for how much should this merchandise be sold?

Ans. $350.00.

2. A dealer pays $126.00 for a rug. He decides to make a profit of 30% of the selling price. For how much should he sell the rug?

Ans. $180.00.

3. A grocer sells a food specialty costing him $180.00 per gross packages, and makes a profit of 25% of the selling price. How much does he receive per gross packages? *Ans.* $240.00.

4. A toy manufacturer makes an average profit of 38% of his sales. If his costs in a month amount to $1550.00, what is the sales value of the toys produced in that period? *Ans.* $2500.00.

★ **5.** An electrical device costing $27.50 is to bring a profit of $33\frac{1}{3}\%$ of the selling price. What should the selling price be?

Ans. $41.25.

90. How to Find the Cost Price, Given the Selling Price and the Per Cent of Profit on the Selling Price. If an article sells for $100.00 at a profit of 25 per cent of the selling price, what is the cost price?

Since the selling price is made up of two things—cost price and profit—and since the profit is 25 per cent of the selling price, it is obvious that the cost price will be 75 per cent of the selling price, for 100 per cent minus 25 per cent equals 75 per cent. Seventy-five per cent of $100.00 equals $75.00. So that the cost price is $75.00.

Example 1: An item sells for $90.00, and the profit is $33\frac{1}{3}\%$ of the selling price. What is the cost?

Solution: If the profit is $33\frac{1}{3}\%$ of the selling price, the cost represents $66\frac{2}{3}\%$ of the selling price.

$66\frac{2}{3}\%$ of $90.00 = $60.00.

Ans. Cost price is $60.00.

Example 2: If a product is sold for $175.00 and the profit is 35% of the selling price, how much is the cost price?

Solution: The cost price is 65% of the selling price.

65% of $175.00 = $113.75.

Ans. Cost price is $113.75.

Example 3: An item sells for $73.50 and the profit is 28% of the selling price. What does the item cost?

Solution: The cost is 72% of the selling price.

72% of $73.50 = $52.92.

Ans. Cost price is $52.92.

PROBLEMS

★ **1.** A manufacturer of a stationery specialty makes a profit of 30% of the selling price. If he sells the product for $1.60, what does it cost him? *Ans.* $1.12.

2. If the total amount realized from the sale of a job lot of merchandise was $300.00, and the profit was 18% of this amount, how much did the merchandise cost? *Ans.* $246.00. (*Art.* 35)

3. An importer makes an average profit of $37\frac{1}{2}$% of his sales. If his sales for the year amounted to $14,248.00, approximately how much did he pay for the merchandise sold?

Ans. $8,905.00. (*Art.* 34)

4. A woolens dealer's total sales for the day amounted to $620.00. If his average profit is 36% of the selling price, what was the approximate cost of the merchandise sold?

Ans. $396.80. (*Art.* 4)

5. A building was sold for $27,500, on which amount a profit of 28% was made. How much did the building cost?

Ans. $19,800. (*Art.* 35)

91. How to Find the Per-Cent Equivalent of a Specified Profit, Given the Cost or Selling Price. If a profit of $10.00 is made on a sale of $100.00, how much is the per

cent of profit on the selling price? We know instantly
that the answer is 10 per cent, for $10.00 is one tenth of
$100.00, and one tenth is equivalent to 10 per cent.

But suppose the sale amounted to $168.00, and the
profit to $21.00, how much per cent of the selling price
would the profit be then? It is really very simple. Just as
we divided $10.00 by $100.00 in the preceding problem to
get one tenth, here we would divide $21.00 by $168.00 to
get one eighth (by cancellation). The profit is, therefore,
$12\frac{1}{2}\%$ of the selling price since one eighth is equivalent
to $12\frac{1}{2}\%$ (Art. 39).

Not all problems of this nature, however, are solved
quite so easily. For example, to determine the per-cent
equivalent of a profit of $40.20 made on a sale of $268.00
calls for a little extra effort. Nonetheless, this problem
resolves itself simply into finding the equivalent ratio of
$40.20 to $268.00, in which the second term is 100. The
problem, in other words, is one of proportion, which subject we studied in Art. 84. Let us take this as our first
example and follow through the solution.

Example 1: How much per cent of the sale is represented by a profit of $40.20 made on a sale of $268.00?

Solution: $40.20 is to $268.00 as x is to 100.

Since the product of the means equals the
product of the extremes (Art. 39), 40.20
times 100 (the product of the extremes)
equals 268 times x (the product of the
means).

40.20 times 100 = 4020

268 times x = $268x$

$268x$ equals 4020.

Therefore, $1x$ equals 4020 divided by 268, which equals 15.

The profit of $40.20 therefore represents 15% of the selling price.

Example 2: A profit of $55.68 is made on a sale amounting to $174.00. How much per cent profit is that on the selling price?

Solution: $55.68 is to $174.00 as x is to 100.

55.68 times 100 = 5568

174 times x = $174x$

$174x$ equals 5568.

Therefore, $1x$ equals 5568 divided by 174. which equals 32.

The profit of $55.68 therefore represents 32% of the selling price.

Exactly the same method of procedure is applied when the profit is based on the cost rather than on the selling price. Thus:

Example 3: If it is desired to sell an item costing $21.00 for $27.00, how much per cent of the cost price is represented by the profit?

Solution: $6.00 (the profit) is to $21.00 as x is to 100.

6 times 100 = 600

21 times x = $21x$

$21x$ equals 600.

Therefore, $1x$ equals 600 divided by 21, which
equals 28.57.

The profit of $6.00 therefore represents
28.57% of the cost price.

An examination of the above proportions shows that in
each instance the profit is multiplied by 100 and then
divided by the selling price or the cost depending on
which is used as the base (Arts. 96 and 98).

Example 4: A product costs $216.00, and it is planned
to make a profit of $50.00 on the sale. How much per
cent of the cost price would this profit represent?

Solution: 50 times 100 equals 5000. 5000 divided by 216
equals 23.15. The profit of $50.00 therefore
represents 23.15% of the cost price.

PROBLEMS

Estimate in the following problems the rates per cent represented
by the profit on the cost price or the profit on the selling price, as
the case may be:

★ 1. A profit of $13.00 on a cost of $52.00. (Hint: 52 is exactly
divisible by 13.)   *Ans.* 25%.

2. A profit of $78.20 on a cost of $340.00.   *Ans.* 23%.

3. A profit of $38.13 on a cost of $93.00.   *Ans.* 41%.

4. A profit of $77.14 on a cost of $203.00.

Ans. 38%. (*Art.* 73)

5. A profit of $36.12 on a sale of $84.00.   *Ans.* 43%.

6. A profit of $57.77 on a sale of $218.00.   *Ans.* $26\frac{1}{2}$%.

7. A profit of $40.95 on a sale of $126.00.   *Ans.* $32\frac{1}{2}$%.

8. A profit of $143.35 on a sale of $305.00.

Ans. 47%. (*Art.* 73)

9. A profit of $30.78 on a sale of $76.00.   *Ans.* $40\frac{1}{2}$%.

92. The Meaning of Mark-Up and Mark-Down.
Mark-up is the difference between the cost price of an
article and its selling price. Thus the mark-up of a dress
that costs $5.00 and is placed on sale for $8.00 is $3.00.

The term mark-up is used extensively in the retail
trade. Its use is confined practically entirely to articles
sold in the same condition as purchased—that is, without
anything substantial having been added or removed from
them. Furniture, hardware, groceries, drug supplies are
just a few examples. Clothing, even when it undergoes
alterations to fit the wearer, is included.

As illogical as it may seem to the reader unfamiliar
with the subject, it is preferable and customary to calculate the mark-up percentage on the selling price rather
than on the cost price. The reason is that the expenses of
running a business are provided by the sales. In most
retail businesses the difference between the gross profit
and the net profit constitutes a percentage which is more
or less constant. Rent, salaries and wages, and commissions earned by salesmen are some of the principal expenses of running a business, and it is the relation between
the sum of these expenses and the total sales which must
be kept in mind in determining merchandise mark-ups.

Mark-down, on the other hand, has an entirely different
meaning. This term is used to denote a reduction in the
selling price. When, for example, the selling price of an
article has been reduced from $8.50 to $8.00, it is said to
have been marked down.

Mark-up, then, refers to the difference between the
cost price and the selling price. Mark-down refers to the
difference between the reduced selling price and the previous selling price.

93. Calculating Mark-Ups and Mark-Downs. Once the per-cent rate of the desired profit on the selling price has been determined, it is a comparatively simple matter to calculate the equivalent value of the profit in dollars and cents.

In a large degree this subject has already been covered in Art. 89, "How To Find the Selling Price, Given the Cost Price and the Per Cent of Profit on the Selling Price."

Example 1: If a product costs $18.00 how much should it be marked up to allow a profit of 25% on the selling price? (Art. 88)

Solution: A 25% (one fourth) profit on the selling price is equivalent to $33\frac{1}{3}\%$ (one third) on the cost.

$33\frac{1}{3}\%$ (one third) of $18.00 = $6.00

Ans. The mark-up should be $6.00.

Example 2: How much of a mark-up should be given to a product costing $125.00 to allow a profit of 15% on the selling price?

Solution: A profit of 15% ($\frac{15}{100}$) on the selling price is equivalent to $\frac{15}{85}$ on the cost.

$\frac{15}{85}$ of $125.00 = $22.06

Ans. The mark-up should be $22.06.

Mark-downs are always calculated on the selling price. A 15% mark-down, for instance, on a product selling for $5.00 would bring the selling price down to $4.25.

Example 3: An article costing $60.00 was marked up 20%, and then marked down 10%, and sold. How much was received for the article?

Solution: A 20% mark-up is equivalent to 25% of the cost.

Cost	= $60.00
Plus 25%	= 15.00

Original selling price	= 75.00
Less 10% mark-down	= 7.50

Price received on the sale = $67.50

Example 4: A machinery dealer's principal expenses of doing business are an overhead expense of 20% of the selling price, and a salesman's commission of 10%. If it is desired to make a profit of 8% on the selling price, how much should the mark-up be on a machine costing $150.00? Compute the answer to the nearest whole dollar.

Solution: A 20% overhead expense, plus 10% commission, and an 8% profit on the selling price adds up to 38%. And 38% on the selling price is equivalent to $\frac{38}{62}$ on the cost price. $\frac{38}{62}$ of $150.00 = $91.94

Ans. The mark-up should be $92.00.

Note the interesting method of procedure in the following illustration of the solution to a problem which is really two problems in one.

Example 5: A dealer pays $50.00 for a garment on which he wishes to make a profit of 35% on the selling price after making an allowance of 15% to the purchaser. What price should the tag on this garment show?

Solution:

First step: A profit of 35% $(\frac{35}{100})$ on the selling price is equivalent to $\frac{35}{65}$ on the cost price.

Cost	= $50.00
Plus $\frac{35}{65}$ of $50.00	= 26.92

The amount to be received
from the purchaser   = $76.92

Second step: If $76.92 is the amount to be received from the purchaser after a 15% allowance has been made him, $76.92 must be increased by the equivalent of that percentage. To facilitate computation, the amount of $76.92 may conveniently be considered as the cost price, and the 15% a profit on the selling price. Thus: 15% $(\frac{15}{100})$ on the selling price is equivalent to $\frac{15}{85}$ on the cost price.

Cost	= $76.92
$\frac{15}{85}$ of $76.92	= 13.57

| Price on tag | = $90.49 |

Proof: Price on tag   = $90.49
                    Less 15% allowance to pur-
                         chaser   =   13.57
                    _____

                    Amount to be received from
                         purchaser   = $76.92

PROBLEMS

Compute the answers to the following problems:

★ 1. What should the mark-up be on an overcoat costing $36.00, if it is to represent 40% of the selling price? *Ans.* $24.00. (*Art.* 88)

★ 2. If a proprietary medicine costing 24 cents is to have a mark-up placed on it of 25%, what should the selling price be?

Ans. 32 cents.

3. A box of cigars costing $2.50 is to be marked up 15%. How much will the mark-up amount to? *Ans.* 44 cents.

4. A merchant's inventory is valued at $7500.00. If the average mark-up in his business is 35%, how much profit may be expected on the sale of this merchandise? *Ans.* $4038.46. (*Art.* 35)

5. A man contemplating the purchase of a retail business is informed that the inventory value is $12,460.00. If the expense of operating the business is 32% of the sales, and if it is desired that the sales yield a profit of 5%, at how much per cent on the cost should the merchandise be marked up? (Hint: Determine the total per-cent profit on the selling price by adding the per-cent rate represented by the operating expenses to the per-cent rate of the desired profit.) *Ans.* 58.7301%.

★ 6. What would a 10% mark-down amount to on an article whose price tag reads $15.00? *Ans.* $1.50.

★ 7. The asking price of a rebuilt typewriter on which a mark-up of $23.00 was placed was $85.00. If the machine sold at a mark-down of 5%, what was the amount of the sale? (Hint: The mark-up amount in this problem may be disregarded.) *Ans.* $80.75.

★ 8. A couch costing $84.00 was marked up 40%. Subsequently the selling price was marked down 20% and the couch was sold at the reduced price. What was the mark-down price? *Ans.* $112.00.

9. A merchant bought a set of pictures for $132.00. His selling price, based on a 36% mark-up, was later revised by a $12\frac{1}{2}$% mark-down. What was the revised selling price of the pictures? Compute the answer to the nearest dollar.   *Ans.* $180.00.

10. A manufacturer's cost of a desk is $210.00. The desired profit is 40% of the amount to be received from the purchaser after allowing him a discount of 10%. What should the asking price of the desk be? Compute the answer to the nearest dollar. (Hint: This problem is similar to the one in Example 5 in the text.)

Ans. $389.00.

CHAPTER XVI

DECIMALS AND FRACTIONS

Because it was planned as a supplement to the main text this chapter has been placed at the end of the volume rather than at the beginning.

Its purpose is to provide a necessary background for two types of readers: those not skilled in the use of decimals and fractions, and those who have had so little occasion to use this knowledge in the past as to have forgotten much of what they possessed of it.

It is hoped, however, that most readers will gain something from the pages that follow. For a knowledge of decimals and fractions will do more than pave the way to a more thorough understanding of many of the shortcuts discussed in this book; it is essential to anyone who has anything at all to do with business mathematics of one kind or another.

94. The Function of the Decimal Point. A quick mental picture of the function of the decimal point can be obtained by considering the origin of the word "decimal." It originated from two Latin words: *decimus*, tenth, and *decem*, ten.

Strictly speaking, the decimal point has many functions. By moving it to the right or left, a number can be multiplied or divided, respectively, by 10, 100, 1000, etc., according to the number of spaces it is moved. Thus to *multiply* 24.38 by 10 the decimal point is moved one place to the right, giving us 243.8; to multiply 24.38 by 100 the point is moved two places to the right, making the result 2438. To *divide* 24.38 by 10 the decimal point is moved one place to the left, changing the number to 2.438; and to divide 24.38 by 100 the point is moved two places to the left, when the number becomes .2438.

The decimal point may be said to separate the figures at the left of a number, which represent the number of *whole* units, from the figures at the right, which represent a *part* of a unit. Thus the figure in the first place *after* a decimal point represents tenths (.3 means three tenths); the figure in the second place after the decimal point, hundredths (.04 means four hundredths); the figure in the third place, thousandths (.007 means seven thousandths), etc.

The figure in the first place *before* a decimal point gives the number of units; the figure in the second place, tens; third place, hundreds, etc.

Here, then, is an important fact to remember: For each place the decimal point is moved to the right, the value of a number is *multiplied* by 10; for each place it is moved to the left, the value is *divided* by 10.

PROBLEMS

★ 1. Multiply 176 by 10.   *Ans.* 1760.
★ 2. Multiply 3925 by 100.   *Ans.* 392500.
★ 3. Multiply 16.4 by 10.   *Ans.* 164.
★ 4. Multiply 3.86 by 100.   *Ans.* 386.
★ 5. Multiply .1257 by 100.   *Ans.* 12.57.
★ 6. Divide 49 by 10.   *Ans.* 4.9.
★ 7. Divide 23863 by 100.   *Ans.* 238.63.
★ 8. Divide 2.475 by 10.   *Ans.* .2475.
★ 9. Divide .1462 by 100.   *Ans.* .001462.
★ 10. Divide 3.875 by 1000.   *Ans.* .003875.

95. How to Read Numbers Containing Decimal Points.
There is no limit to the number of places the decimal
point may be moved. The following illustration presents
a picture of the values of places in decimal numbers and
how they are read:

Millions	Hundred Thousands	Ten Thousands	Thousands	Hundreds	Tens	Units	DECIMAL POINT	Tenths	Hundredths	Thousandths	Ten Thousandths	Hundred Thousandths	Millionths	etc.

0000000 . 000000

14.1 would be read 14 and one tenth.

118.23 would be read 118 and 23 hundredths or, if the
dollar sign preceded it, 118 dollars and 23 cents.

.192 would be read 192 thousandths.

33.0468 would be read 33 and 468 ten thousandths.

146.46328 would be read 146 and 46328 hundred
thousandths.

3.762413 would be read 3 and 762413 millionths.

PROBLEMS

Show how you would read the decimal numbers mentioned in
the following cases:

★ **1.** Music wire is available in a variety of thicknesses. One of
them is .059 inch in diameter.   *Ans.* 59 thousandths of an inch.

★ **2.** One of the over-all diameters of a brand of cable cord having
an insulation thickness of $\frac{3}{64}$ of an inch is .605 inch.

Ans. 605 thousandths of an inch.

★ **3.** The maximum thickness of a brand of asbestos paper is
described as .020 inch. (Hint: When a zero after a decimal point is
not followed by a digit, it may be disregarded.)

Ans. 2 hundredths of an inch.

★ 4. A fingerprint remover that cleans steel and retards corrosion leaves a film of about 0.0002 inch thick. (Hint: When no other figure than a zero precedes a decimal point, the zero may be disregarded.)   *Ans.* 2 ten thousandths of an inch.

★ 5. Sheets of natural cork, 0.0025 inch thick, are sliced from cork blocks and are used extensively on the tips of cigarettes.
                    Ans. 25 ten thousandths of an inch.

★ 6. The disadvantages of a disagreeable odor and acrid taste of fish glue can be avoided if the glue is boiled with a little water with 1% of sodium phosphate and 0.025% of saccharine added.
                    Ans. 25 thousandths of 1 per cent.

★ 7. An electronic stop-watch clocks one millionth of a second. Write one millionth in decimal form.   *Ans.* .000001.

Write each of the following numbers in decimal form:

★ 8. $4\frac{7}{10}$.   *Ans.* 4.7.
★ 9. $200\frac{8}{1000}$.   *Ans.* 200.008.
★ 10. $12\frac{18}{100}$.   *Ans.* 12.18.
★ 11. $19\frac{23}{1000}$.   *Ans.* 19.023.

96. Avoiding Confusion in Moving the Decimal Point. Confusion will be avoided if it is remembered that the insertion of the decimal point designates the figures after the point as a *part* of a unit, whereas the absence of a decimal point signifies whole units. Thus .36 indicates 36 hundredths of a unit; and $2.40, two dollars and forty cents. On the other hand, if, in working a problem, we showed 54 cents merely as 54, without a decimal point, we would have to remember to consider the figures in the answer as cents; it is usually better, however, to include the decimal point whenever possible, so the answer may be read in dollars and parts of a dollar, that is, in dollars and cents.

Another important fact which should be observed is this: When the moving of a decimal point places it before or after a blank space, that is, a space without a figure in it, a zero is inserted. Thus .3 multiplied by 100 equals 30, and .7 multiplied by 1000 equals 700. Similarly, .4 divided by 10 equals .04, and .8 divided by 100 equals .008.

Having in mind the principle discussed in Art. 94, let us study the following simple multiplication problems and the explanations which accompany each solution:

Example 1: Compute the value of 10 units costing .17 each.

Solution: We are to multiply .17 by 10, and so the decimal point is moved one place to the right, giving us 1.7 dollars. Since there is no figure in the second place after the decimal point, a zero is inserted, and our answer is $1.70.

Example 2: Find the cost of 100 articles at $1.02 each.

Solution: Here we are to multiply $1.02 by 100, and the decimal point is therefore moved *two* places to the right, making the result $102.00. Two zeros have been inserted after the decimal point to indicate that there are no cents in the answer.

Example 3: Estimate the value of 1000 units costing .04 each.

Solution: One thousand times .04 equals 40, and since we are dealing with dollars and cents, the answer is $40.00.

Example 4: Multiply 34 cents by 10,000.

Solution: Moving the decimal point in .34 four places
to the right gives us 3400 or $3400.00.

Let us take a few problems in division:

Example 5: Find the cost of 10 units at .80 per 100.

Solution: Notice that the price is "per 100." The quantity with which we are concerned is one
tenth of 100, so we divide .80 by 10. This,
to use a very simple illustration, is effected
by moving the decimal point one place to
the left, which supplies the answer, .08 or
8 cents.

Example 6: Find the cost of 100 units at $24.00 per 1000.

Solution: Here the price is "per 1000." Since 100 is one
tenth of 1000, we divide $24.00 by 10,
which gives us $2.400. Since zeros after a
decimal point, when they are not followed
by a digit, have no value, we drop the last
zero and simply show the answer as $2.40.

Example 7: Compute the value of 10 units priced at
$862.00 per 1000.

Solution: Ten is one hundredth of 1000, so we move the
decimal point in the price two places to the
left, giving us $8.6200. Dropping the two
unnecessary zeros supplies the answer,
$8.62.

When working with per-cent rates remember that "per cent" means per hundred. So that 4 per cent means 4 per hundred, or 4 hundredths, or .04. Similarly, 28 per cent equals 28 hundredths, or .28. Conversely, .32 may also be written as 32 per cent; and .475 may be written as 47.5 per cent, or $47\frac{1}{2}$ per cent.

Example 8: Find 26% of $128.00.

Solution: 25% of $128.00 ($\frac{25}{100}$ or $\frac{1}{4}$ of $128.00) = $32.00
1% of $128.00 ($\frac{1}{100}$ of $128.00)   =   1.28

___

26% of $128.00   = $33.28

Example 9: Find .19 of $20.00.

Solution: .19 means 19 hundredths.
$\frac{1}{100}$ of $20.00   = $0.20

___

$\frac{19}{100}$ of $20.00 (19 times $0.20) = $3.80

Problems

★ **1.** If 100 yards of sheeting costs $13.80, what is the cost per yard?   *Ans.* $0.138.

★ **2.** A printer quotes $142.50 per 1000 booklets. How much is that per booklet?   *Ans.* $14\frac{1}{4}$ cents.

★ **3.** Write the following per cents as decimals: (a) 7%; (b) $8\frac{1}{2}$%; (c) 86%; (d) $91\frac{1}{4}$%.   *Ans.* (a) .07; (b) .085; (c) .86; (d) .9125.

★ **4.** An instrument for the analysis of metals, coal, coke, etc., is said to be accurate to $\frac{1}{5}$ of 1%. Write this as a decimal per cent.
                                                      Ans. .2%.

★ **5.** It costs the government about seven tenths of a cent to make each piece of paper money. Express $\frac{7}{10}$ of a cent (a) as the decimal part of a dollar and (b) as the decimal part of a cent.

Ans. (a) $0.007; (b) .7 cent.

★ **6.** If 300 clasp envelopes cost $15.78, what is the cost per unit? Show your answer to the nearest tenth of a cent. *Ans.* $0.053.

★ **7.** Copper sash cord, $\frac{7}{32}$ inch in diameter, weighs .083 pound per foot. How much will 200 feet of this cord weigh?

Ans. 16.6 pounds.

★ **8.** Iron sash cord, $\frac{1}{8}$ inch in diameter, weighs .023 pound per foot. How much will 300 feet of this cord weigh?

Ans. 6.9 pounds.

★ **9.** A building having an approximate area of 10,000 square feet is offered for sale at 65 cents per square foot. At this rate what would the total cost be? *Ans.* $6500.00.

★ **10.** If a newspaper sheet is .0025 inch thick, what is the approximate depth of a pile of 2000 of these sheets? *Ans.* 5 inches.

★ **11.** A thousand porcelain insulators $1\frac{7}{8}$ inches in height and $1\frac{3}{8}$ inches in diameter weigh 230 pounds. On this basis how much should 100 of these insulators weigh? *Ans.* 23 pounds.

★ **12.** The approximate weight of 1-inch, electrical metallic tubing is 711 pounds per 1000 feet. What weight would be represented by 10 feet of this tubing? *Ans.* 7.11 pounds.

97. The Distinction Between Decimal Fractions and Common Fractions.

In Art. 94 it was demonstrated that a number may be divided by 10 by moving the decimal point one place to the left, so that 7 divided by 10 equals .7. However, .7 may also be written as $\frac{7}{10}$. Similarly, the result of 2.3 divided by 10 may be written as .23 or as $\frac{23}{100}$.

Both numbers, .23 and $\frac{23}{100}$, are known as fractions; .23 is a *decimal* fraction because its relation to a whole unit is indicated by a decimal point, and $\frac{23}{100}$ is a *common* fraction because it is shown with a denominator instead of with a decimal point.

From the foregoing it will be seen that many common fractions can be quickly converted into decimal fractions simply by changing the form of the fraction so that the denominator is a power of 10. Thus the common fraction $\frac{3}{5}$, which is equivalent to $\frac{6}{10}$, may be written as .6; $\frac{23}{25}$, which is equivalent to $\frac{92}{100}$, may be written as .92; and $\frac{7}{20}$, which is the same as $\frac{35}{100}$, may be expressed as .35; $\frac{419}{1000}$ has the same value as .419, and so on.

Problems

Express the following as common fractions:

★ 1. .2.   *Ans.* $\frac{2}{10}$.
★ 2. .45.   *Ans.* $\frac{45}{100}$.
★ 3. .375.   *Ans.* $\frac{375}{1000}$.
★ 4. .025.   *Ans.* $\frac{25}{1000}$.
★ 5. .0069.   *Ans.* $\frac{69}{10000}$.
★ 6. .00073.   *Ans.* $\frac{73}{100000}$.

Express the following as decimal fractions. Remember that when the denominator of a fraction is multiplied by a number, the numerator should be multiplied by the same number in order that the value of the original fraction may be retained.

★ 7. $\frac{3}{10}$.   *Ans.* .3.
★ 8. $\frac{8}{100}$.   *Ans.* .08.
★ 9. $\frac{29}{100}$.   *Ans.* .29.
★ 10. $\frac{17}{50}$.   *Ans.* .34.
★ 11. $\frac{5}{25}$.   *Ans.* .2.
★ 12. $\frac{19}{250}$.   *Ans.* .076.

Without pausing for more than a moment in each problem, write the decimal fractions as common fractions.

★ 13. .25763.   *Ans.* $\frac{25763}{100000}$.
★ 14. 4.3697.   *Ans.* $4\frac{3697}{10000}$.
★ 15. 17.25439.   *Ans.* $17\frac{25439}{100000}$.
★ 16. 10.1001.   *Ans.* $10\frac{1001}{10000}$.
★ 17. 29.4360.   *Ans.* $29\frac{436}{1000}$.

98. How to Convert Fractions Whose Denominators Are Not a Power of 10 into Decimal Fractions. All of us know that the common fraction $\frac{1}{2}$ is equivalent to the decimal fraction .5; that $\frac{1}{4}$ is the same as .25; that $\frac{1}{8}$ equals .125. However, in converting most other common fractions into decimal fractions, even the best of us must "figure it out," and the most practical way to do this is by *simple division*.

Assume we wanted to convert the common fraction $\frac{1}{7}$ into a decimal fraction. Knowing that $\frac{1}{7}$ means 1 divided by 7, we perform a simple operation in division, using exactly the same method as in proving that the common fraction $\frac{1}{2}$ is equivalent to the decimal fraction .5. Let us, then, study the procedure in dividing 1 by 2, showing the answer in decimal form:

$$\begin{array}{r} .5 \\ 2\overline{)1.0} \end{array}$$

The method in arriving at .5 is as follows: 2 into 1 won't go. So we place a zero after the 1, taking care to also insert a decimal point after the 1, so that the zero does not change the value of the dividend.

Two into 10 (the number to be divided is read as 10, even though there is a decimal point after the 1) goes 5 times. So we place a 5 directly above the last figure of the dividend. Our answer is now complete, except for one thing: a decimal point must be inserted in the quotient, directly above the decimal point in the dividend. The answer, therefore, is .5.

The process will be more clearly understood after studying the following illustrations of conversion from a common fraction to a decimal fraction:

```
                    .083                         .333
      [1/12]    12)1.00          [1/3]      3)1.0
                    96                          9
                  ─────                       ────
                    40                          10
                    36                           9
                  ─────                       ────
                                                1
```

```
                    .166                         .143
      [1/6]      6)1.0           [1/7]      7)1.0
                    6                           7
                  ────                        ────
                    40                          30
                    36                          28
                  ────                        ────
                     4                           2
```

```
                    .346                         .2727
      [9/26]    26)9.0           [3/11]    11)3.0
                    78                          22
                  ─────                       ─────
                   120                          80
                   104                          77
                  ─────                       ─────
                   160                          30
                   156                          22
                  ─────                       ─────
                     4                           8
```

Note that in some instances the divisor goes into the
dividend an exact number of times, while in others it does
not. For instance, 4 goes into 1 exactly .25 times, whereas

in each of the foregoing illustrations something is left over. For all practical purposes, and particularly when the figures after the decimal point represent cents, it is not necessary to work the problem beyond the third decimal place. The purpose of the third figure after the decimal point in the quotient is to determine the exact value of the preceding figure—that is, whether it is to be increased by 1. The general rule is that if the figure in the third decimal place is 5 or more, the preceding figure is increased by 1; if the third figure is less than 5, the preceding figure remains unchanged. Thus $1.426 is read as $1.43, and $1.312 as $1.31.

In many instances it would be useless to compute the answer beyond the first, second or third decimal place. Thus in dividing 1 by 3, each figure in the quotient is 3; in the quotient produced by dividing 1 by 6, the 6 repeats itself; and when 3 is divided by 11, 2 and 7 alternate indefinitely.

When the answer is to be expressed to the nearest whole number, it is unnecessary to work the problem beyond the first decimal place. Thus 14.3 gallons expressed to the nearest gallon, is 14 gallons; 2.7 ounces expressed to the nearest ounce, is 3 ounces; and 8.5 pounds would be considered as 9 pounds.

PROBLEMS

Compute to the nearest thousandth of a unit, the decimal equivalents of the following numbers.

1. $\frac{5}{9}$.   *Ans.* .556.

2. $\frac{2}{13}$.   *Ans.* .154.

3. $\frac{3}{7}$　　　　　　　　　　　　　　　*Ans.* .429.

4. $\frac{7}{15}$.　　　　　　　　　　　　　　*Ans.* .467.

5. $\frac{19}{22}$.　　　　　　　　　　　　　　*Ans.* .864.

6. $2\frac{2}{3}$.　　　　　　　　　　　　　　*Ans.* 2.667.

7. $15\frac{5}{6}$.　　　　　　　　　　　　　*Ans.* 15.833.

8. $124\frac{4}{7}$.　　　　　　　　　　　　*Ans.* 124.571.

9. $71\frac{7}{12}$.　　　　　　　　　　　　*Ans.* 71.583.

10. $100\frac{3}{8}$.　　　　　　　　　　　*Ans.* 100.375.

11. The fractional relation of 7 inches to one yard. (Hint: There are 36 inches to the yard.)　　　　　　　*Ans.* .194.

12. The fractional relation of 6 ounces to one pound. (Hint: There are 16 ounces to the pound.)　　　　　　*Ans.* .375.

13. The fractional relation of 5 pints to one gallon. (Hint: There are 8 pints to the gallon.)　　　　　　*Ans.* .625.

14. The fractional relation of 16 square inches to one square foot. (Hint: There are 144 square inches to the square foot.)
　　　　　　　　　　　　　　　　Ans. .111.

15. The fractional relation of 160 acres to one square mile. (Hint: There are 640 acres to the square mile.)　　*Ans.* .25.

99. Addition and Subtraction of Decimal Numbers. In setting down decimal numbers to be added, care should be taken to write all the tenths under each other, all the hundredths under each other, and so on. Thus to add .6, .18, .298, and .0456, we would write these numbers as follows:

$$
\begin{array}{r}
.6 \\
.18 \\
.298 \\
.0456 \\
\hline
1.1236
\end{array}
$$

Proceeding with the addition: There is only one digit in the column at the extreme right (the ten thousandths column)—namely, the digit 6—so we write 6 in that column. There are two digits in the thousandths column—5 and 8; their sum is 13, so we write 3 in that column and carry 1. In the hundredths column we have 4, 9 and 8; their sum is 21 which added to 1 we carried equals 22, so we write down 2 and carry 2. The sum of the digits in the tenths column equals 9 which added to the 2 we carried equals 11, so we write down 1 in the tenths column; and since there are no figures to be added at the left of this column, we write down the rest of the number, which is 1.

The subtraction of decimal numbers is performed in exactly the same way as the subtraction of whole numbers. However, when there are a larger number of figures after the decimal point in the minuend (the number to be subtracted) than there are after the decimal point in the subtrahend (the number from which we are to subtract), it is necessary to insert, or to imagine the insertion of, the necessary number of zeros in the subtrahend. Likewise, if there are more figures after the decimal point in the subtrahend, it is necessary to insert, or imagine the insertion of, the necessary number of zeros in the minuend.

Thus to subtract .34724 from .68, we would write three zeros after the 8 in the minuend, as follows:

$$
\begin{array}{r}
.68000 \\
.34724 \\
\hline
.33276
\end{array}
$$

Let us now subtract 1.4593 from 2.7 without taking the trouble to annex the zeros.

$$2.7$$
$$1.4593$$
$$\overline{}$$
$$1.2407$$

When there are more figures after the decimal point in the minuend than there are after the decimal point in the subtrahend, it is equally unnecessary to annex zeros. Simply imagine the zeros to be there and subtract them from the figures in the minuend. Thus to subtract 3.82 from 15.94763, we would write the numbers as follows:

$$15.94763$$
$$3.82$$
$$\overline{}$$
$$12.12763$$

It is really very simple: 0 from 3 equals 3; 0 from 6 equals 6; 0 from 7 equals 7; 2 from 4 equals 2; 8 from 9 equals 1; and 3 from 15 equals 12.

PROBLEMS

1. Add .47, .035, .6.   *Ans.* 1.105.
2. Add 13.2, 1.48, .967, 103.5682.   *Ans.* 119.2152.
3. Add 147.67, 1.4, 2.78, 39.002.   *Ans.* 190.852.
4. Add 4.0904, 6.703, 90.2, 11.38901.   *Ans.* 112.38241.
5. Add 10.045, 134.1, 4.9607, .32.   *Ans.* 149.4257.
6. Subtract .246 from .869.   *Ans.* .623.
7. Subtract .147 from .8064.   *Ans.* .6594.
8. Subtract .16 from .40372.   *Ans.* .24372.
9. Subtract 4.056 from 92.6274.   *Ans.* 88.5714.
10. Subtract 33.1004 from 106.27965.   *Ans.* 73.17925.

100. How to Multiply a Decimal Number by a Whole Number, or a Decimal Number by a Decimal Number. A very practical method of multiplying numbers, one or both of which include a decimal point, is to multiply the numbers without regard to the decimal points, and then point off, from right to left, as many decimal places in the product as there are decimal places in the multiplicand and multiplier together.

Example 1: Find the product of 236.78 times 43.

Solution:
$$236.78$$
$$43$$
$$\overline{}$$
$$71034$$
$$94712$$
$$\overline{}$$
$$1018154$$

There are 2 decimal places in the multiplicand and none in the multiplier, so we point off 2 decimal places in the product, which gives us 10181.54 as our answer.

Example 2: Find the product of 71426 times .153.

Solution:
$$71426$$
$$.153$$
$$\overline{}$$
$$214278$$
$$357130$$
$$71426$$
$$\overline{}$$
$$10928178$$

There are 3 decimal places in the multiplier
and none in the multiplicand, so we point
off 3 decimal places in the product, giving
us as our answer 10928.178.

Example 3: Find the product of 14.834 times 6.27.

Solution:

$$
\begin{array}{r}
14.834 \\
6.27 \\
\hline
103838 \\
29668 \\
89004 \\
\hline
9300918
\end{array}
$$

Here we have 5 decimal places all together—3
in the multiplicand and 2 in the multiplier,
so we point off 5 decimal places in the product, which gives us 93.00918 as our answer.

Problems

Find the products of the following numbers:

1. 3.7 times 54.   *Ans.* 199.8.
2. 26 times 63.7.   *Ans.* 1656.2.
3. 1.093 times 43.   *Ans.* 46.999.
4. 24.8631 times 5.7.   *Ans.* 141.71967.
5. 1.24563 times 7.43.   *Ans.* 9.2550309.
6. 2167.2 times .3154.   *Ans.* 683.53488.

7. If a gallon of kerosene weighs 6.7 pounds, what will 23
gallons of kerosene weigh?   *Ans.* 154.1 pounds.

8. Estimate the amount due a workman for 37 hours at $1.34
an hour.   *Ans.* $49.58.

9. If one foot of round steel bar, $\frac{11}{32}$ inch in diameter, weighs 0.316 pound, how much will 73 feet of these bars weigh?

Ans. 23.068 pounds.

10. The Owners, Landlords & Tenants' Liability insurance rate on general bakery stores in which beverages and food are served on the premises, in an eastern city, is $1.54 per 100 square feet of area. Estimate the amount of a one-year premium for insurance of this character to cover an area of 1800 square feet. *Ans.* $27.72.

11. A cotton driving rope $1\frac{3}{4}$ inches in diameter transmits, at a speed of 3600 feet per minute, 43.3 horsepower. Estimate the equivalent of this power in watts. One horsepower equals 746 watts.

Ans. 32,301.8 watts.

12. A ton of granite occupies 2.3 cubic yards. Estimate the space that would be occupied by 34.4 tons of this material.

Ans. 79.12 cubic yards.

13. If 100 square feet of 6-inch glass blocks laid with $\frac{1}{4}$-inch visible mortar joints requires the use of 4.3 cubic feet of mortar, how much mortar would be needed for placing 350 square feet of these blocks in the specified manner? *Ans.* 15.05 cubic feet.

14. The pic is an Egyptian unit of measurement which is equal to 22.835 inches. Estimate the equivalent in inches of 2.64 pics.

Ans. 60.2844 inches.

15. In the Philippine Islands in a recent year the average yield of unshelled peanuts was 586 kilograms per hectare. If a kilogram equals 2.2 pounds, and a hectare 2.47 acres, how many pounds of unshelled peanuts would represent the yield of 494 acres? (Hint: 494 acres is exactly 200 hectares.) *Ans.* 257,840 pounds.

101. How to Divide a Decimal Number by a Whole Number.

In dividing a decimal number by a whole number the decimal point is handled in exactly the same way as in dividing a whole number by a whole number. It was seen in Art. 98, for instance, that in converting the common fraction $\frac{9}{26}$ to a decimal fraction, it was necessary to insert a decimal point after the 9 and to insert, or imagine the insertion of, zeros after the decimal point. The illustration as it appears in that article is as follows:

$$
\begin{array}{r}
.346 \\
\hline
26)\overline{9.0} \\
78 \\
\hline
120 \\
104 \\
\hline
160 \\
156 \\
\hline
4
\end{array}
$$

It will be noted that the insertion of a zero after the decimal point in the dividend does not alter its value. The zero simply facilitates the process of division. Thus 26 is not divisible into 9, but it is divisible into 90.

If the dividend had been 9.2352 we would, of course, have divided 26 into 92, taking care to insert the decimal point in the quotient directly above the decimal point in the dividend, as will be seen in the following illustration.

Example 1: Divide 9.2352 by 26.

Solution:

$$
\begin{array}{r}
.3552 \\
\hline
26)\overline{9.2352} \\
78 \\
\hline
143 \\
130 \\
\hline
135 \\
130 \\
\hline
52
\end{array}
$$

Ans. .3552.

Observe that in every problem in division, the figure in the quotient is inserted directly above the last figure of the part of the dividend being divided. Thus when 26 is divided into 92, the 3 in the quotient is inserted directly above the 2 in 92.

Example 2: Divide .049296 by 13.

Solution:

$$
\begin{array}{r}
.003792 \\
\hline
13)\overline{.049296} \\
39 \\
\hline
102 \\
91 \\
\hline
119 \\
117 \\
\hline
26
\end{array}
$$

Ans. .003792.

Example 3: Divide $364.47 by 7.

Solution:

$$
\begin{array}{r}
52.066 \\
\hline
7)\overline{364.47} \\
35 \\
\hline
14 \\
14 \\
\hline
047 \\
42 \\
\hline
50
\end{array}
$$

Ans. $52.07.

The last illustration provides an interesting example of the procedure followed when the deduction of a partial product leaves no remainder, as when 14 deducted from 14 does not complete the solution of the problem. A zero is therefore written down as the difference, and the next figure in the dividend is brought down in the usual way. Seven into 4 won't go, so a zero is inserted in the next space in the quotient and another figure is brought down from the dividend. Seven into 47 goes six times, so 6 is inserted in the next space in the quotient, and the computation is continued in the usual manner.

Problems

Find the exact answer to each of the following problems:

★ 1. Divide 21.872 by 8.   *Ans.* 2.734.
  2. Divide 2.31914 by 17.   *Ans.* .13642.
  3. Divide 330.76159 by 43.   *Ans.* 7.69213.
  4. Divide .4394 by 52.   *Ans.* .00845.
★ 5. Divide .04404 by 12.   *Ans.* .00367.
  6. If it costs $1024.60 to produce 73 dresses, what is the cost per dress?   *Ans.* $14.04.
★ 7. It takes 18.5 hours to assemble 5 electrical units. How much time does that average per unit?   *Ans.* 3.7 hours.
  8. If it requires 308.25 pounds of whole milk to make 137 pounds of condensed or evaporated milk, how many pounds of whole milk would be required to make one pound of condensed milk?
                                                    Ans. 2.25 pounds.
  9. If 137 yards of a Navy balloon cloth weigh 280.85 ounces, what is the weight per yard?   *Ans.* 2.05 ounces.
  10. If 37 cubic inches of wrought iron weigh 10.2786 pounds, what is the weight per cubic inch?   *Ans.* .2778 pounds.
  11. If 43 gallons of water weigh 359.695 pounds, what is the weight of one gallon of water?   *Ans.* 8.365 pounds.
  12. A stack of 3480 sheets of aluminum occupies a space 1.74 inches deep. What is the thickness per sheet?   *Ans.* .0005 inches.

102. How to Divide a Whole Number by a Decimal Number, or a Decimal Number by a Decimal Number. To divide by a decimal number, the most practical procedure is to change the divisor to a whole number. Thus divisor 2.7 would be changed to 27; 8.41 to 841; and so on. The object of making the change is to facilitate computation.

We must remember, however, that when the divisor is multiplied by any number, the dividend, too, must be multiplied by the same number, for it is obvious that unless this is done the quotient will be affected. And this holds true whether the divisor is multiplied by 10, by a power of 10, or by any other number. The following illustrations will serve to make this clear:

Example 1: Divide 28 by 1.4.

Solution: 28 divided by 1.4 is equivalent to 280 divided by 14.

$$\begin{array}{r} 20 \\ \hline 14)\overline{280} \\ 28 \\ \hline \end{array}$$

Ans. 20.

Example 2: Divide 945 by 3.15.

Solution: 945 divided by 3.15 is equivalent to 94500 divided by 315.

$$\begin{array}{r} 300 \\ \hline 315)\overline{94500} \\ 945 \\ \hline \end{array}$$

Ans. 300.

Note that when the divisor is exactly divisible into a part of the dividend which is followed only by zeros, the quotient is completed by the annexation of zeros over the zeros in the dividend. Thus in the foregoing problem, the insertion of 3 in the quotient over the 5 in the dividend is followed by the annexation of two zeros in the quotient over the two zeros in the dividend.

Example 3: Divide 465 by 24.7, and state the answer to the nearest hundredth.

Solution: 465 divided by 24.7 is equivalent to 4650 divided by 247.

```
            18.825
       247)4650
            247
            ────
            2180
            1976
            ────
            2040
            1976
            ────
             640
             494
             ───
            1460
            1235
```

Ans. 18.83.

Example 4: Divide 105 by 3.5.

Solution: 105 divided by 3.5 is equivalent to 1050 divided by 35.

$$\begin{array}{r} 30 \\ \hline 35\overline{)1050} \\ 105 \\ \hline \end{array}$$

Ans. 30.

The reader may find it worth while at this point to refer to Chapter XIII, "The 'Double-and-Double' Method of Division," where some interesting techniques are discussed for dividing by mixed numbers. He will find, for instance, that by changing a divisor to a single-digit number (by the simple process of multiplying it by 2, 3, or 4, etc.) and multiplying the dividend by the same number, a problem can be considerably simplified. Thus 3.5 multiplied by 2 becomes the single-digit number 7; 105 multiplied by 2 equals 210; and quick as a flash it is seen that 210 divided by 7 equals 30.

When the dividend as well as the divisor contains a decimal point, the procedure in changing the divisor to a whole number is exactly the same as when the dividend is already a whole number. There is only this difference: Whereas when the dividend is already a whole number zeros are annexed to it, when the dividend is a decimal number the digits after the decimal point take the place of the zeros. Thus the problem 4.82 divided by .4 would be changed to 48.2 divided by 4; 131.62 divided by .73 would become 13162 divided by 73; 19.1 divided by .645 would be restated to read 19100 divided by 645; and so on.

Problems

Compute the answers to the following problems to the nearest hundredth.

1. Divide 574 by 1.3.   *Ans.* 441.54.
2. Divide 3689 by 21.4.   *Ans.* 172.38.
3. Divide 74 by 5.23.   *Ans.* 14.15.
4. Divide 36 by 1.5.   *Ans.* 24.
5. Divide 82.464 by 81.2.   *Ans.* 1.02.
6. Divide 7.3845 by 3.4.   *Ans.* 2.17.
★ 7. Divide .00562 by .002.   *Ans.* 2.81.
8. Divide 68.625 by 15.25.   *Ans.* 4.5.

9. Compute the number of feet to a pound of wire of which 120 feet weigh 22.8 pounds. State the answer to the nearest hundredth of a foot.   *Ans.* 5.26 feet.

10. If 425 dozen units can be produced in 6.25 hours, what is the production capacity per hour?   *Ans.* 68 dozen.

11. If 6.4 pounds of a pharmaceutical preparation can be made with 32 ounces of a certain ingredient, how many ounces of the ingredient will make one pound?   *Ans.* 5 ounces.

12. Convert 688.975 inches to meters. (There are 39.37 inches to the meter.)   *Ans.* $17\frac{1}{2}$ meters.

13. Convert 19.1646 kilograms to pounds. (There are .4536 kilograms to the pound.)   *Ans.* 42.25 pounds.

14. If 1000 conductor terminals weigh 28 pounds, how many should be contained in a package whose net weight is 18 pounds 2 ounces? (Hint: Divide the net weight of the package by the weight of one conductor terminal.)   *Ans.* 647.

15. The protein contents of wheat and tapioca are 12.35% and .87%, respectively. How many times greater is the protein content of one than the other?   *Ans.* 14.2 times.

16. A molding powder weighs .86 ounces per cubic inch. Compute the number of cubic inches that would be occupied by 29.24 ounces of the powder.   *Ans.* 34 cubic inches.

103. A Word About Common Fractions, Proper Fractions, Improper Fractions, and Mixed Numbers. Frequent reference will be made to these terms in the articles that follow, and the reader will do well to familiarize himself with their meaning.

A *common fraction*, as we have already seen, is distinct from a decimal fraction in that it is written with a numerator and a denominator. Thus $\frac{1}{2}$, $\frac{3}{4}$, $\frac{4}{5}$, $\frac{13}{11}$, are all common fractions.

A *proper fraction* is one in which the numerator is smaller than the denominator. Thus only the first three fractions in the preceding paragraph are proper fractions.

An *improper fraction* is one in which the numerator is greater than or equals the denominator. Thus $\frac{9}{8}$ and $\frac{3}{3}$ are improper fractions.

A *mixed number* is one which consists of a whole number and a fraction. Thus $7\frac{1}{4}$ and $42\frac{8}{9}$ are mixed numbers.

104. How to Reduce Common Fractions to Their Lowest Terms, and How to Increase the Terms of Common Fractions Without Changing Their Value. Imagine yourself at the grocer's, making some purchases. You order half a pound of cheese, and when the clerk is about to remove the cheese from the scale you see the indicator pointing to 8. You know that since there are 16 ounces to the pound, the 8 represents half a pound. In other words, $\frac{8}{16}$ is reduced to $\frac{1}{2}$. In this simple illustration lies the explanation of what is meant by reducing a common fraction to its lowest terms.

It is clear, therefore, that in dealing with fractions, it is frequently advisable to reduce them to their lowest terms. However, if a fraction is to be so reduced, the numerator and the denominator must be divisible by the same number, which number is known as a *common factor*. Thus in the fraction $\frac{8}{16}$ the common factor is 8. Of course, 2 and

4 are also common factors of 8 and 16, but 8 is the largest common factor in this instance.

The following illustrations of fractions reduced to their lowest terms will help to fix in mind this process:

$$\frac{3}{6} = \frac{1}{2} \qquad \frac{12}{21} = \frac{4}{7} \qquad \frac{5}{15} = \frac{1}{3}$$

$$\frac{3}{27} = \frac{1}{9} \qquad \frac{24}{96} = \frac{1}{4} \qquad \frac{14}{26} = \frac{7}{13}$$

$$\frac{17}{85} = \frac{1}{5} \qquad \frac{20}{46} = \frac{10}{23} \qquad \frac{28}{32} = \frac{7}{8}$$

When we speak of increasing the terms of a fraction we usually have in mind changing the denominator to a specific higher number. For instance, it may be desired to change the fraction $\frac{4}{5}$ so that the denominator is 10 instead of 5. As we have already seen, if we multiply both terms of a fraction by the same number the value of the fraction is unchanged. Thus $\frac{4}{5}$ equals $\frac{8}{10}$. Likewise, if it is desired to increase the terms of the fraction $\frac{2}{3}$ so that the denominator is 9 instead of 3, we simply multiply each of the numbers in the fraction by 3, which gives us $\frac{6}{9}$. All we need do, then, in increasing the terms of a common fraction, is to determine the number of times that the original denominator is contained in the desired denominator, and multiply numerator and denominator by that number.

PROBLEMS

Reduce the following fractions to their lowest terms:

★ 1. $\frac{2}{4}$.   *Ans.* $\frac{1}{2}$.

★ 2. $\frac{5}{20}$.   *Ans.* $\frac{1}{4}$.

★ 3. $\frac{3}{9}$.   *Ans.* $\frac{1}{3}$.

★ 4. $\frac{12}{18}$.   *Ans.* $\frac{2}{3}$.

★ 5. $\frac{13}{39}$.   *Ans.* $\frac{1}{3}$.

★ 6. $\frac{25}{100}$.   *Ans.* $\frac{1}{4}$.

★ 7. $\frac{4}{24}$.   *Ans.* $\frac{1}{6}$.

★ 8. $\frac{14}{16}$.   *Ans.* $\frac{7}{8}$.

Increase the terms of the fraction $\frac{1}{4}$ so that the denominator is represented by the number indicated:

★ 9. 12.   *Ans.* $\frac{3}{12}$.

★ 10. 16.   *Ans.* $\frac{4}{16}$.

★ 11. 28.   *Ans.* $\frac{7}{28}$.

★ 12. 36.   *Ans.* $\frac{9}{36}$.

★ 13. 44.   *Ans.* $\frac{11}{44}$.

★ 14. 8.   *Ans.* $\frac{2}{8}$.

★ 15. 72.   *Ans.* $\frac{18}{72}$.

★ 16. 56.   *Ans.* $\frac{14}{56}$.

105. How to Add or Subtract Common Fractions with Unlike Denominators. How would you add $\frac{1}{2}$ plus $\frac{1}{3}$? The two denominators are unlike, and obviously it is just as impossible to add these fractions in their present form as it would be to add oranges to apples and obtain one total.

Before we can add fractions with unlike denominators, it is necessary to find a common denominator—that is, a number into which each of the original denominators is divisible. This is accomplished by multiplying one denominator by the other.

The denominators in the fractions $\frac{1}{2}$ and $\frac{1}{3}$ are 2 and 3; so their common denominator is 6. And since the value of a fraction is not changed when its numerator and denominator are multiplied (or divided) by the same number, it is a very simple matter to convert the two fractions in our problem so that the denominator in each instance is 6: $\frac{1}{2}$ becomes $\frac{3}{6}$, and $\frac{1}{3}$ becomes $\frac{2}{6}$; and the sum of $\frac{3}{6}$ plus $\frac{2}{6}$ equals $\frac{5}{6}$.

This method of finding a common denominator may be applied regardless of the number of different denominators in a problem. Thus to add $\frac{1}{2}$ plus $\frac{1}{3}$ plus $\frac{2}{5}$, we should find a common denominator by multiplying 2 by 3 by 5, which equals 30. Our problem now becomes $\frac{15}{30}$ plus $\frac{10}{30}$ plus $\frac{12}{30}$, which equals $\frac{37}{30}$, or $1\frac{7}{30}$.

In the preceding problem the common denominator happens to be the product of all the denominators in the original fractions. However, to add $\frac{1}{3}$ plus $\frac{1}{2}$ plus $\frac{1}{4}$, it would not be necessary to multiply 3 by 2 by 4 to find a common denominator. Since denominator 4 is divisible by denominator 2, it is only necessary to multiply 3 by 4, arriving at 12 as the common denominator.

A practical way of writing down converted fractions to be added is demonstrated in the following illustrations:

Example 1: Add $\frac{3}{4}$ plus $\frac{2}{3}$ plus $\frac{1}{6}$ plus $\frac{5}{12}$.

Solution: The highest denominator is 12, and each of the other denominators is exactly divisible into it, so we will change the other denominators to 12.

$$\frac{9 + 8 + 2 + 5}{12} = \frac{24}{12} = 2.$$

Ans. 2.

Example 2: Add $2\frac{1}{9}$ plus $8\frac{2}{3}$ plus $\frac{5}{6}$ plus $13\frac{1}{6}$.

Solution: The sum of the whole numbers (2, 8 and 13) = 23. The lowest common denominator is 18, and converting each of the fractions to eighteenths, we obtain

$$\frac{2 + 12 + 15 + 3}{18} = \frac{32}{18} \text{ or } \frac{16}{9} \text{ or } 1\frac{7}{9}.$$

23 (the sum of the whole numbers) plus $1\frac{7}{9}$ (the sum of the fractions) = $24\frac{7}{9}$.

Ans. $24\frac{7}{9}$.

The subtraction of common fractions with unlike denominators calls for exactly the same procedure in converting the denominators as when adding. Thus to subtract $\frac{1}{4}$ from $\frac{1}{2}$ we would simply change the second fraction to $\frac{2}{4}$, and it is seen immediately that $\frac{1}{4}$ subtracted from $\frac{2}{4}$ equals $\frac{1}{4}$. Likewise, the problem $\frac{1}{3}$ subtracted from $\frac{8}{9}$ would be revised to read $\frac{3}{9}$ subtracted from $\frac{8}{9}$, and so on.

To subtract one mixed number from another, subtract one fraction from the other fraction, and one whole number from the other whole number. Thus:

Example 3: Subtract $7\frac{3}{8}$ from $9\frac{1}{2}$.

Solution: $9\frac{1}{2} = 9\frac{4}{8}$.

$\frac{3}{8}$ subtracted from $\frac{4}{8}$ $= \frac{1}{8}$

7 subtracted from 9 $= 2$

$7\frac{3}{8}$ subtracted from $9\frac{1}{2} = 2\frac{1}{8}$

In actual practice, of course, $7\frac{3}{8}$ would be written under $9\frac{1}{2}$, the same as when subtracting whole numbers, as follows:

$$9\frac{1}{2}$$
$$7\frac{3}{8}$$

$$2\frac{1}{8}$$

When the value of the fraction in the subtrahend exceeds the value of the fraction in the minuend, simply borrow 1 from the whole number in the minuend. Thus:

Example 4: Subtract $3\frac{1}{2}$ from $10\frac{1}{4}$.

Solution: $10\frac{1}{4}$ is equivalent to the improper fraction $9\frac{5}{4}$.

$3\frac{1}{2}$ is equivalent to $3\frac{2}{4}$.

$3\frac{2}{4}$ subtracted from $9\frac{5}{4} = 6\frac{3}{4}$.

Ans. $6\frac{3}{4}$.

Problems

Find the sums of the following fractions:

★ 1. $\frac{1}{2}$ plus $\frac{1}{3}$.   *Ans.* $\frac{5}{6}$.

★ 2. $\frac{1}{4}$ plus $\frac{2}{5}$.   *Ans.* $\frac{13}{20}$.

★ 3. $4\frac{3}{8}$ plus $\frac{3}{4}$.   *Ans.* $5\frac{1}{8}$.

★ 4. $\frac{2}{3}$ plus $2\frac{4}{9}$.   *Ans.* $3\frac{1}{9}$.

★ 5. Subtract $\frac{1}{6}$ from $\frac{2}{3}$.   *Ans.* $\frac{1}{2}$.

★ 6. Subtract $\frac{1}{2}$ from $\frac{9}{10}$.   *Ans.* $\frac{2}{5}$.

★ 7. Subtract $\frac{2}{5}$ from $6\frac{13}{20}$.   *Ans.* $6\frac{1}{4}$.

8. Subtract $1\frac{15}{16}$ from $4\frac{5}{8}$.   *Ans.* $2\frac{11}{16}$.

9. A dealer sold 4 lengths of cloth: $3\frac{1}{2}$ yards, $4\frac{1}{4}$ yards, $7\frac{1}{3}$ yards and $5\frac{1}{6}$ yards. How many yards did he sell in all?

Ans. $20\frac{1}{4}$ yards.

10. The treatment of a building exterior required the use of $3\frac{1}{4}$ gallons, $4\frac{1}{2}$ gallons and $5\frac{3}{8}$ gallons of paint. What was the total amount of paint used?   *Ans.* $13\frac{1}{8}$ gallons.

11. Find the total weight of the following upholsterers' shears: a $10\frac{1}{2}$-inch weighing $1\frac{3}{8}$ pounds, an $11\frac{1}{4}$-inch weighing $1\frac{1}{2}$ pounds, a 12-inch weighing $1\frac{5}{8}$ pounds, and a $12\frac{1}{2}$-inch weighing $1\frac{3}{4}$ pounds.

Ans. $6\frac{1}{4}$ pounds.

12. One girl can produce 2 gross units in 6 days, and a second girl, 2 gross units in 4 days. What fraction of a gross would be produced in one day by both girls working together?   *Ans.* $\frac{5}{6}$ gross.

13. From a sheet of metal $4\frac{1}{2}$ feet long 2 lengths are cut: $1\frac{1}{3}$ feet and $2\frac{1}{4}$ feet. Disregarding the amount of waste in cutting, what part of the sheet remained?   *Ans.* $\frac{11}{12}$ of a foot.

14. By how many yards does $\frac{5}{8}$ of a mile exceed $\frac{1}{2}$ a mile? (There are 1760 yards to the mile.)   *Ans.* 220 yards.

15. How much larger is $8\frac{1}{3}\%$ than $6\frac{1}{4}\%$? *Ans.* $2\frac{1}{12}\%$.

★ 16. The first and last sales of a stock issue on a certain day were at $36\frac{3}{4}$ and $36\frac{1}{8}$, respectively. By what fraction of a dollar per share had the price dropped at the close of the day's business?

Ans. $\frac{5}{8}$ of a dollar.

106. How to Multiply or Divide a Fraction by a Whole Number, or a Fraction by a Fraction. In problems such as 3 divided by 5, or 1 divided by 4, both the dividend and the divisor are whole numbers, and so the process of division is quite simple. The answer to the first problem is simply $\frac{3}{5}$, and the answer to the second is $\frac{1}{4}$. But how do we go about multiplying or dividing a fraction by a whole number, or a fraction by a fraction? It is really very simple, as the following rules show:

1. To multiply a fraction by a whole number, multiply the *numerator* of the fraction by the whole number. Thus $\frac{1}{3}$ multiplied by 2 equals $\dfrac{1 \times 2}{3} = \dfrac{2}{3}$.

2. To divide a fraction by a whole number, multiply the *denominator* of the fraction by the whole number. Thus $\frac{1}{3}$ divided by 2 equals $\dfrac{1}{3 \times 2} = \dfrac{1}{6}$.

3. To multiply one fraction by another fraction, multiply the numerator of one fraction by the numerator of the other fraction, and multiply the denominator of one fraction by the denominator of the other fraction. Thus $\frac{2}{7}$ multiplied by $\frac{5}{9}$ equals $\dfrac{2 \times 5}{7 \times 9} = \dfrac{10}{63}$.

4. To divide one fraction by another fraction, reverse the position of the numerator and denominator in the

divisor, and proceed to multiply one fraction by the other fraction. Thus $\frac{2}{7}$ divided by $\frac{5}{9}$ equals $\frac{2}{7}$ multiplied by $\frac{9}{5} = \frac{2 \times 9}{7 \times 5}$ or $\frac{18}{35}$.

It should be remembered that in any mathematical problem, the word "of" means "multiplied by." Thus one-half of 8 means $\frac{1}{2}$ multiplied by 8.

PROBLEMS

The final answers to Problems 1 to 8 are not required; show only how you would write the multiplicand and multiplier or the dividend and divisor, as the case may be, in each of these 8 problems, with a single dividing line.

⋆ 1. Multiply $\frac{4}{11}$ by 32.   *Ans.* $\frac{4 \times 32}{11}$.

⋆ 2. Multiply $\frac{13}{15}$ by 90.   *Ans.* $\frac{13 \times 90}{15}$.

⋆ 3. Divide $\frac{6}{7}$ by 12.   *Ans.* $\frac{6}{7 \times 12}$.

⋆ 4. Divide $\frac{3}{4}$ by 8.   *Ans.* $\frac{3}{4 \times 8}$.

⋆ 5. Multiply $\frac{5}{8}$ by $\frac{3}{8}$.   *Ans.* $\frac{5 \times 3}{8 \times 8}$.

⋆ 6. Multiply $\frac{7}{12}$ by $\frac{1}{3}$.   *Aus.* $\frac{7 \times 1}{12 \times 3}$.

⋆ 7. Divide $\frac{8}{13}$ by $\frac{5}{7}$.   *Ans.* $\frac{8 \times 7}{13 \times 5}$.

⋆ 8. Divide $\frac{2}{3}$ by $\frac{3}{4}$.   *Ans.* $\frac{2 \times 4}{3 \times 3}$.

⋆ 9. What is the height in inches of a stack of 240 sheets of Plexiglas, each $\frac{3}{16}$ inch thick?   *Ans.* 45 inches.

⋆ 10. If it takes 8 hours to complete $\frac{2}{7}$ of a job, what part of the job is completed every hour?   *Ars.* $\frac{1}{28}$.

★ **11.** What fraction of a gross is $\frac{1}{4}$ of $\frac{1}{3}$ of a gross?

Ans. $\frac{1}{12}$ of a gross.

★ **12.** How many times is $\frac{1}{8}$ of an ounce contained in $\frac{3}{4}$ of an ounce?

Ans. 6 times.

107. Cancellation, and How It Simplifies the Process of Multiplying Fractions. Problems in fractions are often solved quickly and easily by the simple process of cancellation, which is really a process of division. Take, for instance, the problem of multiplying $\frac{3}{5}$ by $\frac{10}{9}$:

$$\frac{3}{5} \times \frac{10}{9} \text{ or } \frac{3 \times 10}{5 \times 9}$$

According to the rule, the product of the numerators (3 and 10 in this problem) divided by the product of the denominators (5 and 9) will supply the answer. Often, however, it is unnecessary to multiply all the original numerators by each other and all the original denominators by each other. When a numerator or one of its factors is divisible into a denominator, or vice versa, the process of division should be carried out. Thus in the example $\frac{3}{5}$ multiplied by $\frac{10}{9}$, the denominator 5 can be canceled into the numerator 10, and the numerator 3 into the denominator 9. When the process of division (or cancellation, as it is called) is completed, the problem will look as follows:

$$\frac{\overset{1}{\cancel{3}} \times \overset{2}{\cancel{10}}}{\underset{1}{\cancel{5}} \times \underset{3}{\cancel{9}}} = \frac{2}{3}$$

Note that it is not necessary to cancel a whole numerator or a whole denominator at one time: only a factor may be canceled, as shown in the following solution of the problem $\frac{14}{33}$ multiplied by $\frac{22}{35}$.

$$\frac{\overset{2}{\cancel{14}} \times \overset{2}{\cancel{22}}}{\underset{3}{\cancel{33}} \times \underset{5}{\cancel{35}}} = \frac{4}{15}$$

Canceling the factor 7 into 14 and 35, and the factor 11 into 22 and 33 reduced the problem to the equivalent of 4 divided by 15.

Let us take a more difficult problem:

$$\frac{\overset{1}{\cancel{\overset{2}{\cancel{32}}}} \times \overset{1}{\cancel{\overset{2}{\cancel{6}}}} \times \overset{1}{\cancel{7}} \times \overset{1}{\cancel{3}} \times \overset{1}{\cancel{15}}}{\underset{1}{\cancel{\underset{1}{\cancel{16}}}} \times \underset{1}{\cancel{15}} \times \underset{\underset{1}{3}}{\cancel{9}} \times \underset{2}{\cancel{14}} \times \underset{1}{\cancel{2}}}$$

The step-by-step procedure in working this problem is as follows: The numerator 32 contains the denominator 16 twice, so a line is drawn through each number, and 2 is substituted for 32.

There is a 15 in the numerator and another in the denominator, so these numbers are eliminated by cancellation.

The numerator 7 will go twice into the denominator 14, so a line is drawn through each of these numbers, and 2 is substituted for 14.

Numerator 3 goes into denominator 9 three times, so 3 is substituted for 9.

Now the 3 in the denominator will go twice into the 6 in the numerator, so 2 is substituted for 6.

And since the two 2's in the numerator will cancel the two 2's in the denominator, lines may be drawn through all four 2's, and a 1 substituted for each 2.

We now have nothing but 1's in the numerator and 1's in the denominator. The answer, therefore, is $\frac{1}{1}$, and since 1 divided by 1 equals 1, the answer may be stated simply as 1.

It is important to observe that the cancellation process may be used only when all the signs between the numerators and all the signs between the denominators are *multiplication* signs. If there is a plus or a minus sign between any two numerators or denominators, it is necessary to compute the net value of the figures above the line and the net value of the figures below the line. Thus in the example

$$\frac{6 + 4}{6 \times 5}$$

the plus sign in the numerator prevents the cancellation of one 6 into the other 6. The net value of the numerator is 10, and the net value of the denominator is 30. The answer, therefore, is $\frac{10}{30}$ or $\frac{1}{3}$.

PROBLEMS

The following problems are to be worked by the process of cancellation, as discussed in the text:

1. Multiply $\frac{7}{8}$ by $\frac{16}{25}$.   *Ans.* $\frac{14}{25}$.
2. Multiply $\frac{3}{4}$ by $\frac{5}{6}$.   *Ans.* $\frac{5}{8}$.
3. Multiply $\frac{1}{2}$ by $\frac{8}{9}$ by $\frac{3}{4}$.   *Ans.* $\frac{1}{3}$.
4. Divide $\frac{24}{25}$ by $\frac{12}{13}$.   *Ans.* $1\frac{1}{25}$.
5. Divide $\frac{8}{11}$ by $\frac{16}{33}$.   *Ans.* $1\frac{1}{2}$.
6. Divide $\frac{19}{20}$ by $\frac{3}{10}$.   *Ans.* $3\frac{1}{6}$.

★ **7.** Divide the sum of 12 plus 3 by the product of 10 times 3.

$Ans.$ $\frac{1}{2}$.

★ **8.** Divide the sum of 24 plus 1 by the product of 6 times 25.

$Ans.$ $\frac{1}{6}$.

9. A glass mattress weighs 40 pounds against 55 pounds for a conventional cotton innerspring mattress. If the net weight of a shipment of the cotton product is 693 pounds, what would the approximate weight be of a shipment of the same number of glass mattresses? $Ans.$ 504 pounds.

10. The circumference of a circle is approximately $3\frac{1}{7}$ times the diameter. If the diameter is 56 inches, what is the circumference?

$Ans.$ 176 inches, or 14 feet 8 inches.

11. If one cubic foot holds approximately $\frac{4}{5}$ of a bushel of grain, how many bushels of grain could be placed in a bin whose capacity is 595 cubic feet? $Ans.$ 476 bushels.

★ **12.** How many sheets of wire glass $\frac{3}{8}$ inch thick can be stacked in a pile 24 inches high? $Ans.$ 64.

108. How to Multiply a Common Fraction by a Mixed Number, or a Mixed Number by a Mixed Number.

Having in mind the simple rules given in Art. 106, the multiplication of a common fraction by a mixed number or the multiplication of a mixed number by a mixed number will be found to be a relatively simple matter.

It should be remembered that a mixed number is really two numbers in one: a whole number and a fraction. So that to multiply a common fraction by a mixed number two partial products should be found—the product of the common fraction times the whole number, and the product of the common fraction times the common fraction.

Example: Multiply $\frac{3}{7}$ by $5\frac{4}{9}$.

Solution: $\frac{3}{7}$ times $5 = \frac{3 \times 5}{7} = \frac{15}{7} = 2\frac{1}{7}$.

$\frac{3}{7}$ times $\frac{4}{9} = \frac{3 \times 4}{7 \times 9} = \frac{4}{21}$.

Our problem now is to add the two partial products. The fractions $\frac{1}{7}$ and $\frac{4}{21}$, however, must have a common denominator before they can be added (see Art. 104). But this can be easily effected, for we see at a glance that the denominator 7 is divisible into the denominator 21 three times. Multiplying the numerator and denominator in the fraction $\frac{1}{7}$ by 3 gives us $\frac{3}{21}$, and $\frac{3}{21}$ plus $\frac{4}{21}$ equals $\frac{7}{21}$ or $\frac{1}{3}$. Adding the whole number 2 to the fraction $\frac{1}{3}$ supplies the answer, $2\frac{1}{3}$.

Another way to find the product of $\frac{3}{7}$ times $5\frac{4}{9}$ is to convert the mixed number into an improper fraction ($\frac{49}{9}$) and to multiply one fraction by the other, as explained in Art. 106, canceling the numerators and denominators into each other, as explained in Art. 107, thus:

$$\frac{\overset{1}{\cancel{3}} \times \overset{7}{\cancel{49}}}{\underset{1}{\cancel{7}} \times \underset{3}{\cancel{9}}}$$

See how beautifully the process of cancellation works out here: the 3 cancels into the 9, and the 7 cancels into 49. In an instant we have the fraction $\frac{7}{3}$, or $2\frac{1}{3}$, as the answer.

It will be seen from the foregoing that in multiplying a common fraction by a mixed number it is sometimes a good plan to convert the mixed number into an improper fraction to see if the numerators and denominators cancel into each other, before working the problem by any other method.

Still another method is to multiply the mixed number

by the numerator of the common fraction, and then divide the result by the denominator of the common fraction, thus:

$$3 \text{ times } 5\tfrac{4}{9}: \qquad 3 \text{ times } 5 \qquad\qquad = 15$$
$$\qquad\qquad\qquad 3 \text{ times } \tfrac{4}{9} = \tfrac{12}{9} = 1\tfrac{3}{9} \quad = 1\tfrac{1}{3}$$

$$16\tfrac{1}{3}$$

$$16\tfrac{1}{3} \text{ divided by } 7: \quad 16 \text{ divided by } 7 \qquad = 2\tfrac{2}{7}$$
$$\tfrac{1}{3} \text{ divided by } 7 = \frac{1}{3 \times 7} = \quad \tfrac{1}{21}$$

$$2\tfrac{2}{7} \text{ plus } \tfrac{1}{21}$$

The fraction $\tfrac{2}{7}$ is equivalent to $\tfrac{6}{21}$; $2\tfrac{6}{21}$ plus $\tfrac{1}{21} = 2\tfrac{7}{21}$, or $2\tfrac{1}{3}$.

In multiplying a mixed number by a mixed number, the nature of the numbers is a very helpful guide in selecting the method of procedure. If both numbers are small—as, for example, in the problem $3\tfrac{5}{9}$ times $2\tfrac{1}{8}$—it would be a simple matter to convert both numbers to improper fractions and proceed from there.

On the other hand, if the numbers are large—as, for example, in the problem $348\tfrac{12}{19}$ times $91\tfrac{1}{3}$—it would obviously be better to multiply $348\tfrac{12}{19}$ by 91, $348\tfrac{12}{19}$ by $\tfrac{1}{3}$ (which is equivalent to dividing $348\tfrac{12}{19}$ by 3), and then add the results.

Problems

1. If a girl can sew $\tfrac{2}{3}$ of a gross of bags in one hour, how many can she be expected to produce in $8\tfrac{1}{4}$ hours?   *Ans.* $5\tfrac{1}{2}$ gross.

2. A pharmaceutical manufacturer uses 7 ounces of a certain drug to each dozen bottles of a preparation. If he needed $16\tfrac{1}{2}$ dozen

bottles all together, how many pounds of the drug will be required? Use the apothecaries' weight of 12 ounces to the pound.

Ans. $9\frac{5}{8}$ pounds.

3. If a salesman's commission is $37\frac{1}{2}\%$, how much will he have earned on a sale amounting to \$65.33? (Hint: $37\frac{1}{2}\%$ is equivalent to $\frac{3}{8}$, and consider \$0.33 as $\frac{1}{3}$ of a dollar.) *Ans.* \$24.50.

4. A surveyor reports the width of a field as $23\frac{1}{2}$ rods. Convert this figure to yards. (There are $5\frac{1}{2}$ yards to the rod.)

Ans. $129\frac{1}{4}$ yards.

5. If 100 square feet of a 4-mesh copper wire cloth weigh $65\frac{7}{10}$ pounds, how much will 325 square feet weigh? Compute the answer to the nearest fortieth of a pound. (Hint: Multiply $65\frac{7}{10}$ by $3\frac{1}{4}$.)

Ans. $213\frac{21}{40}$ pounds.

6. One ounce is equivalent to $28\frac{7}{20}$ grams. Estimate the number of grams in $4\frac{1}{2}$ ounces. *Ans.* $127\frac{23}{40}$ grams.

7. If the weight per dozen paint brushes is $4\frac{3}{8}$ pounds, what would the weight be of 32 of these brushes? (Hint: 32 equals $2\frac{2}{3}$ dozen.) *Ans.* $11\frac{2}{3}$ pounds.

8. If a pound of fat supplies $2\frac{1}{4}$ times as much energy as a pound of digestible carbohydrates, how many pounds of digestible carbohydrates would be needed to supply the energy provided by $3\frac{1}{4}$ pounds of fat? *Ans.* $7\frac{5}{16}$ pounds.

9. Compute in square feet the area of a floor of a boxcar 40 feet 4 inches long by 8 feet 4 inches wide. (Hint: 4 inches equals $\frac{1}{3}$ of a foot.) *Ans.* $336\frac{1}{9}$ square feet.

10. A device for producing pure water has a flow rate of $13\frac{1}{2}$ gallons per hour. At this rate, how many gallons would be produced in $3\frac{1}{4}$ hours? *Ans.* $43\frac{7}{8}$ gallons.

109. How to Divide by a Mixed Number.

To divide by a mixed number it is only necessary to convert the mixed number to an improper fraction, invert the numerator and denominator and multiply. Thus to divide 36 by $2\frac{1}{4}$, change $2\frac{1}{4}$ to $\frac{9}{4}$ which, inverted, becomes $\frac{4}{9}$; then revise the problem to read 36 multiplied by $\frac{4}{9}$, which may be written as $\dfrac{36 \times 4}{9}$. If the problem had been to divide $\frac{23}{25}$ by $3\frac{3}{4}$, it would be restated as $\frac{23}{25}$ divided by $\frac{15}{4}$, which is equivalent to multiplying $\frac{23}{25}$ by $\frac{4}{15}$.

PROBLEMS

★ **1.** Divide 6 by $2\frac{1}{2}$. *Ans.* $2\frac{2}{5}$.

2. Divide 144 by $1\frac{1}{8}$. *Ans.* 128.

3. Divide $\frac{11}{22}$ by $1\frac{1}{2}$. *Ans.* $\frac{11}{18}$.

4. Divide $\frac{8}{15}$ by $6\frac{2}{3}$. *Ans.* $\frac{2}{25}$.

5. Divide $9\frac{1}{2}$ by $2\frac{1}{4}$. *Ans.* $4\frac{2}{9}$.

6. Divide $36\frac{2}{3}$ by $3\frac{1}{3}$. *Ans.* 11.

7. If 210 units can be inspected in $8\frac{3}{4}$ hours, what is the average per hour? *Ans.* 24 units.

8. Estimate the number of $1\frac{1}{3}$-yard lengths that can be cut from a bolt containing $49\frac{1}{3}$ yards of rayon cloth. *Ans.* 37 lengths.

9. An oriental rug having an area of $172\frac{1}{2}$ square feet is priced at $850.00. How much does this average per square foot?
Ans. $4.93.

10. If $2\frac{1}{4}$ gallons of chaulmoogra oil can be obtained from 108 bushels of nuts, how many bushels of nuts will produce 1 pint of this oil? (Hint: Divide the number of bushels per gallon by 8.)
Ans. 6 bushels.

11. A paper box manufacturer finds that in $4\frac{1}{4}$ hours $5\frac{2}{3}$ gross rims were secured to the boxes. At this rate how many gross rims may be expected to be secured in one hour? *Ans.* $1\frac{1}{3}$ gross.

12. How many lineal feet of a plastic screen cloth 28 inches wide would comprise an area of $116\frac{2}{3}$ square feet? (Hint: 28 inches is equivalent to $2\frac{1}{3}$ feet.) *Ans.* 50 lineal feet.

13. If the average weight per foot of carbon-and-graphite pipe, having an inside diameter of 4 inches, is $7\frac{1}{5}$ pounds, how many feet would make up a total weight of $201\frac{3}{5}$ pounds? *Ans.* 28 feet.

14. How many shovelfuls would it take to load $8\frac{5}{8}$ cubic yards of dirt onto a truck, using a $\frac{3}{8}$-cubic-yard crawler shovel? *Ans.* 23.

15. The total depth of a stack of cork tile $\frac{5}{16}$ of an inch thick is $32\frac{1}{2}$ inches. Estimate the number of tiles in the stack. *Ans.* 104.

16. How many $\frac{3}{4}$-ounce packages can be made up from $97\frac{1}{2}$ ounces of a botanical drug? *Ans.* 130.

GLOSSARY

Denominator. The part of a fraction below the dividing line; thus in the fraction $\frac{7}{12}$, 12 is the denominator.

Digit. In this book the word is used to designate any of the figures 1, 2, 3, 4, 5, 6, 7, 8 and 9. It should be noted, however, that some authorities consider 0 as a digit too.

Dividend. The number that is divided by another number; thus, in the problem 18 divided by 9, 18 is the dividend.

Divisor. The number by which any number is divided; thus in the problem 18 divided by 9, 9 is the divisor.

Factor. Any of the quantities which, multiplied together, form a product; thus, in the problem 8 multiplied by 4, both 8 and 4 are factors. On the other hand, to factor a number means to break it up into numbers (factors) which, multiplied together, produce the original number; thus the number 6 is composed of the factors 2 and 3, because 2 multiplied by 3 equals 6.

Minuend. The number from which another number is subtracted; thus, in the problem 16 minus 12, 16 is the minuend.

Multiple. A number that is exactly divisible by a given number; thus 100 is a multiple of 10, because it is exactly divisible by 10.

Numerator. The number above the dividing line in a fraction; thus in the fraction $\frac{7}{12}$, 7 is the numerator.

Per cent. "Per hundred," or "hundredths"; thus 2 per cent means 2 hundredths.

Percentage. The result obtained by computing a certain per cent of a number; thus in computing 5 per cent of $100.00, $5.00—the result obtained—is known as the percentage.

Power. The product resulting from the continued multiplication of a number by itself; thus 4, 8, 16, 32 are powers of 2; and 100, 1000, 10000 are powers of 10.

Quotient. The number resulting from the division of one number by another; thus, in dividing 18 by 3, 6—the result obtained—is known as the quotient.

Subtrahend. The number that is subtracted from another number; thus, in the problem 16 minus 12, 12 is the subtrahend.

THESE SYMBOLS GUARANTEE
THE BEST IN READING

POCKET BOOKS, INC. is the largest publisher of books in the world today in terms of the number of copies it has sold and is currently selling. Over 700,000,000 copies have carried the symbol of "Gertrude," the little kangaroo which is the colophon of POCKET BOOKS, INC., or the perky bird which is the trademark of CARDINAL EDITIONS, books of exceptional merit and value, priced at 25c, 35c and 50c.

Only genuine POCKET BOOK and CARDINAL editions carry these symbols. The titles are carefully chosen from the lists of all leading publishers and present the most distinguished and most widely diversified group offered today by any publisher of paper-bound books. Watch for these symbols. They are your guarantee of the best in reading at the lowest possible price.